Engaging Wellness

Corporate Wellness Programs that Work

Published by:
Corporate Health and Wellness Association®
http://www. wellnessassociation.com/

Editors:
Jonathan Edelheit, Esq
Reneé-Marie Stephano, Esq

Assistant Editors:
Daniel Regan Pyne
Sarah Michele Hunt

Editorial Consultant:
Denise Holland

Graphic Design:
Dinier Quirós

Dedication

For our friends, family, and colleagues in the industry who have always supported us in our initiatives. Their passion, commitment and support has kept the momentum going.

To the wellness professionals who have made the commitment to becoming a Certified Corporate Wellness Specialist, and are setting new standards in the industry.

Table of Contents

Chapter 1: Program Design

Chapter 2: Incentives

Chapter 3: Health Risk Assessments

Chapter 4 Biometrics

Chapter 10: Interventions and Best Practices

Chapter 11: Social Media and Corporate Wellness

Chapter 12: Multinational Wellness

Chapter 13: Wellness Program Communication

Chapter 14: Small Group Wellness Programs

Chapter 15: Fully Insured vs. Self-Funded

Chapter 16: Other Important Information

About the Authors and Editors

Jonathan Edelheit, JD

Jonathan Edelheit is Editor-in-Chief of the Corporate Wellness Magazine and Chairman of the Corporate Wellness Conference. Mr. Edelheit is an attorney. Previous to the Corporate Wellness Magazine, he spent over ten years involved in implementing wellness programs in both fully insured and self-funded health plans at a national healthcare administrator. He is a believer in the importance of getting employees engaged and participating in employer wellness programs.

Mr. Edelheit serves on the board of directors of the Corporate Health and Wellness Association. He has been featured and mentioned in hundreds of media publications and speaks all over the world at conferences and workshops. Mr. Edelheit has authored several books in Medical Tourism and in Corporate Wellness. Mr. Edelheit consults U.S. and multinational employers, insurers and insurance consulting firms. Mr. Edelheit organizes one of the largest US health insurance conferences that bring in the senior leaders in the US industry, the Employer Healthcare & Benefits Congress and the Corporate Wellness Conference. He is also editor-in chief of several U.S. insurance magazines, which focus in the areas of Healthcare Reform, Self-Funding, and Voluntary Benefits. He runs some of the largest social networking groups on linkedin for US and International HR, Insurance and Healthcare Professionals.

Mr. Edelheit sits on the Board of Directors for the Global Benefits Association, Self-Funding Employers Association, and the Voluntary Benefits Association. Mr. Edelheit is CEO of the Medical Tourism Association.

Email: jon@corporatewellnessmagazine.com

Renée-Marie Stephano, Esq.

 Renée-Marie Stephano is the President of the Corporate Health and Wellness Association, Co-editor of the Corporate Wellness Magazine and Co-founder of the Medical Tourism Association and Editor-in-Chief of Medical Tourism Magazine and the Health and Wellness Destination Guide Series of books. Ms. Stephano has authored several books concerning healthcare and insurance.

Ms. Stephano is an attorney and specializes in working with governments, hospitals, insurance companies and employers to develop sustainable programs and strategies. She has worked with organizations and governments across the globe. She organizes one of the only annual Ministerial Summits that brings together Ministers of Health to focus on health and wellness initiatives of the local population.

Ms. Stephano is a keynote speaker at international conferences and has spoken at hundreds of events and has been featured and mentioned been featured on major news networks and publications around the world.

Ms. Stephano serves on the Board of Directors for the International Healthcare Research Center, a 501c3, nonprofit health and wellness research center, the Corporate Health & Wellness Association, and two Washington D.C. based lobbying groups focused on lobbying the U.S. Congress.

Ms. Stephano donates her time as president of the Corporate Health and Wellness Association.

Email: renee@WellnessAssociation.com

Preface

We would like to thank everyone who has helped make this book possible, especially the 52 authors who have contributed their time and energy. We would also like to thank the members of the Corporate Health and Wellness Association, and the CHWA advisory board, who over the past few years have providing insight, content and guidance in developing this book and the Certified Corporate Wellness Specialist program. All of you have provided invaluable help in bringing the industry together through collaboration and the sharing of best practices. And finally, to all the passionate wellness professionals out there who often are the difference between a wellness program being successful or not. Keep the passion and momentum going!

- Jonathan & Renée-Marie

Foreword

At the beginning of every fiscal year, business leaders take up the challenge of designing the best financial plan for their company. Year after year, these leaders look to the various markets that influence their bottom lines and look for trends, try to identify current or foreseeable market changes and try to make the best business decision they can to ensure the financial strength and stability of their companies. In the past twenty years or so more businesses are seeing that their employee medical costs are becoming a larger part of their overall operating expenses, and they are trying to identify the best way to rein in those costs. For self-funded companies, the cost of employee healthcare is not just the cost of health insurance premiums. These employers are faced with paying the direct costs of their employees' healthcare and lifestyle decisions.

Rather than making the decision to cut health benefits or increase insurance premiums for employees in order to better afford the rising medical costs, more and more forward thinking employers are turning to corporate wellness programs. Over the past ten or more years these programs have become common and have moved off of the sidelines and into the mainstream – and the results are encouraging. Wellness programs, when designed to educate, encourage, and reward healthy employee lifestyle behaviors have shown in most studies to garner at least a 1:3 return on investment within the first 3 to 5 years, and there are a number of companies who are seeing much higher returns.

This book is a collection of articles written by professionals who are already deeply involved in creating, studying, and/or implementing effective wellness programs for their companies. Who better to tell us about the successes, failures, challenges and opportunities that wellness programs can provide than those professionals who are already brining these programs to life for hundreds of companies nationwide? By reading these articles, it is my hope that you learn from the author's experience and apply their lessons and insights into you own corporate environment or client base. None of these authors provide a complete guide for creating the "best" wellness program – and they shouldn't. Every company, every organization, every group of employees is different. They bring with them the challenges of different corporate cultures, different access to and skill levels for using technology, and different health and lifestyle behavior challenges. There is no one right way to create a wellness program – but there is a base set of skills, knowledge, and philosophies that can help you design the program that meets the needs of any organization. I urge you to read these articles, learn from the authors, and review the key points offered at the end of each chapter. Focus on these points and apply the information to your specific situation.

This book is the beginning of creating a knowledge base around corporate wellness. How you use the information and apply it to your situation is where your real knowledge will come from. I encourage you to get your certification, put your new skills to use in creating the best corporate wellness program that you can for your organization and share your experience with us. We would love to hear about your success! Good luck and enjoy the journey.

CHAPTER 1
Program Design

Using Effective Engagement Strategies to Drive Long-Term Program Success
By: *Barton H. Sheeler*

Introduction
Changing culture and managing change in people follow hand in hand. The key to building a successful wellness program is to first get people to be aware of and understand their health issues, engage them into programs and support them to actively participate in making successful changes toward healthier lifestyle habits and choices. Over the years, I've found that all programs that successfully achieve these goals have three essential ingredients in common:

1) Integrated and personalized programs, tools and services

2) Strong communication and support from top leadership

3) Meaningful incentives to encourage program participation

Let's Be Clear About Engagement
What's the difference between engagement and participation when it comes to wellness? It's a good question. Lately, the terms have become commingled in an effort to quantify and measure interactions with members. However, they are not one and the same. The distinction is an important one that can mean the difference between initial success and sustainable results.

Effective Engagement is a Two-way Street
There are two sides to every conversation. First, there is a person with something to say. Secondly, there needs to be a person who is willing and able to hear and respond. In the same way, engagement is a two-way street – requiring a message to be delivered and feedback to be attained. It requires that both parties be actively involved in moving the discussion forward by interacting along the way.

Optimal engagement, just like effective communication, is give and take, back and forth. It's the difference between "talking at you" and "talking with you." When communication only goes one way, it's impersonal, ineffective and leads to a dead end.

The way to tell if optimal engagement has occurred in wellness is if a closed-loop communication exists and a personal connection has been made. This is more than sending out flyers or notices to employees about an upcoming biometric screening, or the employee submitting an online HRA; both are one-way communications. Optimal engagement requires communication that goes both ways and establishes a relationship, such as a telephone conversation to follow up HRA results, an email string in response to a member question, or a reply to a mail correspondence.

If employees don't respond to an offer to engage, it could be because they don't feel the offer is relevant; or they may feel they don't have the ability to respond because of barriers that exist in their life. In either case, engagement can't happen.

So what's the secret to breaking through the resistance and achieving optimal engagement? First, provide an offer that is relevant and compelling. This starts by understanding that health and wellness are innately personal. People are guided in the decisions they make as much, if not more, by emotion as by logic or reason. For this reason, the most effective communications need to connect with people at an emotional level.

Meaningful participation in health and wellness can only occur when people have truly engaged. Half-measures won't provide sustainable results.

Effective Engagement Strategies Set the Foundation for Participation
Just like two-way communication is critical to effective engagement, building participation requires give and take. In building a wellness program, the key is to get people to first understand their health issues (give awareness), help them become fully invested in the programs (take action) and, ultimately, support them in making successful changes toward healthier lifestyle habits and choices (achieve improvement). You can't just convey the information or post the new rules. Each participant needs to be part of the conversation by interacting with communications, tools, events and providing ongoing feedback.

Three Essential Ingredients to Sustained Participation
Over the years, I've found that successful wellness programs all have these three essential ingredients in common:

1) **Solid programming that is personalized to each participant.** This includes a number of online tools like health assessments, risk reports and educational programming. The key is to provide instant "personalized feedback" to assist participants with understanding their individual health issues and making informed decisions.

2) **Clear communication from the top down.** Programs need a strong, consistent communication plan that is year-round, and support from top leadership within the organization.

3) **Meaningful and tangible incentives.** People don't feel different from Monday to Tuesday, so it's hard to get them to act differently from Tuesday to Wednesday. Incentives help to get the conversation started, and then reinforce active participation over time as people engage with the wellness program.

All three are important to sustained participation and will contribute to the long-term success of the program. Think of it like the three legs of a tripod – removing any one leg causes the program to tumble.

Programming to Meet People Where They Are and Make the Experience Personal

All wellness program platforms need to include the basics, such as an online health assessment and reporting. But in order to be really engaging, the experience should be "member-centric" – personalized for users with features such as individual reports that use predictive modeling to indicate various risks (e.g., the likelihood of the onset of a variety of disease states and educational lessons tailored to each person's individual health risks and needs).

Personalized health assessments, reports and tools will help create greater awareness of one's health risks and issues. From there, a personalized action plan will help break the "path to improvement" into attainable steps and goals. People need to remember that they did not get to an unhealthy state overnight, and they can't fix everything overnight, either. It takes time and sustained effort to change to healthy behaviors.

Combined health trackers allow a two-way method of setting goals and being held accountable along the way. By using personalized tools like an action plan and online lessons or, if possible, working with a health coach to set goals; the trackers reinforce the need to improve personal responsibility for individual health.

The more informed and educated people are about their individual health concerns, the more likely they are to actively participate in modifying unhealthy behaviors and lowering their health risks. Using engaging programs and educational tools will facilitate this educational process and provide the understanding and confidence needed to make appropriate lifestyle changes.

Figure 1.1: Sample Online Educational Lesson

Each member in the program is assigned a series of lessons based on the answers to the health assessment. Just select the lesson category and then click on the lesson title to view. A quiz is available at the end of each lesson to confirm understanding and get credit for completion of the lesson.

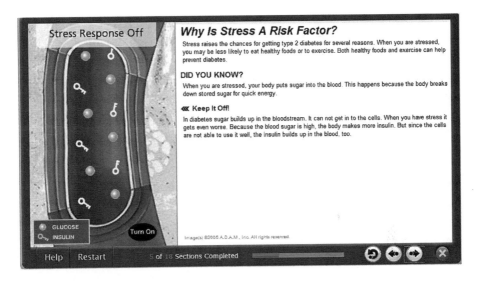

Communication, Communication, Communication – You Have to "Walk the Talk"

The second leg of the wellness tripod is clear communication. Top leadership needs to participate in the program and "walk the talk." They need to lead by example and communicate the importance of wellness by clearly describing annual participation requirements and promoting the incentives each person can earn for completion of various activities.

It's not enough to hire a wellness company and expect the company culture to change overnight. It's a team effort, and it must be managed that way. A vendor can run the program, engage the people and demonstrate ROI, but only if the program is well-communicated year round – not just at benefit selection or when it's time to take a health assessment. Getting key leadership, owners, etc. engaged in the process, promoting the programs, and being visible in their own participation and support of the programs is absolutely essential. In short, they need to "walk the talk" and reinforce the importance of living a healthy lifestyle.

Try using sign-up sheets for the biometric screening event, or require that email confirmations about team selections for an upcoming "health challenge" be sent to a wellness coordinator to ensure the message meets the "two-way communication" standard noted above. Then survey the participants during the year to get feedback on what is working well, what they liked best and what they would suggest in the future.

When selecting a health and wellness company, consider your in-house ability to develop effective program communication campaigns, and then find out what experience the vendor has in assisting with this valuable piece of the program. Ask for examples of welcome letters, posters, postcards, e-mail messaging, etc. More recently, health challenges have become part of progressive wellness programs. Challenges keep the communication about the importance of, and progress within, various components of the wellness program visible and "on the front burner" – a great way to keep the communication process flowing throughout the year.

Incentives Drive Participation and Foster Sustained Participation
The lure of free money is hard to resist. That's why the surest way to foster real program success is to use meaningful and tangible incentives that encourage engagement and active participation. Again, it's the two-way street – if you do a, b and c, we'll give you x, y and z – a reward for the effort!

However, the role of incentives must be carefully considered. Financial incentives sound good in theory, but there is no clear evidence that they alone motivate sustainable behavior change. When it comes to health behaviors, people are human. The decisions we make are not always logical. What's more, health status is a complex product of lifestyle choices, physiological and genetic components. People start from different places in health status; if the outcome goal is viewed as unachievable, those who could benefit the most from health improvement may not engage, even if they initially participate to get the cash incentive.

We know from behavioral economists that people place more priority on the present (the immediate gratification of overeating, for example) than the future (the risk of gaining weight). It's not logical, but it is reality. It's also why financial incentives alone don't achieve long-term behavior change.

By applying the lessons learned from behavioral economics, we can improve incentive program design. Employers should resist putting all of their incentive "eggs" in an outcome-based basket. Rather, you should consider a balanced strategy that integrates extrinsic rewards and intrinsic enticements. A successful incentive strategy should start with the end in mind and be focused to achieve three primary goals:

GOAL INCENTIVE

Participation Extrinsic rewards to generate initial engagement

Behavior Change Intrinsic rewards to support sustained engagement and motivation

Outcomes Extrinsic rewards to recognize progress and achievement

This holistic framework considers the duality of how people make decisions and provides both tangible and intangible incentives to achieve multiple program goals. Extrinsic rewards such as cash, gift cards, prizes and discounts appeal to the emotional need for immediate gratification. Intrinsic enticement such as peer support in a walking club, working with a health coach to set and achieve health goals, friendly competitions and recognition in a company newsletter appeals to psycho-social needs to be accepted.

Using an incentive point tracker to manage individual progress can help people keep score during the year and reinforce healthy living as each new reward threshold is reached. Each program is organized around the needs of each group. The incentive point tracker permits an administrator to set up items like program categories, activities, frequency and related point values which can be modified from one program year to another. The rewards section lists the corresponding reward levels.

Figure 1.2: Sample Incentive Point Tracker

The incentive point tracker takes the work out of managing a health and wellness program which can be modified on a group-by-group basis as needed.

Groups can set up and track incentive time frames and track points in a number of categories, all for a specific period (and not necessarily specific to a calendar year). Administrative reports track the total sum of points earned as members complete activities and accumulate points during the program period.

As the activities tracked in the incentive management tool are completed, they are also reported back to the employer to acknowledge completion of certain events and receipt of sufficient points to earn the corresponding program reward, all while promoting personal responsibility and a culture of long-term program engagement.

In the end, the best advice for employers is that you can't just select a wellness partner and contract out cultural change. However, you can change the health status of an organization with effective engagement in "member-centric" programs, strong year-round communications promoting the value of good health and incentives to maintain sustained participation.

Key Ideas:

- If employees don't respond to an offer to engage, it could be because they don't feel the offer is relevant; or feel they don't have the ability to respond because of barriers that exist in their life. In either case, engagement can't happen.

- The most effective communications need to connect with people at an emotional level.

- The key is to get people to first understand their health issues, help them become fully invested in the programs and, ultimately, support them in making successful changes toward healthier lifestyle habits and choices.

- You can't just convey the information or post the new rules. Each participant needs to be part of the conversation by interacting with communications, tools, events and providing ongoing feedback.

- Three Essential Ingredients to Sustained Participation

  1. Solid programming that is personalized to each participant

  2. Clear communication from the top down

  3. Meaningful and tangible incentives

- In order to be really engaging, the experience should be "member-centric" – personalized for users with features such as individual reports that use predictive modeling to indicate various risks.

- A successful incentive strategy should start with the end in mind and be focused to achieve these three primary goals: Participation, Behavior Change, and Outcomes.

Questions:

1. What is a reason that an employee would not respond to an offer to engage in a wellness program?

    a. The offer is not relevant to them

    b. They have personal barriers in their life which prevent their engagement

    c. All of the above

    d. None of the above

2. What are the three «essential ingredients» to sustaining participation?

    a. Personalized programming, clear communication, meaningful and tangible incentives

    b. A good wellness company, health challenges, and health trackers

    c. Sage, rosemary, and thyme

    d. "Walking the talk," detailed HRAs, group incentives

3. What is meant by "walking the talk?"

    a. Following through with incentives

    b. Having leadership engaged in your program

    c. Having access to a track where employees can walk, and talk business

    d. Using personalized tracking programs

4. The most effective communications need to connect with people at an emotional level.

    a. True

    b. False

Building a Strategic Wellness Program
By Fabien Loszach

The times have changed – the vast majority of employers recognize that their employees' health affects the productivity and the performance of their company[1]. Research shows that employee health directly influences work behaviour, attendance and on-the-job performance, and healthcare costs. Seventy-six percent of American businesses report year-to-year healthcare cost increases of as much as 10 percent.

Surprisingly, the solution to the problem of rising health costs in business is quite simple; it consists of implementing means for employees to access health initiatives like sports activities and nutritious food, and taking measures to encourage these healthy choices. However, disparate initiatives such as offering discounts on a gym membership or others; random incentives typically have results that leave something to be desired.

To ensure that workplace health initiatives change the workplace dynamics, and the corporate culture, to the point of generating a respectable return on investment; a strategic plan must be implemented. This article aims to serve as a guide – it will present the necessary steps to implementing an employee wellness program that is structured and integrated.

Employer Engagement – Straight from the Top
For many employers health is considered to be the responsibility of individuals, not managers or other company leaders. Some believe that health is a matter best handled by the public system. Yet, a careful analysis of the facts shows that businesses today have no choice but to take action if they want to maximize performance in the long run.

It is widely agreed that for any wellness program to succeed, top management must be fully on board. An employer or CEO must lead by example through his or her own engagement and lifestyle; simply paying for the program isn't enough. This attitude should be reflected by a written policy that is approved by management and personnel.

Getting Employees on Board

Employees often say they don't feel supported by their employers when it comes to good health choices, even when there is a wellness program available. Most employees claim that their company is only moderately-to-not-supportive when it comes to their efforts to be healthy[2]. To ensure the success of a wellness program, it is critical to deliver a program that employees want and need.

Employees need to feel that a wellness program fits in line with their personal goals and beliefs, and is not simply part of their job requirements. This will require patience from managers, and planning that includes meetings where employees can present their ideas about what they would like to improve about their health and what they would like to see in a wellness program. Another essential element to ensure employee participation is a strong awareness campaign promoting the program.

Creating a Health and Wellness Committee

A dedicated committee composed of motivated and informed individuals will make a huge difference in the success of a wellness program. Management can decide between a structure that is more or less flexible, depending on the size of the organization, by opting for a committee with elected members or for a less formal structure with a 'wellness leader.'

The mandate of the health and wellness committee will be to organize and administer the program, relay the vision of the employer, promote the program, evaluate ongoing needs and objectives, implement solutions and support employees in their efforts.

True project managers, committee members will simultaneously fill the role of researcher (sharing knowledge and best practices on how to evaluate, strengthen and grow the program), educator (providing employees with tools, training, manuals, etc.), strategist (developing short and long term strategy) and policy maker – they will become bona fide health consultants at work.

Diagnosing the Workforce

The most important step in creating a strategic wellness program is one of the first actions the wellness committee should undertake – evaluating the current situation and the overall health of employees. The diagnostic, assessment or data collection phase is often overlooked by employers, who prefer to implement turn-key activities that provide maximum visibility, but it is a critical first step for guiding future actions and decisions. A good diagnostic tool will allow the committee to understand the overall health status of the company, identify the needs of employees and target activities accordingly, and establish the priorities for implementation.

Ideally, the diagnostic should be conducted through an anonymous questionnaire that covers the four essential components of corporate wellness: lifestyle choices, organizational wellness (workplace environment, management practices, etc.), and physical and emotional wellness. This will ensure that employees answer questions with complete honesty, and that every possible factor affecting health and wellness is covered. The diagnostic should also measure participation and satisfaction rates, as these provide a great first impression of how well the company is faring.

Based on the results of the diagnostic, the committee will be able to identify the specific issues that are driving health costs in the company. They will then be able to decide on a strategy that meets the needs of employees while addressing the problems identified, and define specific goals for the wellness program. At this point, the committee will be able to outline an action plan for the first year. The committee should strive to make the program flexible; rather than laying down a fixed five-year plan, they should plan to reassess and adjust the program each year according to the results.

Branding and Communication

Once the committee has figured out an action plan it must think about branding and promotion. The success of a wellness program will hinge largely on the strength of the communications regarding the program. The committee will need to determine the ideal combination of communication outlets, such as email newsletters, posters and other physical reminders, regular group gatherings and possibly the creation of a website.

The committee may decide to develop a brand image for the program – projects that unify people always have a good signature. A brand image will tie together all communications regarding the wellness program and grow recognition by creating an identifier for employees and their families. A brand image will establish a look and feel for the program at its initial launch and reinforce the overall message through the ongoing communications done via blog or newsletter. The goal is to create a veritable wellness culture and maintain momentum and participation after the launch.

Action Plan and Implementation

Many companies specializing in health services for businesses offer all-inclusive services. They are often quite expensive, while their long-term value remains to be seen. Helen Darling, president and CEO of the National Business Group on Health wrote in Benefits Canada that "consumers are telling us that the one-size-fits-all approach to health and wellness isn't working for them. In order to help with their challenges and reduce costs, they want health programs that speak to their individual and families' healthcare needs." [3]

The best thing to do is build your own program "a-la-carte", taking into account the insights from the diagnostic phase. Contrary to conventional wisdom, building a customized program is not more expensive and it leaves employers free to make adjustments based on the results. It's important to advocate initiatives that will take place in all four areas of intervention (lifestyle, workplace, physical, emotional) through the development of programs for physical activity and healthy nutrition, smoking cessation, team-building, stress management, etc. It goes without saying that any service providers hired, such as fitness trainers, nutritionists, leadership coaches, etc., must be well qualified.

What is absolutely critical is to tailor the program to meet employees' needs, not just the objectives of the company. Without employee engagement, any wellness program will ultimately fail; so knowing what employees want and how to motivate them is essential for the program to succeed.

Evaluating and Adjusting

The goal of building a wellness program is to create a true wellness culture that incites all employees to become involved in the program and become more aware of their own health and what they can do to improve it. To achieve this goal, the committee should demonstrate vision and consistency in their approach by implementing several solutions and building relationships, partnerships and collaborations with internal and external partners. Finally, they should always measure and evaluate their progress by obtaining employee feedback, tracking participation rates and monitoring absentee rates and disability claims. Constant evaluation will allow the committee to determine what works and what doesn't, to ensure that the wellness program is always meeting its objectives.

Key Ideas:

- Random incentives typically have results that leave something to be desired.

- An employer or CEO must lead by example through his or her own engagement and lifestyle; simply paying for the program isn't enough.

- Employees need to feel that a wellness program fits in line with their personal goals and beliefs, and is not simply part of their job requirements.

- A dedicated committee composed of motivated and informed individuals will make a huge difference in the success of a wellness program.

  - Management can decide between a structure that is more or less flexible (often depending on the size of the organization), by opting for a committee with elected members or for a less formal structure with a 'wellness leader.'

  - The mandate of the health and wellness committee will be to organize and administer the program, relay the vision of the employer, promote the program, evaluate ongoing needs and objectives, implement solutions and support employees.

  - Committee members will simultaneously fill the role of researcher, educator, strategist and policy maker.

- The most important step in creating a strategic wellness program is one of the first actions the wellness committee should undertake – evaluating the current situation and the overall health of employees.

- The diagnostic should be conducted through an anonymous questionnaire that covers the four essential components of corporate wellness: lifestyle choices, organizational wellness and physical and emotional wellness.

Questions:

1. A wellness program works best when a employee feels that is part of the job requirement

    a. True

    b. False

2. What are the four essential components of wellness a good corporate wellness program seeks to address?

    a. Lifestyle choices, organizational wellness, emotional wellness, and physical wellness

    b. Profit, ROI, Productivity, and Sustainability

    c. Corporate Leadership, low healthcare costs, better workplace dynamic, a function wellness committee

    d. None of the above

3. Which role of a wellness committee member is missing from the following list: Researcher, strategist, policy maker, and _____?

    a. Manager

    b. Participant

    c. Educator

    d. Reformer

4. What is the first step to creating a wellness program?

    a. Evaluating the overall health situation of the employees

    b. Investigating ROI from the program

    c. Design a list of incentives

    d. Develop a wellness newsletter

Making Wellness Work for You Now and Later
By Mark Roberts

Wellness programs work. But they can quickly turn into money pits if you make one of the classic mistakes, according to HRMorning. com. Wellness Workdays, a corporate wellness program provider, recently wrote an article titled "Top Ten Wellness Program Mistakes," which was published in *Benefits Magazine*. Here's what they said are the biggest pitfalls in wellness programs today:

1. **Being impatient.** Companies typically will not see a return on their investments for years. Don't give up if you aren't seeing savings right away. The goal for the first couple of years should be to ramp up employee participation (say to 25 percent by the end of year one and to 50 percent by the end of year two). In year three or four, you can start looking for savings.

2. **Not collecting enough data.** What activities would interest your employees most? What health risks are most prevalent among your employees? These are the things you need to find out. After that, it's a matter of developing activities that interest employees and target those health risks.

3. **Not setting health goals.** Simply offering programs or setting up a gym does not a wellness program make. These are activities. A program encourages participants to reach personal goals or benchmarks.

4. **Concentrating solely on the unhealthy.** Of course, it's essential to get your high-risk employees involved early. But don't forget to keep your healthy employees, well... healthy. Otherwise you'll see them slipping into your high-risk group.

5. **Having too few options.** The best way to maximize participation? Offer a variety of programs and activities — not just a gym and a walking program. Don't forget about mental wellness. Classes on stress and financial management can also be a boon.

6. **Not offering carrots.** Many employees simply won't participant if there's no incentive in it for them. And no, better health is not an incentive that will grab their attention.

7. **Pinching pennies.** You can't get something for nothing.

8. **Failing to get support from upper management.** This is one area where your leaders will have to lead. If upper management's not involved, employees won't take it seriously.

9. **Not tracking results.** There's no way to tell whether a wellness program is having an impact if you're not at least tracking participation.

10. **Failing to re-evaluate.** Once you've got a successful wellness program in place, you can't just put it on autopilot. Employees' needs and interests change. At least once a year, check to see if new health risks are popping up or if employee's interests in certain programs are changing.

Synopsis
Regardless of your current offerings to employees, wellness should be a key element of any health benefits plan design you offer. To not do so is to ignore the detrimental overall effects that unhealthy employees have on your bottom line. Current studies show that wellness programs work and provide a good return on investment, especially when properly implemented and when engaged by workers.

When considering your investment in human capital, you cannot afford not to have a wellness program in place. Human capital refers to the stock of competencies, knowledge and personality attributes embodied in the ability to perform labor so as to produce economic value, according to Paul Rauseo, Fox Business commentator. The success of a company depends very heavily on the productivity and work performance of its human capital; its people. The ability to function and perform at a high level consistently is greatly enhanced by employee wellness programs. Wellness programs focus on the physical wellbeing of employees, looking after medical requirements and ensuring personal health is a priority.

According to Advanced Benefit Strategies of Virginia, as a result of the PPACA, there is increased interest in employee wellness programs by employers striving to lower the profit demaging cost of offering health insurance to their employees. Healthcare reform has clarified the incentives, both positive and penal that will be allowed by the Department of Labor. Surprisingly, there is wide a latitude employers may use with incentives and penalties tied to wellness plan participation.

There is mounting evidence that wellness programs can significantly lower health costs when implemented with proper incentives. Here are five reasons in synopsis:

1. Although definitive studies have been difficult to quantify in the past, evidence is currently emerging that **strong incentive wellness programs can significantly lower employer healthcare costs.** The key to success lies in getting the participation of all employees. Significant financial incentives such as a $500 cash incentive for completing an evaluation, or significantly lowering contributions for participants who meet certain goals, has proven to be cost effective.

2. **Healthier employees are productive.** With the recession still working itself out, employees are being asked to be more productive than ever, just as business owners must be more productive with the resources they have to stay competitive. Keeping your human resources, people, in top shape with preventive maintenance is a common sense way to gain an edge on the competition.

3. It's been proven that employees utilize medical care more efficiently when they have "skin in the game." In other words, **people care more about making smart choices when they have a financial stake in the outcome.** Wellness programs demonstrate to employees that the employer cares about their wellbeing and that their actions have an impact on the company. The movements toward "consumer driven" health plans with higher deductibles that give employees a greater stake in their care are perfect partners for wellness programs. Employees easily see the advantage of becoming healthier and spending less on out-of-pocket costs.

4. This may seem to be common sense, but **absenteeism and sick leave costs are significant, and improving the health of employees is proven to lower the rate of absenteeism.** Wellness programs educate employees extensively on how to avoid illness and often provide personal health improvement

strategies to engage employees on a specific level and reduce sick days for a large portion of the employee population.

5. Although difficult to put a price on, employers implementing wellness programs report a **surge in employee morale and loyalty to the company.** When employees feel their employer is truly interested in their best interest, they tend to be loyal, hard workers in return. Reduced turnover and recruiting costs are also part of this equation, as a happier workplace results in less turnover.

Many companies that implement wellness tied to meaningful incentives are experiencing double digit decreases in health insurance costs and sick leave. Legal concerns about strong incentive-based wellness programs have been a deterrent to the adoption of programs by some companies. The Obama administration's healthcare reform guidance that permits and actually encourages tough requirements for wellness programs has reinvigorated the market for employer-sponsored wellness plans. Educating your employees on the validity and importance of wellness is critical to your overall business success. According to *Benefits Pro Magazine,* when focused on providing benefits that work, make sure you include a wellness platform that augments your major medical and ancillary benefits. Plus, your corporate bottom line will thank you for years to come. According to Trotter Wellness, programs like health coaching, and Health Risk Assessments, when combined with clinical and lifestyle behavior changes, bring as much as a 5 to 1 Return on Investment. That would put a smile on any CFO's face.

Solutions

Employers are searching for ways to improve the bottom line for both corporate profit and healthy employees, realizing that these assets go hand in hand. Finding solutions that work and are affordable can be a challenge in a tight economy and a down business cycle. You can go direct to a vendor or multiple vendors, but the administration can be challenging. There are companies that can assist with every aspect of a wellness program, from product aggregation, administration and plan design options. The same wellness program will not work for every company or every employee, a plan designed around the needs of the majority of employees will prove to be the most effective option.

Key Ideas:

- The goal for the first couple of years should be to increase employee participation. In year three or four, you can start looking for savings.

- Once you've got a successful wellness program in place, you can't just put it on autopilot. At least once a year, check to see if new health risks are popping up or if employees are becoming more/less interested in certain programs.

- It's been proven that employees utilize medical care more efficiently when they have "skin in the game." In other words, people care more about making smart choices when they have a financial stake in the outcome.

- A plan designed around the needs of the majority of employees will prove to be the most effective option.

- The biggest pitfalls in wellness programs are:
  - Being impatient
  - Not collecting enough data
  - Not setting health goals
  - Concentrating solely on the unhealthy
  - Having too few options
  - Not offering carrots
  - Pinching pennies
  - Failing to get support from upper management
  - Not tracking results
  - Failing to re-evaluate

Questions:

1. What is the best way to maximize participation?

    a. Offer a few activities that many people

    b. Offer a variety of activities

    c. Focus only on mental wellness

    d. None of the above

2. What is the goal of for the first years of a wellness program

    a. Maximize ROI

    b. Focus on employee participation

    c. Look to cut costs

    d. Discover new actives to maximize wellness

3. Which of the following are some of the biggest pitfalls in wellness programs today?

    a. Being impatient

    b. Not offering carrots

    c. Not setting health goals

    d. All of the above

4. What does it mean to have "skin in the game"

    a. People are more likely to make smart decisions if they have a personal stake in the outcome

    b. Wellness programs should offer contact sports like football and basketball

    c. Companies should offer wellness programs that include spa treatment which are good for the skin

    d. By setting personal goals, the wellness program is likely to succeed.

Building A Successful and Sustainable Worksite Wellness Program from Scratch

By William McPeck

Introduction

Your employer has decided to start a worksite wellness program and you have been assigned to develop the program. You have no training or experience in worksite wellness programs. If this describes you, read on; this chapter is for you.

This chapter begins with two assumptions. The first assumption is that the business case has already been made for why a worksite wellness program should be developed and the decision has been made to develop a worksite wellness program. As a result of these decisions, you the reader have been charged with either leading the development of the program or to oversee its development.

The second assumption is that a decision has been made to develop your own internal worksite wellness program rather than outsource the whole program to an outside vendor. This is not to say however, that an outside vendor might not be sought out for specific program interventions as a component of the internal program you are developing.

In this chapter, the term wellness coordinator will be used to designate the person charged with leading the development of the program. In reality, the person may have any number of job titles.

Having studied, worked and consulted in the worksite wellness field for more than 12 years, I believe successful and sustainable worksite wellness programs are based on four principles:

1. Management Support and Engagement
2. Employee Support, Participation and Engagement
3. The Program is Comprehensive in Scope
4. The Program Creates, Delivers and Can Demonstrate Value

Worksite Wellness Program Models

While a number of worksite wellness program models have been put forth in the literature, my sense of them is that they are all very similar, differing only in the number of elements they contain or how they define these elements. My two favorite models are: The Wellness Council of America's Seven Benchmarks of Success [4] and the model put forth in the 2008 wellness program development cycle article by Ryan, Chapman and Rink. [2] This chapter is based on an integration and synthesis of these two models.

The 10 Steps in the Development of a Successful and Sustainable Worksite Wellness Program.

1. Understanding Your Mandate for the Wellness Initiative

2. Engaging All Managers and Supervisors

3. Building Your Wellness Program Infrastructure

4. Researching, Analyzing and Identifying Employee and Organizational Needs

5. Formulate Program Goals and Objectives

6. Program and Evaluation Plan Development

7. Plan Approval

8. Plan Implementation

9. Creating a Supportive Environment

10. Evaluating What Your Program Does

1. Understanding Your Mandate for the Wellness Initiative

One of the four principles of success and sustainability is management support and engagement. A lack of managerial support and engagement is a program- killer. Part of management's engagement is a clear statement by senior management as to their expectations and goals for the wellness program. It is critical that you understand senior management's mandate.

As your organization's worksite wellness coordinator, you will need ongoing engagement from senior management. Here's a list of what you will need from them:

• Ongoing support consisting of:

• Communication to managers/supervisors and employees

- Resources; financial and personnel
- Visible participation; leading by example
- Creation of supportive organizational policies
- Integration of health and wellness principles and practices within the organizational structure
- Education of managers and supervisors
- Help with the alignment of the wellness program with the company's mission, vision and goals

Tasks for the wellness coordinator during this phase include:

- Identify a senior management wellness sponsor or champion
- Understand your organization's priorities
- Identify your organization's values
- Know the values and benefits your program can bring to the organizations
- Gather information on your senior leaders' leadership styles
- Create a plan as to how you will periodically communicate with senior management about the wellness program
- Understand how decisions are made in your organization
- Develop communication tools and templates for senior management to use

2. Engaging All Managers and Supervisors

Many of the worksite wellness models limit management support and engagement discussion to just the C-suite. My experience has taught me that limiting support and engagement to the C-suite is insufficient. Mid-level managers and supervisors have a critical role to play in supporting your worksite wellness program. What you need from mid-level managers and supervisors consists of:

- Support
  - Communication with their direct reports
  - Provide opportunities for their direct reports to participate in the worksite wellness program's interventions

- Visible participation in the wellness program's interventions

Tasks for the wellness coordinator in this phase include:

- Develop and share with managers and supervisors communication tools and strategies they can use with their direct reports
- Educate managers/supervisors about the value to the work unit of having healthy employees
- Work with managers/supervisors to identify and remove barriers to employee participation
- Work with managers/supervisors to identify times for the scheduling of wellness program interventions so they will be least disruptive to work production, flow and schedules
- Actively promote toward and engage manager and supervisor participation in the wellness program's interventions

3. Building Your Wellness Program Infrastructure

Now that you have your guidance and marching orders from senior management, it is time to move on to creating your program's infrastructure. A worksite wellness program infrastructure generally consists of three levels. These levels and their roles are:

- Wellness Champion(s)
- Advocacy and communication
- Wellness Team or Committee
- Advocacy, communication, planning, participation, motivation and support
- Wellness Coordinator
- FT, PT, volunteer or contractor

Wellness Champions

Within the worksite wellness community, wellness champions have historically been defined as line-level employees who encourage health and wellness within their work unit level through direct contact with their fellow employees. Champions have also been labeled as wellness ambassadors, sparkplugs, wellness associates, peer mentors and similarly related terms.

Through the use of leadership, passion, enthusiasm and friendship, the wellness champion serves as a go-to resource for co-workers and a wellness program leader. The wellness champion provides information and monitors employee reaction to wellness program initiatives. Wellness champions work informally at their worksite to encourage their peers and to vitalize the program's initiatives. Worksite wellness champions can also, depending upon their interest and level of training, organize on site wellness events and coordinate other wellness-related interventions.

The skills and qualities of a successful wellness champion include:

1. Passion, but not fanaticism, about health and wellness
2. Confidence and credibility
3. Being friendly and approachable and demonstrating a positive attitude
4. Being a good listener and effective communicator
5. Being a person who walks the wellness talk
6. Demonstrating caring and commitment to the goal of wellness
7. A recognition of the importance of having a culture of health and wellness
8. Having an insight into the work unit's social network
9. Serving as a positive buffer between line employees and the wellness program
10. Helping to energize and engage employees in wellness

Wellness Team or Committee
Why do you need a team or committee? The simple answer lies in continuity. If your wellness program is driven by a team or committee, your program will survive the loss of any one individual leader (champion or coordinator) of your program.

Having a solid, functional wellness team or committee is fundamental to the success of your wellness program. Before creating a new stand-alone wellness committee, look around to see if an existing committee is willing to expand its role to encompass employee wellness.

The committee's membership should reflect a cross-sectional representation of your organization, including work units, shifts, etc. The size of your wellness committee will be a function of the size of your organization. In large organizations, the committee should probably be no larger than 10-15 members. I have seen an organization with just 10 employees have a very successful 3-person wellness committee.

I firmly believe that the leadership of the wellness team or committee should not, by default, fall to the wellness coordinator. I recommend that the wellness coordinator serve as a staff person to the committee.

Make sure that the wellness team or committee's responsibilities are clear.

Four Necessary Functions of a Wellness Committee

1. Analyze annual employee health and wellness interest survey data, along with any other relevant employee-related data routinely collected by the organization. This other relevant data might include data from the following sources:

   a. Employee health risk assessment data

   b. Health insurance medical and behavioral health aggregate claims data

   c. Safety and workers' compensation data

   d. Absenteeism and productivity data

   e. Short- and long-term disability data

2. Develop or assist in the development of an annual wellness program operating plan. The operating plan should include monthly, quarterly and annual wellness program goals. These goals should be" SMART" Goals:

   a. Specific

   b. Measurable

   c. Attainable

   d. Realistic (but also requiring effort)

   e. Time-specific

The committee should track, review and, if necessary modify the goals.

3. Monitor the implementation of the wellness program. Be on the lookout for program implementation issues. The committee should monitor such things as the implementation schedule, implementation practices and employee participation levels. The committee should also be monitoring employee feedback about the various program interventions.

4. The committee should be involved in the auditing and evaluation of the wellness program. All aspects of the program should be evaluated using process, output and outcome evaluation strategies. Program interventions and the worksite's physical environment should be subject to periodic auditing practices.

All wellness committees, at a minimum, should perform these four functions. Additional functions may result from the organization's practices, the work environment and the organization's culture.

Wellness Coordinator

The wellness coordinator may either be a full-time, part-time or contracted position. The wellness coordinator is generally responsible for the implementation of a wellness program and its day-to-day operation. If an existing full-time or part-time employee is tasked with the added responsibilities of implementing a wellness program, it is important that this employee's wellness duties, expectations and responsibilities be clearly spelled out in his or her job description.

Tasks for the wellness coordinator in this phase include:

- Identify wellness champion(s)

- Define wellness team composition

- Assemble the team

- Establish team protocols

- Staff, don't lead, the wellness team

4. Researching, Analyzing and Identifying Employee and Organizational Needs

When it comes to establishing and implementing a wellness program it is important to establish that your wellness program is data driven and not just a series of feel-good activities. There should be a rational purpose behind what you do.

It is critical that you research, analyze and identify employee and organizational needs. Strategies for accomplishing this include:

- Identify existing employee and organizational data sources
- Identify needs for data that does not currently exist
- Gather the data
- Analyze the data
- Identify program's target needs

Identify Needed Data:
Do you have access to the following data sets?

- Employee Needs and Interest Survey
- Health Risk Assessment
- Biometric Screening Data
- Organizational Cultural Audit
- Worksite Environmental Scan

Gather the existing data already being collected by your organization.

Analyze the existing data; what does it reveal to you?

Identify your wellness program's targeted needs; what are the gaps between your goals and the existing data?

Develop a report of your findings and communicate these findings to all interested parties (e.g., your wellness champions, wellness team and senior management).

Tasks for the wellness coordinator in this phase include:

When it comes to identifying potential programming interventions, these interventions can be one of two types:

- Accepted best practice
- Evidence-based

Accepted best practices are interventions that have been used by many and appear to achieve health promotion goals in a given situation. The success of these interventions often depends upon the wellness coordinator's degree of awareness, articulation, clarity and reflection. The use of accepted best practices is often based on intuition or the experience or practice of another wellness coordinator who has used the intervention successfully. An example of an accepted best practice would be programming or interventions offered by a national health-related non-profit.

Evidence-based interventions are the result of a process of planning, implementation and evaluation of programs or interventions that have been copied or adapted from tested models or interventions. Simply stated, evidence-based interventions are research or evaluation based. Sources for evidence-based programming or interventions can be found at the end of the chapter.

When it comes to programming, your challenge as a wellness coordinator is to determine which interventions you are going to offer on site, which interventions you are going to offer electronically and how the site-based and virtual interventions integrate into one seamless wellness program.

When choosing program interventions, it is important to remember that health promotion remains both an art and a science. While there is some good science supporting what we do, practices continually run ahead of the science. Therefore a good mantra to keep in mind is that we should be guided, as opposed to governed, by the science.

Whether you end up choosing an accepted best practice or an evidence-based intervention, you should endeavor to match the best intervention available with your objective and target population. Once you have selected your intervention, you should identify the evaluation or assessment methodologies you will be using to measure the implementation of the intervention and its impact on your objectives.

Your operating plan should spell out who will be responsible for delivering each intervention in your program. Will the intervention be delivered internally or by an outside vendor? If an outside vendor will be used, you need to determine how that vendor will be selected.

With the number of wellness vendors in the marketplace today, it is incumbent upon you to select a vendor carefully. Do your due diligence; don't rush into making a decision.

Look for vendors who are accredited by either URAC or NCQA. While these accreditations are voluntary, they offer you a good starting point.

Elements of sustainable, winning wellness interventions include:

- The program's interventions are realistic, given available resources and the target audience

- Potential program risks have been identified, assessed and plans for these risks have been developed

- Designated interventions are technically feasible and achievable

- Adequate funding has been secured to accomplish the intervention's stated goals and objectives

Tasks for the wellness coordinator during this phase include:

- Identify all potential interventions

- Match targeted employee population with the best intervention

- Plan the interventions

- Plan appropriate evaluation/assessment methods for each intervention

- Develop an annual operating plan

- Vet all intervention vendors

7. Plan Approval

Once your annual operating plan is complete, it is necessary to share the plan and to seek approval of the annual operating plan. At a minimum, share the plan with and seek approval of the plan from your wellness team and senior management.

Tasks for the wellness coordinator during this phase include:

- Present the plan to wellness team for review and approval
- Present the plan to senior management for review and approval

8. Plan Implementation

When it comes to implementing your plan I can't emphasize enough that the role of the worksite wellness coordinator is to deliver results, not just coordinate activities.

Organizations, worksites and individuals are dynamic in nature. As you implement your plan, it is important to keep in mind that you need to balance managerial, organizational and employee needs, desires and interests within available resources. In today's fast-paced, ever-changing environment, it is important that you remain flexible enough to accommodate last-minute changes or issues that arise during the year.

While it is important to be flexible, implement the plan per the schedule you developed. Avoid falling into the trap of chasing the latest and greatest shiny object or program idea.

When it comes to implementing your programming, there are four keys you need to keep in mind:

1. Implement interventions and programming that continually raise employee awareness
2. Your interventions need to create opportunities to enhance employee motivation
3. Your interventions need to give employees the opportunity to learn new knowledge and skills associated with new behaviors
4. Your interventions need to provide opportunities for employees to practice the new behaviors they are learning

Implementing your plan is all about managing your interventions. This will require you to juggle many different elements. Time, budget, vendors, employees and management must all be coordinated. Employees and management must also be satisfied. Simply stated, program management is the control of your program's allocation, utilization and direction of resources in relationship to time and costs.

As a wellness coordinator, you are responsible for the coordination of the interventions outlined in your operating plan. You are therefore tasked with looking after the:

- Financial elements
- Program delivery
- Communications
- Program evaluations necessary to justify your program

It is therefore important to structure your wellness program interventions so all aspects of each intervention can be easily viewed and tracked. This is where your operating plan will come in handy.

No discussion about programming implementation would be complete without some discussion about motivation and incentives.

Motivation exists at three levels:

- Innate
- Intrinsic
- Extrinsic

Innate motivation is, according to Christine Robinson, "The naturally endowed needs, drivers, or desires that motivate a person to a particular action or behavior." [5] Steven Reiss, Ph.D. at Ohio State University has identified 16 innate drivers of behavior. [46]

Intrinsic motivation is the engagement in a task or behavior for its own sake, because the task itself is interesting, appealing or satisfying, with no apparent reward except for the enjoyment gained from performing the task or behavior. Intrinsic drivers of behavior include:

- Feelings of autonomy

- Self-efficacy or self-confidence

Extrinsic motivation is engagement in a task or behavior because of a separate outcome or reward gained by doing the task, recognition gained from doing the task or because the individual has been directed to do the task by someone else. Examples of extrinsic motivators include:

- Use of tangible incentives
- Social supports
- Environment that fosters choice

By definition, then, wellness program incentives are extrinsic motivators. While there is still much heated debate in the field about the use of incentives, my perception is that the use of incentives has become a core part of today's worksite wellness programs.

My understanding of the latest research about incentives is that extrinsic motivators are helpful to get employees to participate in a wellness intervention, but it has not yet been clearly demonstrated that wellness incentives lead to employee engagement in wellness or that they lead to long-term involvement resulting in changes in employee behavior. So for the time being, in addition to providing incentives, wellness coordinators should look to help employees identify and develop their own personal intrinsic motivators based on their personal innate drivers.

Effective program management is critical to keeping your wellness program on track.

Tasks for the wellness coordinator during this phase include:

- Implement interventions
- Manage the interventions
- Problem solve

9. Creating a Supportive Environment

This element is about how the organization can and should support its employees participating in healthy lifestyle changes. When it comes to helping employees develop and maintain a healthy lifestyle, the role of a supportive environment cannot be overemphasized. A critical role for today's wellness coordinator is leading the charge in creating a supportive environment. A supportive environment consists of the following elements:

- Physical environment

- Social environment

- Organizational culture

- Policies

The worksite wellness coordinator should look at the worksite's physical environment from three perspectives:

- What is it like to work here?

- How can I use or improve the existing physical plant and environment to support or enhance wellness initiatives or interventions?

- What opportunities exist that I might be overlooking?

Humans, by their very nature, are social beings. Social support provides motivation, encouragement and accountability to the individual seeking to make a healthy change. As the wellness coordinator, seek out ways to make this need for social support work for you.

Within the field, there is a lot of discussion about creating a healthy culture within an organization. While there might be a lot of discussion, the discussion is seriously lacking in the area of offering the wellness coordinator specific guidance on how to change an organization's culture. Of all the wellness coordinator training programs I have participated in, none have addressed the issue of how to go about changing an organization's culture.

Organizational change initiatives fail as frequently as individual behavior change. While I have previously written about and taught organizational culture change, I am now rethinking this strategy. When it comes to organizational change, the basic question the wellness coordinator needs to ask is this: "Do I want to invest the time and energy necessary to change the organization and its culture, or is it easier for me to identify and understand the organization and its culture and tailor my wellness program strategies and interventions to the existing organization and its culture?"

Working with management to adopt, implement and promote health and wellness policies is a great way to fully support both individual employee and organizational health and wellness goals. Health- and wellness-related policies are just as important as safety and other organizational policies. Policies clearly impact the organization's culture and environment.

Tasks for the wellness coordinator during this phase include:

- Modify the physical environment where possible

- Create social opportunities

- Ensure the wellness program interventions fit with the organization's culture

- Change the organizational culture

- Create health- and wellness-related policies

10. Evaluating What Your Program Does

In most, if not all wellness program models, program evaluation is often listed as the last program element. This is unfortunate as program evaluation is critical to the success and sustainability of your wellness program. What is equally unfortunate is that less than 40 percent of the wellness programs in existence today conduct any type of program evaluation.

If you wish your program to be successful and sustainable, you must evaluate every intervention and activity you engage in. It is critical that you establish your program's results and value from the beginning, because sooner or later someone will ask you for them. At the very least, it will be embarrassing for you to have to admit that you have no results or information to provide the decision makers who are asking. Of equal importance, if you don't measure what your program is doing, how will you know when you need to change what you are doing? Remember the old adage, what gets measured gets done!

I believe that as wellness coordinators, we are better off establishing ways our wellness programs deliver value to the organization. Just like value-based benefits, seek to establish value-based wellness.

Basically, program evaluation consists of one or two types:

- Quantitative
- Qualitative

Program evaluation strategies consist of three types:

- Process evaluation
- Output evaluation
- Outcomes evaluation

The following evaluation measures, as well as others, can be linked to your program objectives and strategies and can be measured as part of your evaluation strategy:

- Participation levels
- Participant satisfaction
- Changes in knowledge, attitudes and behaviors
- Changes in the environment and culture

Important evaluation questions include:

- Did the program meet its objectives?
- How did the users like the intervention?
- What improvements in individual health or risk factors occurred?
- What positive effects did the program have on your organization?
- How much did the program cost?
- What was the net economic effect of the program?
- Based on the current year's efforts and results, how should the program be changed next year?

Tasks for the wellness coordinator during this phase include:

- Appropriately evaluate each and every intervention or activity
- Share your evaluation results with all interested persons
- Use your evaluation results to modify your interventions and your operating plan

Remember, what gets measured gets done.

Conclusion

As a wellness coordinator, you have both an awesome responsibility and opportunity. Worksite wellness works! Your role as a worksite wellness coordinator is to develop a successful and sustainable worksite wellness program.

There are 10 steps to creating a successful and sustainable worksite wellness program. This chapter has outlined these 10 steps. Experience and research have shown that these 10 steps are critical to success and sustainability.

Your challenge becomes how to apply these 10 steps within your organizational context. Cookie-cutter wellness does not work. One-size wellness programming does not fit all. These 10 steps, when modified to your organization, will serve you well.

Resources

U.S. CDC Healthier Worksite Initiative
http://www.cdc.gov/nccdphp/dnpao/hwi/index.htm
U.S. NIOSH Total Worker Health
http://www.cdc.gov/niosh/TWH/
Toronto Health Communication Unit – Comprehensive Workplace Health Promotion
http://www.thcu.ca/infoandresources/resource_display.cfm?res_topicID=16

US Government
CDC – Workplace Health Initiative www.cdc.gov/nccdphp/dnpao/hwi/index.htm
CDC- National Healthy Worksite Program www.cdc.gov/nationalhealthyworksite/index.htm
NIOSH – Total Worker Health www.cdc.gov/niosh/TWH

Canadian Government
Health Canada - Environmental and Workplace Health
www.hc-sc.gc.ca/ewh-semt/index-eng.php

Sources of Evidence Based Programming
Physical Health – United States
The Community Guide to Preventive Services
www.thecommunityguide.org
The Cochrane Library
www.thecochranelibrary.com
Research Tested Intervention Programs – National Cancer Institute
http://rtips.cancer.gov/rtips

Physical Health – Canada
Health Evidence Canada
www.health-evidence.ca

Canadian Best Practices Portal
Public Health Agency of Canada
http://cbpp-pcpe.phac-aspc.gc.ca/

Mental Health – Substance Abuse, United States

National Registry of Evidence Based Programs and Practices
http://nrepp.samhsa.gov

Examples of Accepted Best Practice Programming
Physical Health – United States Non-Profits

American Heart Association – www.heart.org
Search using workplace wellness

Start A Walking Program
www.startwalkingnow.org/start_workplace.jsp

Mental Health – United States

American Psychiatric Association – Partnership for Workplace Mental Health
Employer Case Examples
www.workplacementalhealth.org/Pages/EmployerInnovations/Search.aspx

Key Ideas:

- Successful and sustainable worksite wellness programs are based on four principles:

  1. Management Support and Engagement

  2. Employee Support, Participation and Engagement

  3. The Program is Comprehensive in Scope

  4. The Program Creates, Delivers and Can Demonstrate Value

- As your organization's worksite wellness coordinator, you will need ongoing engagement from senior management. Here's a list of what you will need from senior management:

- Ongoing support consisting of:

  - Communication to managers/supervisors and employees

  - Resources (both financial and personnel)

  - Visible participation (leading by example)

- Creation of supportive organizational policies

- Integration of health and wellness principles and practices within the organizational structure

  - Education of managers and supervisors

- Help with the alignment of the wellness program with the company's mission, vision and goals

- Having a solid, functional wellness team or committee is fundamental to the success of your wellness program.

- Before creating a new stand-alone wellness committee, look around to see if an existing committee is willing to expand its role to encompass employee wellness.

- Goals are a broad statement of what the program intends to accomplish within a specific period of time. Develop goals that require effort to achieve. Make your goals SMART goals:

  - Specific

  - Measurable

  - Attainable

  - Realistic

  - Time-Specific

- Objectives are a refinement of the goal statements into more specific, concrete action statements.

- Motivation exists at three levels:

  - Innate

  - Intrinsic

  - Extrinsic

Questions:

1. Which is **not** one of the four principles sustainable and successful programs are based on?

   a. Management Support

   b. Comprehensive in Scope

   c. Demonstrated Value

   d. Can be run without supervision

2. Having a solid, functional wellness team or committee is not fundamental to the success of your wellness program.

   a. True

   b. False

3 Which of the following is not a description of creating SMART goals?

   a. Specific

   b. Measurable

   c. Meaningful

   d. Attainable

4. What are the three levels of motivation?

   a. Needs, Wants, and Undesirable

   b. Innate, Intrinsic, and Extrinsic

   c. Fear, Pride, and Humiliation

   d. Risk Aversion, Risk, and Reward

Employees Are What They Eat: The Importance of Integrating Nutrition in Corporate Wellness
By Amanda Carlson-Phillips

For many years, corporate wellness programs focused almost entirely on movement programming, ranging from on site fitness centers to group classes to online modules around general fitness. All of these options deliver significant value to the employee, but for too many years, optimal nutrition integration has been a missing part of the puzzle. Here we have outlined five reasons why employees are what they eat, and why onsite nutrition programming should be top of mind for employers in evaluating wellness solutions.

1) **Rising Medical Costs:** Simply put, employers can't afford to ignore the impact of heart disease and diabetes on their healthcare premiums—the American Heart Association estimates heart disease costs alone will triple by 2030. Lowering the risk factors for diabetes and heart disease alike requires more than just fitness programming: employers must provide integrated, dynamic and engaging nutrition education content and support so that employees think differently about how they eat each day. To quantify potential impact, we recently did a program with Intel that included both onsite fitness and personalized nutrition. Over just fourteen weeks, the average percentage decrease in cholesterol was 5.03 percent, average fat loss was 14 pounds, and VO2 scores increased by an average of 19 percent. There was a 30 percent change in participants characterized as "at risk" based on their lipid profile—a staggering number when you consider the potential impact on claims data.

2) **Meeting People Where They Are:** For many employees, the notion of working out is simply too big of a jump given their current health state. Nutrition is a great way to reach non-movers with simple, actionable programming they can incorporate slowly into their lives. For many years, nutrition has become synonymous with weight loss. While trying to lose weight people often lose sight of why we really eat. Bringing in dynamic and supportive nutrition programming can help guide people to choose foods that nourish the body, provide

sustainable energy, and improve the way they feel as opposed to short-term fixes to lose five pounds. Every employee has to eat, so finding a way to meet them where they are and make small upgrades to their daily rituals can lead to the sustainable change employees and employers are looking for.

3) **Nutrition is a Family Affair:** Employers have offered a wide range of onsite solutions for corporate wellness, but continue to struggle with ways to engage the employees' families in a meaningful way. The result? Often poor nutrition habits are fostered at home, leading to higher claims for the entire family. Finding ways to meaningfully engage with employees around nutrition can have a positive impact at home. By way of example, one of our wellness clients at Intel said he always knew he should eat breakfast, but didn't know how to create a quick, convenient, and healthy option. After figuring out what worked best for him, he purchased healthy breakfast options, including whole-grain, high-protein cereal, for his entire family, the start of what we call "an upward spiral" in their home toward healthier habits.

4) **The Results Speak for Themselves:** Simply put, many people sabotage even their best efforts at fitness with poor nutrition. At C&S Wholesale Grocers, based in Keene, NH, we watched as many of their employees worked eight hour shifts with significant physical exertion without consuming a single ounce of water throughout the day. As little as 2 percent weight loss due to sweating can lead to up to a 25 percent decrease in productivity, so even educating employees about small changes in hydration can lead to significant improvement in how an employee feels throughout the day at work. To address this issue, we provided simple education tools at warehouse sites, along with urine charts for their bathrooms so that employees could monitor their own hydration levels. These simple reminders and changes can lead to noteworthy results for employees and employers alike.

Now that we've addressed the importance of nutrition in wellness programming, I've outlined a few key considerations for employers when considering nutrition programs at their corporation:

- **Integrate Nutrition into Fitness Programming:** Nutrition programming often lives in the medical and clinical side of corporate wellness programs. This creates an association of nutrition with disease management or a reactive solution that needs to be addressed when something is wrong. A new avenue for the delivery of nutrition content and programming should be in parallel with the fitness programs. Fitness programs focus on having more energy, stamina, and strength. Linking nutrition to these goals allows for employees to see nutrition as fuel for their performance and a way to expedite the process of reaching their goals.

- **Re-frame the Approach:** Everyone can benefit from a nutrition tune-up. The foods we choose to eat are linked to the energy we have to be productive in our careers, present with our families, and enjoy the activities that make us who we are. Learning to choose the right foods, in the right amounts, at the right time is the key to feeling and performing the best you can in whatever you choose to do. Nutrition programming should focus on food as the fuel for our lives and provide the education and simple strategies to take advantage and get the most out of every time we eat.

- **Keep it Simple:** Employees need simple strategies that they can incorporate in their daily lives, so focus on key priorities like hydration, increasing fruit and vegetable intake, or upgrading healthy snack options on your campus, and create simple ways for your employees to learn more and take part.

- **Make it Fun:** Nobody wants to be lectured on what they are doing wrong, so making nutrition programming fun and relatable is imperative to its success with your teams. Creating nutrition challenges, remake a recipe contests, or lunch and learns where employees can have interaction with one another and have fun while learning more are all great options to keep employees excited rather than tired by nutrition programming.

- **Build Community:** Invite employees and their families to participate in a healthier barbecue or picnic lunch on campus and work with a local grocery store to provide a coupon for employees to try out healthier breakfast fare for a week. Engaging a broader audience in the conversation with leads to broader engagements and results for everyone involved.

Whether your employees are unloading pallets every day, manning a service center, or traveling non-stop nutrition has the ability to transform their lives, increasing energy levels, improving performance, and advancing their health state. To date, most employee nutrition programs have been stand-alone online modules or education seminars without the personalization, ongoing support, and integration necessary to make them a sustainable success. To create impactful nutrition programming, it's imperative that companies consider integrating nutrition education and support with fitness, maximizing each individual's ability to make sustainable changes to their overall health.

Key Ideas:

- The American Heart Association estimates heart disease costs alone will triple by 2030.

- As little as 2 percent weight loss due to sweating can lead to up to a 25 percent decrease in productivity, so even educating employees about small changes in hydration can lead to significant improvement in how an employee feels throughout the day at work.

- A new avenue for the delivery of nutrition content and programming should be in parallel with the fitness programs. Fitness programs focus on having more energy, stamina, and strength. Linking nutrition to these goals allows for employees to see nutrition as fuel for their performance and a way to expedite the process of reaching their goals.

- Nutrition programming should focus on food as the fuel for our lives and provide the education and simple strategies to take advantage and get the most out of every time we eat.

Questions:

1. Why is hydration important for productivity?

    a. It is not, productivity decreases because employees are constantly going to the restroom

    b. Up to 2 percent weight loss from sweat can lead up to 25 percent in decreased productivity

    c. More fluids in the body gives people greater ability to concentrate

    d. None of the above

2. Nutrition programs should focus on food as the fuel for our lives.

    a. True

    b. False

1. The American Heart Association estimates heart disease costs alone will_____ by 2030.

    a. Double

    b. Triple

    c. Stay the same

    d. None of the above

Ten Reasons Why Your Wellness Program Lacks Participation
By: Todd McGuire

This article will discuss ten common pitfalls that can derail your efforts to reach as many of your employees as possible. Avoid these common mistakes and you should be able to optimize the participation level in your wellness program.

PITFALL 1: NO INCENTIVES

It's tempting to take the position that *"good health is its own reward, so everyone should sign up for this program."* Unfortunately, that doesn't get most people to take action. I call that "Wellness 1.0 Thinking." The "motivated minority" will respond to this approach, but they are the minority. You are trying to get to the non-participating majority that usually sits on the sidelines.

Modern wellness programs attract the most people when incentives are involved. Done properly, incentives will create a buzz in your workplace. That's "Wellness 2.0." Instead of expecting your employees to leap at the opportunity to improve their HDL cholesterol, try appealing to their inherent interest in rewards. This will get your employees to take notice of your program and hopefully attend an information session that should lead to them signing up. Juicy gossip spreads fast, so there's nothing better than having your employees ask one another *"Did you hear about that new program that actually pays you to lose weight?!"* Plan on using incentives every year as an integral part of your program.

TAKE ACTION: Structure your program to offer incentives for your employees to take charge of their health.

PITFALL 2: MISPLACED INCENTIVES

So now you know that incentives are a key ingredient of a successful wellness program. This is just the beginning. Early attempts at incentive-based wellness programs tried applying the incentives to the first step of the process: reach (or participation). This is tempting because it seems like the natural way to get people to join your program. The problem is that it leads to short term thinking, *"I just need to sign up and then I'll earn the incentive,"* and short term programs filled with participants who aren't really committed to changing their behavior. True behavior change is essential to a meaningful program that will help your employees and your bottom line.

To achieve this holy grail of behavior change, try to align the incentives with real outcomes that can be measured. If your program is focused on reducing hypertension, then measure pre and post blood pressure levels and align your rewards based on improvement. If you are aiming for weight loss and decreasing obesity, then help your employees track their baseline weight and Body Mass Index (BMI) and reward them for progress every three months (or whatever interval fits your organization) as measured by their new and improved weight level. This shift from "pay for participation" to "pay for performance" is crucial to create a long-term culture of health.

TAKE ACTION: Align your incentives with outcomes, not participation.

PITFALL 3: PULL VS. PUSH

Wellness 1.0 was all about "Pull" models of coaching - books, passive web sites, posters. They can have great information, but they suffer from a critical flaw: They require the employee to be motivated to seek out the information. There is a "motivated minority" that will do just that, but you're missing the majority who won't make the effort.

Your employees are busy. They often have more projects on their plate than they can reasonably handle. Ask most people what they do with 5 minutes of downtime between projects and they will be much more likely to get a quick news fix at CNN.com or ESPN.com on their phones than they are to diligently look up some nutrition information or log what they ate for lunch today. Fortunately Wellness 2.0 has the answers: email, SMS text messages, Facebook, Twitter.

TAKE ACTION: Investigate tailored email and SMS/text messaging to communicate with your employees.

PITFALL 4: WRONG COMMUNICATION CHANNEL

What could be better than getting a personalized phone call from a nurse or coach who is dedicated to helping you improve your health? For some folks, that is ideal. But for a lot of busy, stressed out employees who already spend all day on the phone for their job (see Pitfall 3 above), the threat of another phone call is enough to scare them away from a wellness program. Survey your employees. Ask them what would make wellness easier for them. We did, and the results were clear: 91.5 percent of our respondents are on Facebook (N=1,893) and 77 percent use social media tools at least weekly. So we now interact with our participants through those channels.

TAKE ACTION: *Survey your workforce. Would your employees rather get a text message at 11:45 AM reminding them to eat the proper portion at lunch instead of a phone call from a coach?*

PITFALL 5: SHORT TERM THINKING

Another Wellness 1.0 mistake is to think wellness is a 6 week contest or a 12 week boot camp. Those things can be part of the answer; but you really need to stress the expectation that you're asking your employees to adopt a new lifestyle where they know how to choose proper sized portions of healthy food, where they build the habit of taking the stairs instead of the elevator, where they make their health a daily priority. Unfortunately some of the reality shows on TV condition us to think getting healthy is something that can be achieved once and then forgotten.

Speaking of reality, it's more like brushing your teeth. The results don't last, which is why it's recommended daily! Undoing 15, 20, even 30 years of bad habits takes time. Usually more than 6 weeks. Most people will stumble a few times before finding success. I have seen the best success when we've told employees that this is the start of a multi-year campaign. The first stage is one year in duration. You're going to earn incentives every three months for achieving, and maintaining, improvements in your health.

TAKE ACTION: *Your minimum program should be at least a year long.*

PITFALL 6: PRIVACY IS JUST A LEGAL ISSUE

HIPAA does a good job of making the protection of personal health information a priority. It may also make us obsess over the legal requirements and perhaps overlook the reality that good privacy can actually increase participation. With the use of private screening kiosks, anonymous Q&A with health coaches over email, and online tools that allow team competition without revealing individual stats, Wellness 2.0 can attract the ideal demographic to your wellness efforts. As an example, the typical profile of a participant in wellness programs we've run is as follows: 43 years old, 33 BMI. These are great stats in terms of getting the people who need the most help to join your program.

Many executives we've discussed this with are thrilled because this demographic is the exact opposite of what they see when they put in a corporate gym. Gyms are great resources, but they often attract folks who are already working out and in shape. The 43 year old with the 33 BMI is often intimidated by all those healthy gym goers (which is why over 70 percent of the employees we've coached choose the home-based exercise option that is emailed daily at 3:00 AM to their computer or smart phone). We hear from a lot of participants that they are doing simple strength exercises at home for the first time because they feel comfortable following an email and grabbing a soup can or set of resistance bands to do the exercises. That's real world behavior change taking place!

TAKE ACTION: Attract the right demographic by stressing privacy, perhaps using a vendor who can help you maintain an "arm's length" between the employer and the employees' health data.

PITFALL 7: WELLNESS IS A SERIOUS MEDIAL ISSUE

Health and wellness is as serious as a heart attack. Unfortunately that doesn't translate into how you should market your wellness program to your employees. The reality is that most people are not motivated by stern lectures from their physician. They usually just want to look and feel better. We've asked thousands of employees to rank their motivation for improving their health, and the top answer is always the same: "To fit in my old jeans." And there are some other really good options on the list like "My doctor told me to get healthy" or "To have more energy for my family." Maybe in another article I'll dive deeper into some of the neat stats we've collected over the years about what the most common barriers and motivators are for people trying to improve their health.

As wellness professionals, we know that the health of our employees is critical for them and for our organizations. But when we're focused on getting people to take the first step and enroll in a wellness program, we need to move beyond just the medical reasons and highlight how joining the program will help each employee reach goals that matter to them. Now that we know our participating employees' number one motivator is to fit in their old clothes, we highlight the fact that all participants using our kiosk for screenings get a private, full length digital photo of every one of their screenings. As a result, many employees use the kiosk once a week. We only require that they return to the kiosk once every 3 months, but they tell us they really like seeing the pictures of their progress! Motivation is a personal matter. Your job is to find out what that motivation is and harness it.

TAKE ACTION: Use humor, video, pictures. Make wellness fun!

PITFALL 8: WELLNESS IS NOT ALWAYS A TEAM SPORT

One of the most popular features in corporate wellness programs are team challenges. Many people love them and get very competitive, which is great! But for everyone that loves team-based approaches, there is someone (and usually many "someones") who is sensitive about their health and would rather make it a personal journey. Make sure you respect that difference, especially when it comes to incentive programs. I have seen programs run the most smoothly when there are individual incentives for everyone who reaches benchmarks, and then group incentives for those who opt to participate in the team challenges.

TAKE ACTION: Offer both individual and team incentives.

PITFALL 9: OVERLY THOROUGH ENROLLMENT PROCESS

Data is good. More data is often better. As wellness professionals, we usually thrive on data. But there's a very real risk of trying to get too much data. I'm not talking about overstepping privacy borders. I'm talking about enrollment forms that are just too long. You'll know you're guilty of this pitfall when you have to resort to incentives just to get people to sign up. A well-designed—and short—enrollment form will get people started in 5 minutes or less and you won't need to spend a dime on participation. Save those dollars for rewarding progress!

TAKE ACTION: Enrollment in 5 minutes or less.

PITFALL 10: OFFER THE WRONG PROGRAM

Tell me if this sounds familiar. You conduct a comprehensive Health

Risk Assessment (HRA). The HRA stratifies your workforce according to prevalence of health risks. You then find and implement wellness programs that address each of these areas. You communicate with your employees that have hypertension something like this: "Hello Employee 2314, we have a great program to help you lower your blood pressure." This makes perfect sense on paper, but again there's a fatal flaw. Except for that "motivated minority" we talked about, many of your employees will see the information about that hypertension program and file it away in their "Health Plan" folder as something to look at when they get the time. And if you entice them with an incentive to use your hypertension program, some will reluctantly do it for just long enough to get the incentive. That's not real behavior change.

Instead, find out what's motivating your employees and try a more foundational wellness approach to get things moving. Virtually every HRA finds the same thing: Your workforce is overweight, stressed out, sedentary, has high blood pressure and has (or is heading for) heart health issues. Guess what is recommended (to accompany the medications that are prescribed) for each of these issues? The answer: Healthy eating and active living. If your employees are like the ones I've worked with over the years, they are already thinking about how to look and feel better and fit into their old clothes. So give them a program that helps them do just that while also addressing just about every risk found in your HRA. Once your employees take those first steps and start feeling better, they just might be more receptive to the specialized programs that you have waiting in the wings.

TAKE ACTION: Give your employees what they want.

Key Ideas:

- Pay for performance is a more effective incentive program than pay for participation.

- Align your incentives with your outcomes, not participation

- Structure your program to offer incentives

- Your minimum program should be at least a year long.

- Attract the right demographic by stressing privacy and

consider having a vendor who can put distance between the employer and the employee's health data.

- Make wellness fun

- Other both individual and team incentives

- You are trying to get to the non-participating majority that usually sits on the sidelines.

- True behavior change is essential to a meaningful program that will help your employees and your bottom line.

Questions:

1. Pay for performance is a more effective incentive program than pay for participation.

   a. True

   b. False

2. True or False? A good wellness program uses primarily team activities and incentives.

   a. True

   b. False

3. Fill in the Blank: We need to move beyond just the medical reasons and highlight how joining a the program will help each employee reach _____.

   a. The level to get the incentive

   b. Goals that matter to them

   c. A break on their insurance

   d. A higher pay grade

Case Study: East Coast Wellness Innovations
By Renée-Marie Stephano

Introduction and Background
The Gowrie Group is a smaller business dealing in personal and business insurance, headquartered in Westbrook, Connecticut with other branches over New England and the east coast of the United States. Another associated company is Maritime Program Group who is engaging in this wellness program with them. They have 127 employees in 5 locations, 30 percent of their employees are men, and 70 percent women with a median age of 48. The goal of their wellness plan is to promote health and reduction of lifestyle risk factors. Their medical plan is fully insured, while their wellness program is self-funded.

The Problem
As insurance agents and underwriters there is a lot of inactivity throughout the day, coupled with the stress of the line of work. The medical trend prior to implementation was 16.8 percent, which was a top priority for the program. Their medical expenses fluctuated greatly since 2000, from as low as 4 percent to as high as 44 percent. It was seeing the 44 percent increase in medical expenses that prompted them to reexamine their employee's health. The primary health drivers were orthopedic rheumatology, which are bone and joint problems, gastroenterology which are problems with the stomach, and behavioral problems like smoking and use of sleeping aids and mental health drugs. They examine these problems through a cost annualization report, which benchmarks their health expenses to similar companies of similar sizes.

The wellness program was initiated to create a healthy culture. By doing this they hoped to create happier employees who were not as stressed as they were before. The idea was also to reduce injuries so that the medical trend and annual increase could improve.

The Solution
Gowrie began by researching a carrier for their wellness program which would match their corporate culture. They realized that a program that did not engage their employees would just be wasted money. The wellness team met with the owners of the company

and told them of their decision, and they came to the conclusion to appoint twelve wellness "super champions" who would be in various locations and from various departments. The super champions would be motivators of a like mind to help the participants and advertisers for the program. They posted fliers about the program, and created a video with the owners and super champions demonstrating the program and key exercises.

The wellness program centers on the use of pedometers, which was one of the larger costs. They also had to purchase scales and tethers to connect the pedometers and scales to a computer. The scales and pedometers connected to a web portal where they could track steps taken and weight loss. The information was private, and use of the scales were not required. In order to stem the tide of the costs of the pedometers, which are $40 to $45 each, employees are required to sign an agreement that if they do not use the pedometer for three months they must return them.

The program in Gowrie is still new, having been launched July of 2012. Some of the instant results they have seen is a sense of camaraderie from both the employees and management, and employees from different departments working and mingling with each other. They use health risk assessments to determine trends in the population and to educate their employees in their health. They have had 51 percent participation in the health risks assessments. The program also reimburses 50 percent of gym memberships for their employees up to $250, and will offer classes based on the results of the assessments and having a professional examine the results. The program does not offer incentives or penalties, believing the quality of the program, the new relationships formed and the improved health and activity is its own reward. They also honor the people who have made the largest gains and the Super Champions who have done the most work.

The Results

It is still too early to determine any health improvements as a result of the program. But excitement and participation is high. In order to get their step count high, there are arguments about who will walk to someone else's office, and people walking whenever the opportunity presents itself. The CEO of the company even has employees entering his office to thank him for the program. In order to augment health even more they have banned smoking on the premises and in cars in the parking lot.

A culture change has taken place at Gowrie. The employees are eating healthier, and employees are encouraged to give points to each other through the web portal to those they see engaging in healthy behavior. This seeking and giving of points encourages employees to live healthy, and promotes the camaraderie they want. This initiative is called "Caught ya Healthy." Through the web platform they can compete in "jousts" which are small health challenges which result in points and encouragement for healthy activities. Although the exact numbers will not be available until June of 2013, the signs are encouraging.

Some of the advice they give to employers seeking to create a wellness program are to do the research and find a program relevant and engaging to your employees and your company culture. They also advise to keep the program fresh and fun so the program is enjoyable.

Case Study: Building a Culture of Wellness
By Renée-Marie Stephano

Introduction and Background
Premier is a healthcare company based out of Charlotte North Carolina. They have approximately 1400 employees in multiple states, 40 percent of which are men and 60 percent are women. The median age of their employees is 40. The goal of their program is to promote health and reduce the lifestyle health risks. Their program is self-funded and administered by a Large Health Plan.

The Problem
As a healthcare company, part of their mission statement is the health of their community. They have a wellness program to "walk the talk"; to make sure what they want to do for communities they are doing within their own community. The medical trend for the company varied over the years averaging around 6 percent, but some years it was as low as 0 percent, or as high as 15 or 20 percent. They average annual healthcare increases of 5 to 6 percent. The main issue facing their employee population is high-cost claims many of which are cancers.

The creation of the wellness plan began in 2005 when a number of passionate employees, many of which were certified instructors, began a grassroots effort to create a program. They formed a wellness committee where they exchanged ideas and activities. The original emphasis was on having a program that is fun. They did not originally have a large budget, until around 2009. The original grassroots effort created a strong foundation which plays a large part in the future success of the program.

Communication was key in the early stages, as was making fun activities. One of these a was biggest loser competition, or an office Olympics. To increase communication they used the internet, and held "lunch and learn" sessions.

The Solution
In 2009 the committee began to think about the program strategically. It began by changing from an outcome based incentive structure to a participation and an activity based one. Premier began with a "New

Year's Incentive" where they would reimburse any activity intended for health, such as a gym membership or a massage, up to $300 in the first quarter. The money came from reserves the program already had. This has since changed to "Be Well Bucks" and receiving the money is contingent upon participation in a biometric screening and a health risk assessment. In 2011 a meeting with a health coach every quarter was added as well. The coach could either be done in person or on the phone at no cost to the employee.

Again in 2012 the "Be Well Bucks" program was changed. This time an employee could make $500, half based on participation and half based on screenings. The health coach was removed for a program they called "Move 365" where the participants were given a wireless pedometer that tracked the steps taken. An employee must take 500,000 steps a quarter to get this portion of the $500. The pedometers connect to a web portal where steps can be tracked, and other exercises can be logged, as can nutritional information. The quarterly screenings were changed to one screening in November. If there was a 10 percent increase from the last screening taken, then the person qualified for the rest of the money. Finally they have added a $50 monthly payroll deduction for smokers.

Among the screenings used are measurements of blood pressure, total cholesterol, HDL cholesterol and tobacco usage. They also test for BMI but received pressure from some of the participants who were actively exercising, but were putting on a lot of muscle.

They have also had extensive CEO help, which culminated in a competition between two executives. They challenged each other to see who could take the most steps, and their progress was visible to everyone. The loser of the competition would be forced to sing karaoke.

The Results
Their pedometers do a lot of the measuring, as does the screening the employees engage in. This give a lot of data, so the program can be assessed and changed as needed. Value was created for the employer and employees in many ways. Premier has a deal with YMCA, where they can use the facilities there; and the instructors go to the company's building to teach courses. The YMCA also allows Premier the use of their fields where they have quarterly sports

meets in activities like flag football, volleyball and basketball. These meets get the employees excited, and allows them to meet some of the employees they would not interact with regularly, which is great for workplace morale and productivity.

There has been a noticeable change in the culture of health, with more and more people taking the stairs. It has also increased productivity by decreasing stress. It becomes clear to employees, that while they may be worked hard, the company cares about them and their wellbeing.

Allison Golding Senior Director of Total Rewards at Premier has a few words of advice. The first is to keep it simple and fun. Originally they were building their own web portal but abandoned it when it was clear it was too complicated, and thus a waste of resources. The second is to know your workforce, and tailor the program for their needs. A final is communication, if you are changing a part of your program that is fine, but let the people know about it in advance.

CHAPTER 2
Incentives

Incentivizing Wellness: Money for Nothing?
By: Glenn Risely

Americans – leading their peers across the developed world - are fast getting sicker, sadder and more sluggish than ever before. Succumbed to soft and stationary lifestyles, America ingloriously leads the world in the obesity stakes and epidemic levels of chronic and degenerative health conditions which are crippling the nation both physically and financially.

Incredibly, the chronic conditions topping the charts are amongst the leading causes of disability, death and crippling increases in healthcare spending. Heart disease, type 2 diabetes, stroke and many incidences of cancer are common "lifestyle diseases", and are preventable through simple improvements to daily physical activity levels and nutrition. Yet the bulk of the American population remains psychologically rooted to their unhealthy habits, stuck fast in a downward spiral.

And they're taking the social and economic fallout sitting down.

American employers, however, are rising to the challenge. Driven to divert the double threat of lost productivity and soaring healthcare spending and feeling a social duty of care to employees, progressive organizations have embraced workforce wellbeing as a critical business priority. Over the last decade especially, workplace wellness initiatives have taken center stage and snowballed across the business landscape.

Typically corporate wellness initiatives address one or a combination of "usual suspects": sedentary living, poor nutrition, smoking and stress. Common, costly and moreover *modifiable*, these are the health risk factors at the root of most chronic conditions. They're also the lifestyle improvements which can stem the tide of illness, lost productivity and healthcare expenditures across individual organizations and the nation as a whole.

Motivating employee participation has proved a common stumbling block for organizations. A recent Aon Hewitt survey reveals more than half of all employers surveyed considered motivating participants to change unhealthy behaviors as the most significant challenge to accomplishing their healthcare goals[7]

In the haste to "repair" their workforces many American employers have reached for traditional "carrot-and-stick" incentives to swell participation levels and hasten behavior change. Front-loaded, back-loaded, cash and kind...the spectrum of popular participation lures and penalties called upon are many and varied.

A popular participation hook across American organizations, incentives – predominantly financial - are now woven into wellness interventions more often than not, with recent 2009 Buck Consultants research revealing 56 percent of American organizations incentivize their wellness program participation[8], with another 26 percent planning to do so[9].

Furthermore, the value of incentives is on the rise[10], as is the practice of directing incentive dollars towards reducing healthcare premiums, or making cash contributions to healthcare-related spending accounts[11]. With healthcare reform and relaxed incentive parameters on the horizon, incentive prevalence and spending is on the cusp of a boom period. This, despite the fact that most American employers remain unconvinced of their incentive ROI[12].

And so notwithstanding commercial America's largely incentivized efforts, the obesity epidemic and healthcare boom continue unabated. Why? Because when it comes to wellness, the use of lures which speak to extrinsic motivations are a big step backwards.

Here's why:

- Rather than motivate behavior change and health acquisition, they motivate financial or material acquisition. The financial incentive can effectively extinguish or "crowd out" any meaningful self-improvement motivation[13], leading to diminished emotional commitment, without which long-term behavior change is impossible.

- Material incentives can encourage unhealthy, even dangerous conduct. In weight loss-focused wellness programs particularly there is a long history of financial incentives unintentionally creating unhealthy behaviors in the workplace (such as taking laxatives, diuretics, heat exhaustion or over-strenuous exercise just before being weighed) [14]. This purge mentality also makes it highly likely that employees will revert back to unhealthy lifestyles and put weight back on once the incentive is removed[15].

- At best, financially driven participation may drive short-term, superficial participation; but only if the price is right. Despite numerous studies, there is no magic number for amount, frequency or method of financial incentives an organization can successfully offer employees for wellness program success. There's simply no proven financial formula or universal incentive design that works.

- Furthermore, based either on participation or some sort of goal attainment, incentives are typically awarded at the end of the program or at designated intervals. Commonly, this time lag in recognition reduces an employee's motivation, increasing the likelihood of program drop-off[16].

- Finally, for participants who make it through to their reward point? Externally motivated and 'in it for the money' - not to change their lifestyle - they're more likely to quit the program once they get their reward[17]. No real behaviour change, no long-term improvement and no sustained ROI.

While the obesity epidemic and the cost of healthcare reform are popular topics for the media and our politicians - and a compelling platform for workplace wellness intervention - what's not so popular is addressing the hard truth underpinning it: a crisis of personal responsibility. And it's the key. More than an immediate and acute economic threat, America's sick state of health is an enormous social problem that can only be overcome by empowering individuals to take personal responsibility for their health, to change their behaviors and the course of their lives.

Empowerment to turn around unhealthy lifestyle behaviors can only come from changing the personal beliefs, attitudes and mindsets of unhealthy individuals – not their bank account balance.

Let's take a closer look at the reason behind the need for these "carrots" and "sticks", their primary function being to goad participation from otherwise reluctant employees – often those who perceive a prescribed health program as an unnecessary grind and/ or high-risk individuals who've given up on themselves. Rather than peel back and address the factors behind this reluctance, material incentives ignore and furthermore underscore the cynicism and suspicion that already exists in the minds of unhealthy staff – either that the program being offered is boring or uninteresting, or that becoming active and healthy is painful and unpleasant. Probably both. Doomed from the outset, the financial or material "sweetener" seals the negative deal, irrevocably erodes the quality of employee engagement and derails the potential for any long-term behavior change.

A better approach? Fun!

Yep, fun is a powerful motivator and employers would be far better off spending their money on engaging employees in an exciting wellness program than luring them to participate in a stock-standard, sensible-but-dull one. After all, if you think of the things in life that are actually good and fun, people don't need to be paid to do them; they do them because they are their own reward. Human beings are social animals, designed to seek out and enjoy fun and some level of social engagement. A wellness program that is genuinely fun and engaging effectively taps into this intrinsic desire and draws enthusiastic employee participation from each and every employee. It facilitates both the registration numbers and the commitment critical for real ROI. No "carrots", no "sticks."

Also, behavior change can only be achieved alongside an individual's genuine, intrinsic desire to achieve improved health, and some belief in their ability to do so. Appealing to an employee's sense of fun opens this door. Negative attitudes and beliefs – defeatist ("it's too late for me"), delusional ("a pill will fix it – and besides, that's what insurance is for") and in denial ("illness won't happen to me") – can be successfully challenged step-by-step as participants otherwise enjoy program participation.

By taking an intrinsic approach to incentives, a wellness program can deliver employees meaningful recognition, through their own healthy behavior. Over time, (supported) self-rewarding lifestyle improvements such as increased physical activity, continuity of positive behavior and understanding of nutrition best practice over the course of the program steadily builds confidence, commitment and mastery to empower employees to take charge of their health. Once the reward resonates with a person, it facilitates real perception change and behavior change for sustained impact.

Plus, implementation of a fun and holistic approach is extremely employer-friendly. Universally appealing to all employees across all risk levels, fun resonates with everyone. Ditto the desire for autonomous achievement and recognition – they speak to us all and are powerful, personal motivators. A single-minded, straight-forward program geared intrinsically is simple to implement (requires no complex incentive structure or heavy "sell") and effectively engages the high-level and internally motivated employee commitment that cash incentives can't.

What's more, such a program delivers a host of business benefits alongside employee health and wellbeing, including a positive and productive culture of health – not entitlement. Not to mention the incentive dollars saved, available to be repurposed for more effective wellness or business needs. For employers and employees alike, it's a win-win.

Need proof? The world's leading and largest program, the Global Corporate Challenge® (GCC) hangs its hat on this fun and empowering approach. Parallel to this decade's rise of incentivized wellness schemes, the GCC has rocketed from humble Australian origins to become the most proven and popular corporate health program in the world. Nine years of data, 2,000 organizations and half a million people are living, breathing proof.

First, it's fun. The GCC's unique virtual, around-the-world journey (built in line with the World Health Organization's 10,000 daily step recommendation for a healthy, active lifestyle) engages employees in a fun and effective globetrotting pathway to better health, and one that employees stampede to sign up for. Year on year, GCC registration has soared as more and more employees witnessed their colleagues enjoy and change through the program. In 2012, a record 180,000 employees stampeded to participate in the GCC, prompting total sell-out and the program's biggest year yet. A fun program, it's an easy sell that doesn't need financial "sweetening" - stampedes don't lie.

Secondly, it's empowering. Guided by neuroscientists, behavioral psychologists, physicians and the very participants whose lives have been changed, GCC harnesses the dynamics of the modern workplace and fundamentally changes how people think and act. Using a framework where intrinsic gratification and feedback are delivered in just the right dose and at just the right time to keep employees on track and motivated, GCC facilitates powerful autonomous engagement. In fact, a 2011 industry study commissioned by the Foundation for Chronic Disease Prevention in the Workplace (FCDP) and conducted by Lancaster University's Center for Organizational Health and Wellbeing showed that the GCC effectively engaged 82 percent of participants to achieve step counts of at least 7,500 per day [18] – more than double that of the average office worker. GCC drop-out rates are also extremely low, with more than 90 percent of participants completing the 112-day challenge and achieving improved lifestyle habits for the long term. Fun, supportive and wholly self-rewarding, the GCC instills self-belief and resilience, both key elements for sustained success.

From a cultural perspective, the day companies announce to their staff that they are offering access to health and wellbeing without cash or any other kind of incentive, they are making a big statement: "We believe in you." Employees quickly recognize that they are being empowered to achieve the greatest reward – a long, healthy and happy life. Bringing money into the conversation undermines the entire intention. Money changes everything.

Key Ideas:
- Recent 2009 Buck Consultants research revealing 56 percent of American organizations incentivize their wellness program participation, with another 26 percent planning to do so

- Rather than motivate behavior change and health acquisition, they motivate financial or material acquisition. The financial incentive can effectively extinguish or "crowd out" any meaningful self- improvement motivation, leading to diminished emotional commitment, without which long-term behavior change is impossible

- Implementation of a fun and holistic approach is extremely employer-friendly. Universally appealing to all employees across all risk levels, fun resonates with everyone

- Autonomous achievement and recognition are powerful, personal motivators. A single-minded, straight-forward program geared intrinsically is simple to implement and effectively engages the high-level and internally motivated employee commitment that cash incentives can't

Questions

1. Why does this author feel that incentive structures do not lead to behavior change?

   a. Incentives lead to material and financial acquisition.

   b. The people spend their incentive money on Fast Food

   c. The money never arrives

   d. The money is taken out of people pay checks to incentivize them

2. Rather than offer incentives, how does this author feel a wellness program should motivate employees to participate

   a. Offer extra vacation days

   b. Make to program fun and exciting

   c. Fast track those who participate for promotions

   d. Recognize those who improve the most in the company newsletter.

What's My Incentive?: Designing Wellness Program Incentives to Maximize Participation

By Ryan L. Turnbull

Employer-sponsored wellness programs have seen a resurgence in recent years; a trend that is expected to continue in an effort to curb escalating healthcare premiums. Unfortunately far too many wellness programs fail to achieve the desired employee participation and return on investment. Given that a successful wellness program can result in hundreds of thousands, if not millions, in healthcare premium savings, employers must design a strategic incentive strategy that will be appealing to, and motivate the majority of employees.

A recent comment by Dr. Peter Tippett at the 2012 HIMSS Health IT Conference sums it up well; "whatever it is we think of is going to work for a few people but not most". This holds true for your employee wellness program incentive strategy, and quite frankly all components of your corporate wellness program.

Let's be realistic. The typical employee will not change their lifestyle simply because we supply them with a pedometer and website to track their daily steps, and a $5 gift card to Starbucks for it. That is not to say that these types of programs do not have their place. They do — 10-15 percent of employees will embrace any single wellness program component or incentive. Remember our earlier conclusion — *whatever it is we think of is going to work for a few, but not most.* The challenge lies in designing an incentive structure that appeals to the majority of employees to maximize participation and promote sustained long term behavior change.

The carrot vs. the stick: which approach works best? Unfortunately the answer is not black and white. Every workforce is different and there are likely multiple employee segments within a single workforce, each with its own motivations. Thus employers must strive to design an incentive strategy, or multiple strategies, so that the wellness program offers something that appeals to and motivates all employee segments.

The biggest challenge for employers these days is that much of the wellness program provider space has evolved into a 'product driven' marketplace that offers primarily off-the-shelf, high priced, online programming that claims to provide a 'one size fits all' workplace wellness solution offering ineffective incentives. Be leery. 'One size fits all' seldom translates into wellness program success. Avoid these plug-and-play wellness products, minimal cash rewards, gift cards, and other traditional ineffective incentives. They have been shown to be poor motivators of any real long term behavior change, nor do they appeal to the majority of your workforce. Instead such incentives are often abused by employees, costing employers tens of thousands of dollars in incentive related spending. In fact, when the effect of such incentives are put under the microscope we typically find participation spikes correlated with wellness campaigns offering a quick 'cash grab' opportunity, but very little in the way of ongoing participation.

A recent study of employer wellness programs by ShapeUp, Inc. concluded that incentive programs vary widely in their structures, with diverse employer views on appropriate dollar amounts, the use of rewards versus penalties, incentivizing participation versus outcomes, and the use of cash versus other types of rewards (2011 ShapeUp, Inc. Employer Wellness Survey). Though it is clear that most employers continue to experiment, and that best practices in incentive strategy design continue to evolve, there are some strategies that have been more effective than others at encouraging ongoing wellness program participation and sustained behavior change. Let's take a look at some of them.

Tie incentives to employee monthly medical premiums. Whether they are actually aware of it or not, employees respond well to wellness incentives that are tied to the monthly medical premium deducted from one's paycheck. When given the opportunity to participate in a wellness program to qualify for a reduced monthly premium most employees choose to participate. Penalizing employees who choose not to participate can have a similar effect. Be cautious however; choosing to implement a premium penalty can backfire if not communicated effectively in advance and implemented strategically. Regardless of which strategy best fits your workplace, employers are wise to consider premium differentials based on wellness program participation as an incentive strategy proven to maximize long term employee participation.

Use fewer, more significant incentives. Studies have shown that employees respond poorly to incentives with minimal nominal value. Instead of a $10 gift card to Starbucks or other retail establishment consider offering an incentive of significant value that is rewarded to some, but not all, and based on achieving long-term significant results. Employees respond well to the opportunity to obtain a reward of significant value, whether it is a wellness retreat/vacation or personal training for one year, employees will engage and will enjoy competing with their colleagues. Setting lofty, long term goals in order to qualify will also assist to facilitate long term behavior change and sustainable healthy habits. And remember, it's ok that not all employees actually receive the reward.

Target 'intrinsic' motivators. Given the many flaws surrounding the use of traditional incentives, a new form of incentive is emerging, one that targets intrinsic motivators, specifically those tied to philanthropy. This type of incentive leverages one's intrinsic motivation to assist those in need through charitable giving as a means to drive participation in a wellness program. The more you participate, the more money you raise for your charitable cause. Though its effectiveness has yet to be proven, many wellness practitioners see merit in it and are currently testing it within employer wellness programs. For more information check out http://www.plus3network.com/.

Build it right and they will come. Successful incentive design begins with an investigation of employee wellness desires, motivators, and potential roadblocks to success. The most effective wellness programs are customized to the needs of an organization's employees and incentives designed around barriers to participation.

In the end, one size does not fit all. A wellness program and incentive strategy is only as effective as its ability to meet the needs of one's unique employee culture and its ability to break down the barriers to employee participation.

When designing your wellness program, or attempting to improve on a poorly designed one that lacks employee support and participation, take a step back to be sure you truly know your employees and what will work for them. Doing so will allow you to tailor an incentive strategy to meet their needs. Build it right to begin with and you can achieve majority employee participation with minimal use of costly incentives. Build it poorly and you will end up spending thousands of dollars on incentives, many of which may be ineffective.

Employers who begin the wellness program design process with a clear understanding of employee wellness needs can be confident their program will be embraced by employees. Those who omit this critical step in best practice wellness program design should not be surprised if their wellness program fails to achieve the desired participation and return on investment.

Key Ideas:

- The challenge is to design an incentive structure that appeals to the majority of employees to maximize participation and promote sustained long term behavior change

- Employees respond to wellness incentives that are tied to the monthly medical premium deducted from one's paycheck.

- Use fewer, more significant incentives. Studies have shown that employees respond poorly to incentives with minimal nominal value.

- A wellness program and incentive strategy is only as effective as its ability to meet the needs of one's unique employee culture and its ability to break down the barriers to employee participation.

Questions:

1. The challenge of incentives is to appeal to the majority of employees to:

   a. Maximize participation

   b. Promote long term behavior change

   c. B only

   d. Both A and B

2. Fill in the blank: An incentive strategy is only as effective as its ability to meet the needs of its _____.

   a. Return on Investment

   b. Short term goals

   c. Long term goals

   d. Unique employee culture

3. An example of creating an intrinsically motivating incentive is to offer employees the the ability to earn rewards to give to charity

   a. True

   b. False

Case Study: Three Steps to Success, an Intel Case Study
By Renée-Marie Stephano

Background and Introduction
Intel is a well-known technology firm. If you are reading this electronically chances are you are using an Intel product of some kind. In 2011 they had a record year and reported $54 billion in total sales, with over 82,000 employees.

The Program
Intel's program revolves around three simple yet powerful steps. The first step of the program, named Health for Life, is to get a biometric screening whose results are sent to the individual confidentially. Next the person completes a health risk assessment. After this the employee is invited to speak to a personal health coach where they discuss the results of the exams and develop a plan to improve the individual's health. The three step program began in the United States, but since has moved globally with programs in Malaysia, Israel, Costa Rica, Great Britain, India and China. Originally when someone engaged in the three step plan, the participant was given $25 for each step for a total of $75. Now the incentive is $250, which has a greater impact on the employee's wallet, and hopefully encourages more people to participate and go through all of the steps.

Another perk of the Intel plan is the presence of onsite clinics. In 2008 the first clinics opened on their Arizona campuses. At these clinics employees can get all of their primary care needs taken care of, close to work. The program began in Arizona but is being unrolled to all major sites in the Unites States. There are no financial incentives for using the clinic. The clinic is considered its own incentive because of its ease of access and quality of the facility.

Success for 'Health for Life' is not measured in ROI. The measurement is in healthier and more productive employees. There has been an overall reduction in health risks for the entire population, which is an indication of success.

Case Study: Innovative Incentive Stratgies from Sprint

By Renée-Marie Stephano

Introduction and Background

Sprint is a well-known company in the world of communications. They have 39,000 employees spread everywhere. The goal of their wellness program is to help employees and their families thrive. They offer an innovative program, because as a technology company they thrive on innovation. Because of the high stress work environment, a wellness program is important to maintain a healthy and productive workforce.

The Program

Originally the program focused almost solely on physical wellness. Recently they have shifted to an overall wellbeing approach based on the following pillars; physical wellness, financial wellness, community wellness, social wellness, emotional wellness, and career wellness. Some of these pillars overlap; for example career and financial wellness go together as do community wellness and social wellness.

Sprint offers a multi-tiered approach to wellness. One of the wellness initiatives is the Sprint Get Fit Wellness Challenge. The challenge is an eight week activity program open to all employees. Of the 39,000 employees, 9,811 participated in the challenge in 2011, which is 25 percent of the company. Of the participants, 54 percent had competed in 2011, and a total of 18 percent of participants were labeled as high risk. The participants lost a total 21,597 pounds which is roughly the weight of two elephants, walked a total of 2,364,674,204 steps almost the distance from the Earth to the moon five times, and exercised 11,267,209 minutes which is over 21 years.

Another tier of the Sprint wellness program is known as "Sprint Alive!" which is their regular wellness program. Recently every employee and eligible dependent was given access to a personal health advocate. The act of contacting your advocate was incentivized, with all participants getting a $5 Starbucks gift card, and then being entered in a raffle to win a Sprint tablet computer. Launch emails were opened at a rate of 31.6 percent, which is above benchmark. The first and second reminder emails were opened at rates of

24.7 and 19.1 percent respectively. They have had 1093 people enroll in the program, which is 92 percent of their goal.

Incentives are important to the Sprint wellness program. The incentives offered are varied because what incents one person will not for another. Sprint offer everything from gift cards, Sprint products like phones, Amazon Kindles, and charity contributions. Another program they offer is their online recognition portal, which turns their health activities into points, which are turned into the incentives like gift cards.

CHAPTER 3
Health Risk Assessments

Beyond the Questionnaire: Using the Health Assessment as a Tool for Behavior Change
By Barton Sheeler

Opening the Door to Awareness and Engagement

A health assessment (also known as a health risk assessment) is one of the most widely used screening tools in identifying current health status. It's also often the first step in a health promotion or wellness program. Whether they are taking the HA in response to an incentive offer or other promotion, the act of completing the questionnaire is personal and self-directed. In this way, it is the first step on the path to self-awareness and behavior change.

As individuals take the time to answer questions, each one becomes a decision point for them to reflect on the impact that their current lifestyle choices have on their health. This awareness must be present before there can be real change, which makes the HA a critical tool in the overall success of a health and wellness program.

Health assessments identify an individual's health risks, and his or her healthy and unhealthy behaviors through a set of specific and focused questions. They can be designed to ascertain disease-specific risk profiles, or to provide a comprehensive overview of the whole person. An HA is:

- a tool for moving an individual to consider, or even take action, to change health behaviors aimed at improving their quality of life and health

- a way to identify and suggest areas for improvement

- a means for providing a baseline to track outcomes and improvement

High-quality HAs are individualized and dynamic, yet structured and controlled. Generally, they cover a combination of topic areas such as:

- Demographics

- biometric and physical health information

- exercise and nutrition patterns

- conditions of personal risk (e.g., motor vehicle safety, alcohol and tobacco use, etc.)

- components of daily life

- stress status

- productivity

- readiness-to-change

While they can be delivered on paper, most progressive companies see the value in using online assessments for the ease-of-use and flexibility in applying the results – especially when coordinating other components of the health and wellness program. Regardless of the delivery method, the design and structure of the HA is an important point for leveraging this teachable moment for education and engagement.

Selecting a Health Assessment
When selecting an HA tool, you first need to consider the goals you are trying to achieve. Why do you need an HA? What need are you trying to meet or fill? The answers to these questions will give you your first criteria against which you will judge the HAs available in the marketplace. It doesn't matter if an HA is top-notch or developed by a leader in the field; if it cannot meet your outlined objectives it will not be of good use to you.

Once you have decided on an HA that can meet your needs, consider its origin. Where and why was it developed and what credibility does it have? An assessment that is evidence-based and includes readiness-to-change indicators is best in returning accurate and pertinent information to individuals. There are several areas to consider in evaluating assessment tools, for example:

- Is it evidence-based?

- Was it designed by experts in medical and biostatistical/epidemiological fields using current, nationally recognized reference standards to measure risk?

- Are questions based on validated data collection tools developed by reviewers in the field of data collection and analysis as well as subject specialists?

- Does it incorporate the concept of readiness to change states along with individual risk factors as part of the initial collection of key data from each participant?

- Does it include a simple registration process for each member with simple navigation and links to find the health assessment?

- Is the HA question format segmented into clearly titled sections for quick reference and ease of updating?

- Can the participant come back and "finish later" – saving the data entered without having to start all over again?

- Is the user experience fun and valuable?

Making the Most of a Teachable Moment
While the HA is the critical first step on the path to behavior change, what follows the assessment is just as important in moving an individual down a path to better health. An effective HA not only captures information but also provides a clear understanding of the results to prompt follow-through at both the individual and organization levels.

A comprehensive HA generates a vast amount of raw data. In addition to basic identification and demographic information, data can (and should) encompass as many as seven different categories of health and lifestyle questions.

In its most basic form, HA data is often represented as individual points on a graph with a general health score indicating whether the individual's biometric measures, such as blood pressure or cholesterol, fall within a range that is low, moderate or high. This information is useful but begs the question, so what? The data alone without context doesn't provide any actionable information about what the results mean. A more impactful HA report goes beyond presenting raw data to put information in a context that allows understanding.

Put another way, what is more actionable: an HA report that simply says an individual is at high risk due to elevated glucose levels, or one that informs the individual that she has a 9.2 percent chance of developing Type 2 diabetes in the next five years and that 70 percent of her risk is within her control to change through modifiable lifestyle behaviors?

Many times participants are initially motivated with an incentive to take the HA. A report that is clear and actionable can provide the motivation to take the next step to enroll in appropriate lifestyle or disease-management programs. It can also bridge gaps created by low health literacy, which impacts as many as 80 percent of American adults.

Questions to consider in evaluating the value of HA reports:

- Does the HA generate a personalized health report that reviews where a person is currently and identify risks that can be modified for a healthier lifestyle? [Figure 1]

- Does it offer follow-up content that is based on the specific responses and health issues identified in the HA awareness stage?

- What other resources are immediately available to the participants to keep them engaged in the process?

- Is the report coupled with a personalized action plan and/or health advising resource to review individual results?

- Is the HA integrated to link with personalized action plans, participant education resources and incentive tracking?

- Does it incorporate an administrator portal to support easy member activity look-up and report processing?

These are all important points to weigh when deciding on an HA for an effective health and wellness program. Tools and features like these can take much of the hard work out of managing an integrated health and wellness initiative.

Figure 3.1

The report example below shows the risk of disease onset for CHD, Stroke, Diabetes and CHF. It includes the modifiable risks associated with each disease state and the contributing behaviors to visually educate individuals about the impact of lifestyle on future health risk.

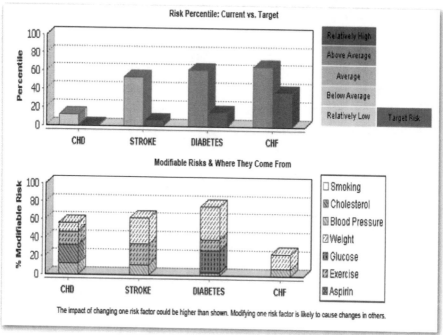

The impact of changing one risk factor could be higher than shown. Modifying one risk factor is likely to cause changes in others.

Summary

The benefits of a good HA report can extend to businesses, too. More meaningful results that assign risks (both modifiable and non-modifiable) for specific conditions can provide more meaningful aggregate data for assessing, managing and improving the health of your population. Having a full picture of health allows for better prediction of near-term and future avoidable disease burden. It also provides greater insight to inform where and how to focus wellness initiatives for maximum impact and to document program outcomes over time.

In the end, the focus is not as much about evaluating the HA as much as it is a thorough consideration of your program goals. There is no shortage of HA tools in the marketplace. The key is finding one that meets the needs of your health and wellness program from both a cost and comprehensive health management standpoint.

An HA that supports a complete wellness program will result in a more effective engagement and better outcomes. If it enables members to create a personalized action plan based on areas that are both meaningful and appropriate at the current stage in an individual's life, it is more likely to be the first step in making lasting change.

Creating awareness is the foundation to building a roadmap toward a healthier lifestyle and ultimately provides greater opportunities to improve health status over time.

Key Ideas:

- The act of completing the questionnaire is personal and self-directed. In this way, it is the first step on the path to self-awareness and behavior change

- Health assessments identify an individual's health risks, and his or her healthy and unhealthy behaviors through a set of specific and focused questions.

- When selecting an HA tool, you first need to consider the goals you are trying to achieve. Why do you need an HA? What need are you trying to meet or fill? The answers to these questions will give you your first criteria against which you will judge the HAs available in the marketplace

- Having a full picture of health allows for better prediction of near-term and future avoidable disease burden. It also provides greater insight to inform where and how to focus wellness initiatives for maximum impact and to document program outcomes over time.

Questions:

1. Why is an HA the first step on the path to behavior change for employees?
   a. It provides feedback to get someone started
   b. It provides an exercise and nutritional guideline
   c. It is self-directed an requires thought
   d. All of the above

2. An HA identifies an individual›s risks through a medical examination.
   a. True
   b. False

3. Why are HA›s beneficial to employers?

a. It provides secret information

b. Employers get benefits from insurance companies for implementing them

c. It provides insight into possible near and future disease problems, and strategies to combat it

d. It costs the company nothing

HRAs – The Heart of Wellness
By Don Hall

Introduction

Today, most organizations – big and small – recognize the great value of an employee wellness program. Even the *Harvard Business Review* agrees. Per an article by Berry, Mirabito, and Baun, "Wellness programs have often been viewed as a nice extra, not a strategic imperative. Newer evidence tells a different story." A result of their discovery is that healthy employees cost companies less.

The issue now is not whether or not you should have a wellness program, but rather how it should be designed. If your company›s wellness program is not delivering the value you hoped for, and your employee health improvement is minimal, is it because the program is poorly designed? Are some elements missing? And can it be turned it around?

In most cases, three simple things are at the heart of the problem:

1) Expecting immediate improvements.

2) Expecting employees to change unhealthy behaviors without offering them meaningful help and incentives.

3) Expecting a single wellness tool to make a program successful.

No one thing – not an annual wellness day, free health screenings or even a powerful health risk assessment (HRA) – can make a company healthy all by itself. No one tool can reveal the full picture or reliably affect the lifestyle changes that can improve employees' health or a company's bottom line.

The recipe for worksite wellness success has many ingredients. It needs a first-rate HRA to gather and organize health data. Then it needs blood work and other biometrics to add objectivity to each person's self-reported story. It also needs appealing incentives to boost participation, interventions that motivate, skillful health coaching, follow-up, and, of course, management's earnest support. But the fundamental ingredient is a thorough evidence-based HRA. Everything else relies on it, draws from it and doesn't make sense without it. A great HRA is at the heart of every successful wellness program.

What Do HRAs Do Best?

An HRA's primary job is to identify the level of an individual's health risk and invite those who are at risk to get well. When people read the results from their first health risk assessment, they're often surprised. Many learn for the first time that they're in an increased risk category, maybe for diabetes or heart disease. And they realize that they need to do something to get healthier. When this happens, an HRA creates an "Aha!" moment. That's when the lights go on, and the desire to change old habits into healthier, new ones is set in motion.

The more comprehensive the HRA, the more good it can do. If the questions are thorough and the scoring is sophisticated, it can recommend health interventions that the individual will likely be interested in. These could be as simple as an outline of a more nutritious way of eating, or a list of new ways to be active.

But how likely is it that a person will actually follow through with making needed lifestyle changes? And what change does a person think is important? A good HRA answers those questions by providing personal health interest and readiness-to-change surveys. And health coaches love it when they do! This incredibly valuable information helps health coaches customize programs for individuals so they have the best chance of success.

For your organization as well as employees, HRAs establish an invaluable information baseline. Year after year, as data accrues, employers can see early more trends develop. (For example, are employees gaining weight? Are blood pressure levels increasing? Are more people exercising and eating better?) If health trends are positive, you'll see the economic benefits that come with reduced absenteeism, increased productivity, and fewer healthcare claims. And you'll see a measurable improvement in employee health. Through HRA reports, the real value of your investment in wellness can be measured.

A crucial step to take on the road to assessing individuals' health is to ask key health indicator questions. For example, "How many servings of fruits and vegetables do you eat each day?" "During the past month, have you felt sad, discouraged or hopeless?" "Do you smoke?" Gathering and interpreting personal data with a comprehensive HRA can help a company's wellness team see the health strengths and health weaknesses of its employees. (Be certain that your HRA includes questions about mental health. Depression is a primary indicator for high health claims.) An HRA is a gateway to a broader and more meaningful worksite wellness program. It can help you know what steps to take next.

Improvements Take Time

For Individuals
Making a lifestyle change – and making it stick – usually takes time. Setbacks, lapses and procrastination are part of being human. It also takes time to see the results of earnest and steady efforts. An extra 20 pounds of fat doesn't show up overnight, and it can't be lost overnight either. High cholesterol, high blood pressure, high blood sugar levels and obesity are especially challenging conditions and generally take a lot of time and a big effort to reverse.

But even at the start, when the effort to replace a bad habit with a good one has just begun, people often feel better right away – sometimes physically, but mostly emotionally. That's because they're taking care of themselves and they feel good about it. Annual HRAs can measure these changes and give supportive feedback on the positive changes individuals are making.

For Employers
The number one goal for most employers with wellness programs is to get employees engaged in healthy pursuits. A company's health costs go down – or at least rise more slowly – when employee health improves. Healthier people are generally also happier people. And a by-product of being happier is increased productivity. Even if the dollars saved aren't easily measured at first, other tangible benefits can usually be seen early on.

The key is getting as many employees as possible participating in your wellness program. An excellent way to increase participation is by offering an attractive HRA (one that includes health tests and personal reports). It's important to promote it well so that people can see the value it would have for their own health. Once people take an HRA, they usually become more interested in making lifestyle changes after they've read their personal report, which makes specific suggestions for positive changes.

Seeing a significant return on investment could take a few years. But there are a few quicker ways to improve the bottom line. For instance, many companies use the HRA to identify those who have an existing disease. They then motivate this group to participate in a targeted wellness program. These high-risk employees likely have the highest number of health claims. By reducing these, you could see a greater and more immediate reduction in health-related costs.

Incentives are a vital part of an effective wellness program. But they have to be what's right for your population if they're going to work. Ask for your employees' input in your HRA or in a participant survey. People will usually tell you what they want if you ask. The best, proven incentive is to offer your employees a discount on their potion of health insurance when they take the HRA. This can increase engagement in your wellness program and follow-up events.

The Indisputable Value of HRA Data

Self-Reporting Plus Biometrics – Getting the Whole Picture
Self-reported information is more than just reliable. It's the most common way health information is collected. When an HRA is conducted properly and people are assured that their information will be used only for their own benefit and will not be seen by management, the information gathered is quite reliable. Nearly all health studies conducted by the government and research programs are based on self-reported questionnaires.

All good HRAs also collect biometric data such as height and weight measurements, body composition, blood cholesterol and glucose levels, blood pressure, depression scores, and results from fitness tests. These data increase the HRA's accuracy by balancing self-reported data with objective data. If you collect data, you need to record it in a database so you can track any changes, do group statistics, and show individuals their results. An HRA does all of this automatically.

Better than Just Health Insurance Claim Data

If a person is taking a beta blocker, does he or she have high blood pressure, coronary heart disease or a heart arrhythmia? Do you want to wait until a person is taking diabetes medication to identify who has diabetes? Or would you rather have the ability to identify pre-diabetes (currently 79 million Americans age 20 and over have it) or those who are at risk of developing diabetes long before they have to take medication?

People with undiagnosed diabetes (a large part of the population) who also have depression or pre-hypertension won't be found at all just by looking at health claims. But they would be identified with a good HRA and biometric screening. Claims data will give you some information, but it can't paint a complete picture. It is largely *reactive* – identifying people who already have a disease rather than finding those at risk for developing one.

Knowing Family History Helps, But...

No good doctor would ever treat a patient without gathering a medical history and doing health tests and examinations. But government regulations have limited data-gathering on HRAs. Family health history and personal genetics questions can no longer be asked. And while family history is important, it isn't critical. In fact, in the esteemed Nurses' Health Study, women with modifiable risk factors for diabetes had the same risk for the disease whether or not they had a family history of it. A good HRA report will still point out to individuals that if they have a family history of early heart disease, diabetes or cancer, they may be at higher risk themselves.

The Four Biggest Mistakes Employers Make with HRAs

When an HRA is used correctly, it engages individuals and makes them – and the whole wellness program – more successful. But when it's used incorrectly, success is harder to come by. These are the most common and most costly mistakes employers make with HRAs:

1. **They think an HRA *is* a wellness program.**
   An HRA is a pivotal part of a wellness program, to be sure. It gathers data that is used to invite people to health classes or programs they need. But it isn't designed to be a change agent all by itself.

2. **After employees take an HRA, the employer expects them to understand the results and know what to do to improve their health.**

   These same employers often decide that HRAs are not effective because their employees didn't make many changes. This is similar to a doctor making a diagnosis without offering treatment, then being disappointed that the patient didn't get well. Employees need direction to learn which steps to take. This can be accomplished with a one-on-one, over-the-phone, group meeting or with a video presentation that explains the results.

3. **They didn't get enough people to take the HRA.**

   If only 20 percent of your population participates in your wellness program, even using the best HRA won't have a measurable impact on your healthcare costs. To see a real ROI, aim for an 80-percent participation rate. Advertise your Wellness Day, and generate excitement around it. Offer incentives that employees find meaningful. A reduction in health insurance premiums reliably boosts participation.

4. **They don't offer enough follow-up.**

   Employees may learn from the HRA which lifestyle changes they need to make to get healthier. But unless employers make these programs available, most people won't follow through. Offer access to weight-loss programs, online interventions to lower blood pressure, plans to eat healthier, personal health coaching, exercise classes or, at the least self-study programs.

How HRAs Pull It All Together – A Summary

When you start your wellness program with a good HRA, you automatically improve your chances for a positive outcome. Here's how:

HRAs show individuals their personal risks and ways to prevent serious disease. Individuals need to know their major health risks. Some are obvious, such as smoking and obesity. Others are not so obvious. Those include risks for high blood pressure and high cholesterol, specifics about poor eating habits (e.g., low intake of fiber, fruits, vegetables and whole grains) and symptoms of depression.

HRAs give each individual a personal plan. Each person needs to know the specific steps they need to take to lower identified risks and improve their health. A good HRA includes these recommendations. It also gives personalized guidelines for lowering the risk of heart disease, diabetes, cancer, improving eating habits, improving fitness level and more.

HRAs establish benchmarks and document change over time. Are individual health scores improving, staying the same or getting worse? Without establishing a benchmark, then re-testing, you simply won't know. When companies start a wellness program, it is important for them and their employees to know their baseline. This is vital for individuals (with their weight, cholesterol levels, activity levels, eating habits, etc.) and for the organization (with the number of smokers, sedentary individuals, those with signs of depression, etc.). It's the only way to measure change and improvement over time and to know what interventions are needed.

Before HRAs became readily available, people ran wellness programs "blindly" – without knowing anyone's health needs, company-wide health needs or benchmarks. Then when administrators were asked if their wellness programs were successful, no one knew. Were there fewer smokers now? Were more people eating healthy? Were more people exercising now? How can you tell a person that he or she has improved (or not improved) this year unless you can compare current results with earlier benchmarks? With an HRA, you have a way to track improvement year by year, and show if your program is beneficial.

HRAs help you identify groups with specific needs for intervention. If you are a wellness coach, you probably want to have a wealth of information with recommendations at hand so you can talk to people intelligently and specifically about their health. A good HRA lets you query the database to find specific groups that need special attention. For example, it would be extremely helpful to know who has signs of depression so you can invite them to a stress management class. Why wait until people have pre-diabetes before encouraging them to make lifestyle changes? Run your queries and intervene early. This can help prevent costly and serious health problems.

HRAs motivate people to make positive lifestyle changes. It's the ultimate goal of a wellness program, since it leads to better employee health and an economic benefit for the organization. For so many employees, an HRA creates the "teachable" moment – after the assessment has been taken and the personal report is in the individual's hand. Be sure the language in the report is encouraging and clear, and be ready with follow-up opportunities.

As more employers use an HRA in their wellness programs, and use it correctly, they will gain insights, health information and the ability to connect to their employees' needs with solutions. With a comprehensive HRA at the heart of your wellness initiative, you'll also gain the coveted ability to run a successful, ongoing wellness program and document the improvements that will come.

References:

1. Berry L, Mirabito AM, and Baun, WB. What's the Hard Return on Employee Wellness Programs? *Harvard Business Review.* Dec 2010.

2. Brewer P, Gallo A, and Smith M. Getting Fit with Corporate Wellness Programs, *Strategic Finance,* May 2010.

3. O'Donnell M. Making the Impossible Possible: Engaging the Entire Population in Comprehensive Workplace Health Promotion, The Science of Health Promotion, *American Journal of Health Promotion,* 2010; 24(6):iv-v.

4. Nash D, Reifsnyder J, Fabius R, Pracilio V. Making the Case for Population Health Management: The Business Value of Better Health, *Population Health: Creating a Culture of Wellness,* Jones and Bartlett Learning, 2011.

5. Staley P, et al. *Interim Guidance for Health Risk Assessments and their Modes of Provision for Medicare Beneficiaries.* Office of Prevention through Healthcare, Center for Disease Control and Prevention, March 15, 2011.

6. Edington D. Zero Trends: Health as a Serious Economic Strategy, Health Management Research Center, University of Michigan, 2009.

7. Byrne DW, Goetzel RZ, et al. Seven-Year Trends in Employee Health Habits from a Comprehensive Workplace Health Promotion Program at Vanderbilt University. *Journal of Occupational and Environmental Medicine,* Dec 2011; 53(12):1353-1493.

8. Colditz GA, Willett WC, Rotnitzky A, Manson JE. Weight Gain as a Risk Factor for Clinical Diabetes Mellitus in Women. *Annals of Internal Medicine.* April 1, 1995; 122(7):548-9.

Key Ideas

- The four biggest mistakes employers make with HRA's:

  1. Thinking that an HRA is a wellness program

  2. Expecting employees know what to do with the information they received from an HRA to improve their health.

  3. Gettign too few people to take the HRA.

  4. Not offering enough follow up to employees after the HRA is complete.

- The recipe for worksite wellness success has many ingredients. It needs a first-rate HRA to gather and organize health data.

Then it needs blood work and other biometrics to add objectivity to each person's self-reported story. It also needs appealing incentives to boost participation, interventions that motivate, skillful health coaching, follow-up, and, of course, management's earnest support. But the fundamental ingredient is a thorough evidence-based HRA. Everything else relies on it, draws from it and doesn't make sense without it. A great HRA is at the heart of every successful wellness program.

- An HRA's primary job is to identify the level of an individual's health risk and invite those who are at risk to get well. A good HRA answers those questions by providing personal health interest and readiness-to-change surveys

- Employees need direction to learn which steps to take. This can be accomplished with a one-on-one, over-the-phone, group meeting or with a video presentation that explains the results.

Questions:

1. Most wellness programs do not need an HRA
   a. True
   b. False

2. What is the primary purpose of an HRA?
   a. Identify an individual›s health risk
   b. Reducing insurance costs
   c. Being the entire wellness program
   d. None of the above

3. True or False: In some circumstances an HRA can stand alone as a complete wellness program.
   a. True
   b. False

4. True or False: Biometrics add significantly more actionable data to a wellness program than a health insurance claims review alone.
   a. True
   b. False

CHAPTER 4
Biometrics

Biometric Screening: the Linchpin of Wellness
By Justin Bellante

Introduction: Counting the Cost

As the wellness industry has matured over the past decade, there has been a growing need for improved health measurement. Wellness efforts are most successful when driven by timely, specific information about risks that drive costs, such as heart disease, diabetes, hypertension and obesity. This has led to an increased emphasis on health screening, both to guide wellness activities and to measure outcomes.

The importance of these endeavors is plain to see. With nearly 60 percent of individuals in the U.S. receiving healthcare coverage through employer-based health insurance,[19] and average annual per employee healthcare costs projected to surpass the $10,000 milestone in 2012,[20] employers are increasingly investing in wellness solutions to reduce costs. Studies from Wellness Councils of America and other reputable sources reveal that, on average, every dollar spent on wellness yields three to five dollars in savings, which has spurred over 81 percent of U.S. employers to enact cost-saving wellness programs.[21]

When screening is done properly it can greatly enhance the entire continuum of corporate wellness – from engagement, measurement, and action to measuring outcomes. Since screening typically sits on the front end of wellness (measurement before prescription), a good screening program should actually increase overall wellness program engagement. To do so, it must be offered to the entire population. In addition, if the screening experience is friendly and compelling, it creates "stickiness "(reinforcing the decision to engage).

Data integration is the final step. Many companies navigate the wellness spectrum admirably, but fail when it comes to connecting critical, timely, money-saving data with actionable interventions. To verify progress and ensure positive health outcomes companies must be able to obtain quantifiable results of their wellness efforts and dollars spent. This includes both measurement of health trends and an assessment of cost savings.

Screening Trends

Wellness increasingly relies on screening in order to match risks with interventions and to measure outcomes. There are three key trends to be aware of: Engagement, Incentives and Accountability.

Engagement

As companies continue to emphasize engagement, the wellness sector is responding by adapting consumer-centric solutions that address access, design and usability needs. The impact on screening has been an increase in the number of screening methods available in the typical employer program and improved customer experiences. A complete screening program should include options for getting tested at the workplace (onsite testing), at home (via a home test kit), at a local lab and by your primary physician.

Incentives

The use of incentives to drive engagement has been steadily increasing. Employers are beginning to base incentives not only on engagement, but increasingly on outcomes, making screening essential to establish health baselines and achieve overall wellness goals.

Accountability

The maturing wellness industry is under mounting pressure to deliver results. Screening helps employers establish a baseline understanding of which types of wellness activities are most needed and whether the chosen activities are getting results.

Screening Methods

Modern screening programs include a variety of methods to engage individuals and measure health. If possible, it is advantageous to offer as many screening methods as possible to meet population needs and achieve wellness goals.

Screening methods, descriptions, and advantages are listed on the following page:

Method	Description	Advantages
Onsite	Nurses and/or technicians conduct screenings at the work-site via fingerstick testing or venous draw. If fingerstick, then post-results counseling is typically offered.	· Convenient for large locations / campuses · Drives buzz / awareness through the physical presence · Can include direct measurement of height, weight, and blood pressure
Lab Visit	A participant locates a lab, prints a lab form and visits the lab to have blood drawn and results sent at a later date.	· Uses the gold standard venous draw and laboratory processing familiar to both patients and physicians
At-Home	A participant orders a test kit, collects a sample via fingerstick in the comfort of his or her home, and sends the sample via mail to be processed by a licensed laboratory.	· Higher fasting compliance · Increased privacy and convenience · Ideal for people in remote locations, dispersed workforces, new hires throughout the year, 2nd or 3rd shift workers, and small companies

Method	Description	Advantages
Physician Results Form	A participant prints a form and takes it to his or her physician to complete (enter updated biometric values) and fax back to the screening vendor	· Promotes relationship with primary care physician · Convenient for those who see their physician regularly · Avoids duplicate billing (if screening is done within 6 months of corporate program) · Testing done using gold standard venous draw and lab processing · Includes height, weight, blood pressure direct measurement

Each of these methods should be accessible via web-based and non-web-based platforms in order to maximize access and engagement. Non-web-based platforms include phone ordering or paper sign-up at a work-site location.

In order to determine which options are right for your population you must first identify and prioritize your wellness goals. If engagement is your goal, as is often the case during first- or second-year wellness programs, then it is critical to collect as much data as possible to establish a population baseline from which to make knowledgeable decisions. In this case, you should give people as many options as possible to measure their health. In subsequent years employers can emphasize preferred screening options yet still provide other options as alternatives.

While many organizations offer a single screening method to reduce overhead and minimize the time required of HR personnel, it is much more effective to offer multiple screening options, automated by a cohesive technology platform with a single screening portal and consolidated billing. The screening platform should include proven engagement tools to drive participation and compliance. These typically take the form of email or phone communications that encourage people to sign-up and remind them to follow through to completion.

The best screening platforms utilize proven methods from behavioral science to increase participation – often by as much as 40 percent. Such firms also leverage focus groups and usability studies to fine-tune these communications vehicles, increasing compliance and boosting customer satisfaction with the overall screening experience.

Participant Experience

Great companies and products are measured by the satisfaction of their customers. Successful screening programs include much more than a test and a lab result. They are marked by measurable results, market credibility, consumer engagement and customer satisfaction – the combination of which produces the best screening experience and the highest ROI.

Make sure your screening vendor offers a uniform platform for all screening methods, including at-home screening, onsite screening, lab visits and doctor visits. It should provide the same user-friendly promotion, sign-up, scheduling and communication tools, along with uniform reporting and data integration. No matter how your population gets screened, they share a common program and you obtain consistent results.

Connections: Since screening is typically situated at the beginning of the wellness program, it is not only responsible for driving engagement, but ensures that customers are satisfied and that there is no drop during subsequent wellness activities and interventions. Many firms fail to connect screening and subsequent wellness activities. As with all consumer products, the sign-up process should be simple and appealing to avoid confusion and drive participation. Participants should always know where they are in the process, and what the next steps are. Market-leading screening vendors conduct regular usability testing to enhance this experience.

Simplicity: One of the primary goals of screening is to create awareness of health issues. Unfortunately, many lab reports are confusing, outdated and unclear about recommended actions. Poor design can lead to missed opportunities if participants can't easily identify risk and take appropriate action. This is not only the case for individual lab reports, but also for aggregate reports delivered to the employer and supporting wellness consultants.

Service: Another important contributor to satisfaction is the level of customer service. Given the variety of employer types and working hours, screening companies should have 24/7 live customer support to address issues as they occur.

In a nutshell, effective screening programs must be flexible and efficient while fulfilling the needs of your covered population. The greater the participation in your screening program, the more complete set of data you will have to measure your progress and make decisive adjustments. Providing access to every covered member of your population is the first step in achieving high engagement.

A comprehensive screening offering should provide a seamless, uniform platform for all participants, no matter which screening method is employed (at-home, onsite, lab visit or physician forms). All methods should be driven by comprehensive communications that remind people to sign-up, complete the screening and review their lab reports. All methods should be supported by comprehensive, 24/7 customer service.

Here are some of the hallmarks of a well-crafted screening solution:

- Flexible sign-up and scheduling tools
- Flexible delivery models including at-home test kits, workplace test kits, onsite testing, lab visits, doctor visits, or clinic visits
- Engagement tools that increase participation by 30 percent or more
- Consumer-tested reminder systems and communications for all screening methods
- Actionable results and integrated, customizable interventions

- Year-over-year online participant reports and employer aggregate reports

- Seamless data integration with third-party vendors, interventions, and health plans, at no extra charge

- Comprehensive, live 24/7 customer support

Planning, Implementation and Monitoring

The complexity of planning and implementation can vary depending upon the type of screening methods employed. At-home screening, lab visits and physician results forms typically involve the least amount of complexity. While onsite screening has more logistical challenges, a good screening service can simplify these challenges and minimize the effort that must be expended by in-house HR and benefits personnel.

All screening programs should include an automated set-up process with a master timeline outlining the program set-up, launch and administration. A checklist or other tool for simplifying and organizing the workload should guide each step of the process. The vendor should provide access to a secure HR dashboard that lets you set up and monitor the program, along with communications templates to simplify setup and ensure that your key messages and brand shines through.

Effective communication springs from thorough research with an emphasis on ensuring a positive and informative customer experience. Initial messaging should address key issues such as privacy, incentives, and deadlines. Reminder emails should be sent on an individual and population level in order to drive compliance and maintain momentum. Progressive screening vendors establish a timeline and template for all key communications, including initial signup, reminders, screening confirmations, availability of lab reports and various types of follow-up to connect participants with relevant interventions. Each step is automated by the platform and monitored through the HR dashboards.

Screening programs typically require lead-time of 30 to 45 days for setup, planning and scheduling of any screening events. The timing of the actual screening can depend upon company goals, but it is best to create a sense of urgency and momentum by concentrating screening events into a one- to three-month period. Following these annual events, you can offer at-home, lab visit, and physician results forms for new hires throughout the year.

Beware of Hidden Costs!

In order to ensure a positive return on your wellness investments you must avoid the hidden costs associated with many screening programs. If you are selecting a vendor based on price, don't overlook some of the indirect costs, and ask your vendor how it will mitigate these costs.

HR Setup Time: How much is your time worth? How many hours do you spend preparing for a screening program? Does your screening vendor give you tools to organize all your screening and wellness information? Does the vendor create free communications and collateral to drive engagement? Many employers spend thousands of unnecessary dollars to set up and manage these programs.

Lost Productivity: How much does your average employee make per hour? The real cost of screening is the combination of what you pay for the screening and the lost productivity or hourly wage of each employee during the screening. A $35 screening can easily cost $75 once these other factors are considered. Time spent setting up and managing a screening program is time spent outside of your core responsibilities. A good screening vendor should be able to show you how to plan and launch a population-wide screening program by spending only one hour of your time.

Data Integration, Handoff and Reporting

To help employees make positive changes, you must integrate screening data with other wellness services, disease management tools, health interventions, Third-Party Administrators (TPAs), health plans, and electronic health records. Fast, accurate and pervasive data integration is what makes a screening solution more successful, enabling you to produce better outcomes and ensure a positive ROI.

A single data point in time has limited use, whether it is a health metric or a key business measurement. However, a trend can show you where you are headed and lead to meaningful action. Health data, on an individual or population level, must be accessible over time so that you can measure progress, view results and analyze the effectiveness of your overall wellness program. Individuals need data that they can track over time, and HR professionals need aggregate reports with year-over-year values in order to see progress, spot worrisome health trends and calculate ROI.

In addition, individuals need actionable results with interventions tied to the 'teachable moment,' the point in time when results are viewed and action is most likely. Health coaching and other wellness resources should be presented alongside professionally designed reports in order to motivate people to take the next step.

Key Ideas:

- Effective screening programs must be flexible and efficient while fulfilling the needs of your covered population.

- There are three key trends to be aware of:

  1. Engagement

  2. Incentives

  3. Accountability

- A complete screening program could include options for getting tested at the workplace, at home, at a local lab and by your primary physician. If possible, it is advantageous to offer as many screening methods as possible to meet population needs and achieve wellness goals.

- There are advantages to each of the screening methods:

- Onsite: Convenient for large locations, drives awareness through the physical presence of the screening event, can include direct measurement of height, weight, and blood pressure.

- Lab Visit: Uses the gold standard venous draw and laboratory processing familiar to both patient and physicians.,

- At-Home: High fasting compliance, increased privacy and convenience, ideal for people in remove locations or those who work non-traditional shifts.

- Physician Results: Promotes relationship with primary care physician, convenient for those who see their physical regularly, avoids duplicate billing, testing done using gold standard venous draw, includes height, weight, and blood pressure direct measurement.

- Individuals need actionable results with interventions tied to the 'teachable moment,' the point in time when results are viewed and action is most likely.

Questions:

1. Which of the "three key trends" is missing from the following list: Engagement, Incentives, _____?

   a. Progress

   b. Accountability

   c. Sustainability

   d. Return on Investment

2. Which screening method has the advantage of avoiding duplicate billing?

   a. Physician Results

   b. At Home

   c. LabVisit

   d. Onsite

3. What is meant by a "teachable moment"?

   a. The point after results are given and action is most likely

   b. The point after a person fails their wellness goal, and has to learn a lesson

   c. The point where the employees are taught about the wellness programs

   d. None of the above

4. It is best to offer only one form of screen process

   a. True

   b. False

Biometric Screening for a Successful Wellness Program
By Lisa M. Holland

Once an employer has decided to implement a wellness program, they must then determine the most appropriate interventions that will have the biggest health impact on their population in order to reduce population health risks as well as produce a relative return on their wellness investment.

Data collection is a key element of any wellness program because it helps the employer target population health risks and track risk migration. Employers should focus efforts on the most important and practical data gathering methods that will help them simplify their wellness strategy maximize their wellness dollars and support a sustainable program.

There has been significant emphasis on the use of a Health Assessment as the primary data collection method for any wellness program. However, Health Assessment tools are self-reported measures of an individual's personal perception of their health and may not provide a true representation of the individual or the population. While much of the wellness literature to date incorporates this self-reported data, generally speaking, the outcome measures do not provide sound information for targeting population health risk that cannot be achieved through objective data collection, such as biometric screenings. The use of biometric screening provides an employer with reliable and valid genomic information, in aggregate, of the population's current health status and predictors of future health risks. In fact, the USPSTF found good evidence that screenings improve health outcomes and offer health benefits that substantially outweigh any harm from obtaining health screenings. [2]

The inclusion of biometric screening in a company wellness strategy assists with raising health awareness among employees, offers the opportunity to establish baseline health information or discover personal health issues that may have been previously undetected. For employers, the aggregate information can be used to formulate and create targeted health interventions, forecast future healthcare costs, assist with benefit design planning and calculate a return on investment.

The goal of the screenings are to engage the population into action-able behaviors to maintain or improve biometric measures within established clinical ranges to prevent or delay the onset of chronic disease and achieve optimal population health, productivity and healthcare affordability.

Seventy-five percent of chronic disease is preventable through simple lifestyle and behavior change. [3] To assist individuals with understanding which behaviors to change in order to prevent or delay disease, the following four critical health factors should be measured: blood pressure, body mass index (BMI), Lipids (Cholesterol panel) and tobacco use. Each of these measures contributes directly to the total health of an individual and the overall population health risk status.

Blood Pressure

Blood pressure refers to the force exerted by circulating blood on the walls of blood vessels. The term blood pressure generally refers the systolic arterial pressure, defined as the highest pressure in the arteries, which occurs near the beginning of the cardiac cycle over the diastolic arterial pressure which is the lowest pressure at the resting phase of the cardiac cycle.

According to recent estimates, nearly one in three U.S. adults has high blood pressure. Because there are commonly no symptoms associated with high blood pressure, nearly one-third of these people don't know they have elevated blood pressure. This is why high blood pressure is often called the "silent killer". Uncontrolled high blood pressure can lead to a wide range of health conditions such as stroke, heart attack, heart failure or kidney failure. A simple screening is the only way to tell if high blood pressure is evident. Blood pressure can change from minute to minute, with changes in posture, exercise, stress or sleeping. Ideally, blood pressure should be equal to or less than 120/70 mm Hg (millimeters of mercury) for an adult. [4]

Body Mass Index (BMI):

BMI is a number calculated from an individual's height and weight. BMI is a reliable measure of an individual's weight in relation to height, not body composition. BMI does not measure body fat directly, but research has shown that BMI correlates to direct measures of body fat. BMI is an inexpensive and easy-to-perform method of screening for overweight and obesity categories.[5] According to recent data from the CDC, 63 percent of adults in the United States are now overweight or obese and this trend continues to rise.[5]

These increasing rates raise concern because of their implications for Americans' health and healthcare affordability. Being overweight or obese increases the risk of many chronic diseases and health conditions, including the following:

- Hypertension
- Dyslipidemia (for example, high total cholesterol or high levels of triglycerides)
- Type 2 Diabetes
- Coronary heart disease
- Stroke
- Gallbladder disease
- Osteoarthritis
- Sleep apnea and respiratory problems
- Some cancers (endometrial, breast, and colon)

Lipid Panel (Cholesterol, HDL, LDL, triglycerides and cholesterol risk ratio):

A comprehensive lipid panel screening measures the total amount of fatty substances (cholesterol and triglycerides) in the blood. A lipid profile measures total cholesterol, LDL cholesterol, HDL cholesterol and triglycerides. The body uses cholesterol to help build cells and produce hormones. Too much cholesterol in the blood can build up along the inside of the artery walls, forming what is known as plaque. Large amounts of plaque increase the chance of having a heart attack or stroke. HDL cholesterol helps remove fat from the body by binding with it in the bloodstream and carrying it back to the liver for disposal. HDL is sometimes called the good cholesterol. A high level of HDL may lower the chance of developing heart disease or stroke. LDL carries mostly fat and only a small amount of protein from the liver to other parts of the body. It is sometimes called the bad cholesterol. A high LDL level may increase the chance of developing heart disease. Triglycerides are a type of fat the body uses to store energy. Only small amounts are found in the blood. Having a high triglyceride level along with high LDL cholesterol may increase the chance of having heart disease more than having only a high LDL level.[6]The USPSTF found good evidence that lipid measurement can identify asymptomatic middle-aged people at increased risk of coronary heart disease.

Tobacco Use (Cotinine Screening)

Cotinine is a metabolite (by product) of nicotine as it is "processed" by the human body. It is an indicator that nicotine has been inhaled or otherwise introduced into the body. [8] Screening for the presence of cotinine can be accomplished through a variety of immunoassay testing procedures to determine if a person is a tobacco user. Cotinine can be found in urine and in blood samples. Because of the complexity of this type of screening as well as the cost implications, most employers do not choose to offer this type of screening as part of their wellness strategy. However, because of the health implications as well as associated medical costs of tobacco use, most employers are implementing some type of tobacco-free programming such as a smoking surcharge program, a tobacco-free workplace policy and the use of self-reported Tobacco Affidavits. According to the Centers for Disease Control and Prevention, tobacco users cost on average $3,500 in direct medical costs and $1,700 in lost productivity per user.[10]

If you are an employer and are thinking about implementing a worksite wellness program or already have a program in place, be sure to include, at a minimum, these four critical biometrics indicators as part of your program's core data collection methodology. Biometric screening provides quantifiable and reliable population health information that will assist you with determining the most appropriate clinical interventions as well as support benefit plan design strategy for the future of your organization.

References

1. B. Swift (2011) Wellness & Benefits Administration Benchmarking Study: An analysis of how companies are leveraging wellness programs and automation to control healthcare costs.

2. The Guide to Clinical Preventative Services 2006, Summary of Recommendations, 9 August 2007, accessed online at www.ahrq.gov/clinic/uspstf/uspstopics.htm

3. Centers for Disease Control and Prevention. http://www.cdc.gov/chronicdisease/resources/publications/AAG/chronic.htm

4. American Heart Association, 13 August 2007, accessed online at www.americanheart.org/presenter.jhtml?identifier=2114.

5. Centers for Disease Control and Prevention (CDC), 15 August 2007, accessed online at www.cdc.gov/nccdphp/dnpa/bmi/adult_BMI/about_adult_BMI.htm.

6. Centers for Disease Control and Prevention. Overweight and Obesity, the Health Consequences. http://www.cdc.gov/obesity/causes/health.html

7. WebMD Medical Reference from Healthwise, updated October 6, 2005, Healthwise Inc., 15 August 2007, accessed online at www.webmd.com/cholesterol-management/Cholesterol-and-Triglycerides-Tests?page=2

8. The Guide to Clinical Preventative Services 2006, Summary of Recommendations, 15 August 2007, accessed online at www.ahrq.gov/clinic/uspstf/uspstopics.htm

9. Foundation for Blood Research, 18 March 2012, accessed online at http://www.fbr.org/publications/pamphlets/cotinine.html

10. Centers for Disease Control and Prevention. Annual Smoking-Attributal Mortality, Years of Potential Life Lost, and Economic Costs—United States, 1995-1999. Morbidity and Mortality Weekly Report 2002; 51 (14): 300-03.

Key Ideas:

- Seventy-five percent of chronic disease is preventable through simple lifestyle and behavior change.

- In order to prevent or delay disease, the following four critical health factors should be measured: blood pressure, body mass index (BMI), Lipids (Cholesterol panel) and tobacco use.

- Biometric screening provides quantifiable and reliable population health information that will assist you with determining the most appropriate clinical interventions as well as support benefit plan design strategy for the future of your organization.

Questions

1. What percentage of chronic disease is preventable with simple lifestyle changes?

   a. 20 percent

   b. 40 percent

   c. 65 percent

   d. 75 percent

2. Which of the four biometric screen types is missing from the following list: Blood pressure, _____, Cholesterol panel, tobacco use

   a. Glucose

   b. BMI

   c. Drug Use

   d. Blood type

3. Biometric screening does not provide quantifiable information

   a. True

   b. False

A Healthy Workforce and a Healthy Bottom-line: 10 Medical Tests that Can Save Lives and Money
By Maureen Young

Corporations spend millions of dollars every year on medical expenses for employees, including medical insurance and productivity losses. In many instances, corporations lose half or even more of their profits to medical care costs[1]. Many of these costs are for diseases and conditions that, if caught early, can be halted by procedures and treatments that could save lives. With the economy struggling and corporate America's need to pinch pennies it is important to be aware that the average age of American workers is increasing faster than that of most of our global competitors; and according to a study conducted by the Centers for Disease Control (CDC) 75 percent of healthcare costs are for diseases that are preventable[2].

Organizations that implement a health and wellness program for their employees see a reduction in absenteeism and an overall reduction in healthcare costs in the long term. The most effective programs include initial health assessments to identify mid- to high-risk individuals in conjunction with incentives and access to information on healthy lifestyle options. Large improvements in absenteeism are the single most critical positive impact from these programs and the evidence reveals slightly more than a 25 percent average reduction in sick leave, health plan costs and workers' compensation and disability costs with comprehensive programs.[4] The financial benefits of corporate wellness programs has profound implications for American employees and could lead to an increase in properly designed and executed health programs in all companies as organizations reap the rewards of them. According to a survey by consultants Aon Hewitt, such corporate programs increased 5 percent; from 49 percent in 2010 to 54 percent in 2011. The same survey found that additional employers plan to adopt them beginning in 2014 if the national health law is upheld by the Supreme Court. The Patient Protection and Affordable Care Act (PPACA) would allow corporations to offer larger incentives for positive lifestyle practices like lunchtime walking, smoking cessation or taking medical tests and reaching specific health standards. Conversely, corporations will be able to impose larger penalties on employees who don't participate or don't meet stated health criteria. Providing programs that keep employees healthy is a key factor in maintaining a productive workforce for all corporations.

The importance of early testing in identifying disease or the potential for chronic conditions cannot be underestimated. Whether preventable or not, diseases are more easily treated if they are diagnosed early. The difference in cost between a procedure, which can run to $15,000, and each medical incidence due to chronic disease at a cost of as much as $45,000, is clear[3]. The difference in the impact to the individual goes deeper than cost and hits the quality of life, the ability to continue working and the security of providing for themselves and their families. Corporations have a unique opportunity to make a difference in their employees' lives and their own financial health, by providing critical baseline testing, providing information about the most important tests and/or encouraging employees to seek them out through incentive or reward programs.

Top 10 Tests Employees Should Take
Out of the hundreds of medical tests available, the following 10 medical tests can provide targeted insight into your employees' current medical state and serve as a baseline against which future health can be measured. Some of these tests are familiar, while others are newer and go deeper to examine the specifics of cardiovascular health, which in many instances is a preventable disease. The tests offer insight into which employees are high-risk individuals who can then be targeted for specific healthcare programs and monitoring. "Results from well-conducted randomized trials suggest that providing opportunities for individual risk reduction counseling for high risk employees within the context of comprehensive programming may be the critical component of an effective worksite health promotion program. Just offering low-intensity, short-duration programs aimed at increasing awareness of health issues for the entire employee population may not be sufficient to achieve desired outcomes."[3]

Ten tests to consider providing for employees or promoting with informational programs are:

1. **Smoker's (Cotinine/Nicotine) Test** – Some corporations have decided to take the precaution of testing current or potential employees for nicotine use with a cotinine test. Cotinine is a

nicotine by-product (a metabolite) that is present in the urine of smokers 2-4 days after tobacco use.

The test identifies smokers who the corporation may require to pay higher insurance premiums based on their increased health risks. The CDC reports that a worker who smokes costs an employer approximately $1,300 more per year in healthcare costs than one who doesn't. Support groups, incentives and competitions can help to get more employees to stop smoking and remain smoke-free.

2. **VAP (Vertical Auto Profile)® Cholesterol Test** – Identifying employees with high cardiovascular disease risk offers an opportunity for corporations and their employees to prevent debilitation and death from stroke and heart attack. Cardiovascular disease is the leading cause of the death in the United States and one in three deaths is due to heart disease and stroke, accounting for 2,200 deaths per day.

    The VAP® cholesterol test is one of the most accurate and comprehensive cholesterol tests available today. It measures 18 separate components of blood cholesterol, compared to just 4 components in the standard cholesterol test.

3. **PLAC® Test** – This test measures Lp-PLA2, a vascular-specific inflammatory enzyme that is implicated in the formation of rupture-prone plaque. Plaque rupture and thrombosis (formation of a blood clot inside a blood vessel) cause the majority of cardiac events (stroke and heart attack). Stroke is the number three killer in the United States and the main cause of disability.

    Cholesterol is not an accurate predictor of stroke risk, but a high level of the enzyme Lp-PLA2 can indicate the need for more aggressive cardiovascular treatment. When arterial walls become inflamed, Lp-PLA2 is produced. Standard cholesterol tests cannot indicate inflammation or pinpoint that the specific type of cholesterol a person has may be the type that is more likely to rupture, creating a blood clot which can cause a heart attack or ischemic stroke. Sixty-eight percent of all heart attacks and strokes are caused by clots, not from narrowing of the arteries.

4. **Diabetes Test** – A simple Glucose (Serum) test, also known as the Fasting Blood Glucose Test, can identify higher- or lower-

than-normal blood sugar levels and diabetes. Undetected diabetes can be a silent killer and is the leading cause of blindness and kidney disease. Many people with type 2 diabetes have no symptoms. Low activity level, poor diet and excess body weight can increase the risk of developing type 2 diabetes.

Early awareness of hyperglycemia or high blood sugar can allow an employee to take action to prevent the development of, or even reverse, the disease by losing weight and improving diet and activity levels. A high amount of fat in the body makes it harder for the body to process insulin correctly. Type 2 diabetes can also develop in thin people who are elderly, which can make it even harder to detect or to suspect.

5. **Nutritional tests** – A Micronutrient Test measures your body's ability to absorb 32 vitamins, minerals, antioxidants and other essential nutrients within your white blood cells. It provides valuable information on how to correct deficiencies and would work well in a corporate wellness program that combines healthy eating and exercise.

    Vitamin deficiencies are associated with disease processes and overall health. Vitamin, mineral and antioxidant deficiencies have been shown to suppress immune function and contribute to chronic degenerative diseases including arthritis, cancer, Alzheimer's, cardiovascular disease and diabetes.

6. **Basic Chemistry Panel** – This panel is a combination of 16 essential tests that measure the major components listed below to get a better overall picture of health:

    a. Electrolytes that could indicate salt/water or acid/base imbalances,

    b. Proteins and enzymes which show liver function and possible abnormalities, and

    c. Kidney tests that check for a range of kidney functions and measure waste in the blood, which indicates the quality of kidney filtration.

The tests in the Chemistry Panel can provide early warning signs for a multitude of conditions and diseases, including kidney disease, liver disease, anemia and lymphoma.

7. **Flu shots** – Although not a test, providing these onsite or at a discounted cost can help to keep the workforce healthy through flu season.

   Although the flu vaccine doesn't always line up exactly with the specific flu strains that spread in the community, there are substantial benefits when the viruses and the vaccine match well. Not only will the individual who received the vaccine be protected, but that individual will not be spreading the flu in the office before realizing he or she is sick.

   Reminders to wash hands to prevent the spread of disease amongst co-workers can limit the spread of many diseases, of which the flu is only one.

8. **Blood pressure** – A simple test that offers quick, targeted insight into a critical health value. About 1 in 3 adults in the United States have high blood pressure, and many may not realize it. The test measures the force of blood pushing against the walls of the arteries as the heart pumps blood. If blood pressure rises and stays high over time it can damage the heart, blood vessels, kidneys and other parts of the body, ultimately leading to coronary heart disease, heart failure, stroke and kidney failure.

   Early identification of chronic high blood pressure with treatment and lifestyle changes can prevent damage to the body and debilitating health events.

9. **Colonoscopy** – Definitely not a test that can be offered in the office, but a test that can reduce the incidence of cancer by identifying polyps before they become a problem. This test can be encouraged with incentives or rewards.

   Colonoscopies are recommended for everyone over the age of 50 and those at a high risk for the disease. Nearly all colon cancers begin as noncancerous polyps that slowly develop into cancer. The rate of death for colon cancer has dropped in the last 15 years, possibly due to increased awareness and screening. Colon cancer can almost always be caught with a colonoscopy in its earliest and most curable stages.

10. **Sexually transmitted diseases (STD)** – No one likes to think about the possibility that they are carrying an STD around,

but long-term consequences can be devastating. One of the major problems with STDs is that many of them have no symptoms until it's too late.

The long-term consequences of undiagnosed and untreated STDs can be disastrous; infertility, chronic pelvic pain, brain damage, liver damage and blindness are just a few. Modern medicine is a powerful weapon against these diseases; the earlier they are caught, the better. Ensuring that the corporate healthcare plan covers these tests so that employees can receive anonymous, confidential testing may encourage them to be tested before an STD causes long- term health issues.

How Corporations Can Make a Difference
Corporations can review their health insurance claims to determine which types of conditions employees are seeking treatment for or review an in-depth, aggregate report derived from a company-wide baseline health screening program. This analysis will help management to focus company wellness programs more effectively for their employee base. A comprehensive health program that is developed to reduce healthcare costs, improve employee satisfaction, and enhance the employer's image is one that contains multiple aspects of wellness. Key features of the program should include a health risk assessment (HRA), lab testing and biometrics, and wellness or fitness programs. Incentives are one way to ensure that employees are motivated to participate and can be provided in the form of reduced healthcare costs, gift cards or flextime for those who participate in the program.

One study, conducted on the impact of a worksite health program on short-term disability with 1628 employees over a three-year period, showed a significant difference between participants and non-participants. The number of net days lost to short-term disability was 6 days less for participants than non-participants and represented a potential savings of $1.37 million over 2 years and a 20 percent program impact.[5]

While it is frequently difficult to determine the exact Return on Investment (ROI) for wellness programs because they vary so significantly from company to company, the evidence points to risk reduction based on identifying high-risk individuals as a critical factor in the clinical and cost success of a health program. Ensuring that health insurance covers basic tests that can highlight moderate and high-risk health concerns early and/or providing opportunities for the testing will put your employees and your company on the path to a successful wellness program. Early tests that identify risk factors and behaviors may increase healthcare costs initially, but they will reduce costs in the long run as individuals take steps to improve their health either through procedures, exercise, medication and/or changes in diet.

The healthcare crisis in the United States has put a spotlight on the lack of sufficient insurance for many people. Limiting health insurance to minimal services and crisis care is detrimental to employees and their employers. In fact, the leading cause of personal bankruptcy in the United States is outstanding medical bills. According to a study conducted by Harvard University and referenced in Forbes[7], 62 percent of all personal bankruptcies are caused by medical expenses. Of these bankruptcies, 78 percent of the filers had health insurance. Since the majority of illnesses are preventable, catching these diseases early is an obvious way to keep your employees productive and able to continue working.

In the end, retaining good employees by keeping them healthy and motivated to work benefits everyone. Productivity losses related to personal or family health problems cost U.S. employers $1,685 per employee per year; that's $225.8 billion annually[6]. The old adage "An ounce of prevention is worth a pound of cure" is definitely true, not just for individuals but for corporations as well. Help your company thrive by taking care of your employees.

References

1   Robert Rosen, The Healthy Company, Putnam., Oct. 1, 1992.

2   Centers for Disease Control and Prevention. The Burden of Chronic Diseases and Their Risk Factors: National and State Perspectives 2004. http://www.cdc.gov/nccdphp/burdenbook2004. February 2004.

3   Chapman L. Meta-Evaluation of Worksite Health Promotion Economic Return Studies. Art of Health Promotion Newsletter 6(6): January/February 2003

4   Pelletier, KR A review and analysis of the clinical- and cost-effectiveness studies of comprehensive health promotion and disease management programs at the worksite: 1998-2000 Update. Am J Health Promotion: Nov/Dec 2001, Vol. 16, No. 2, pp. 107-116.

5   Citation Serxner, Seth PhD, MPH; Gold, Daniel PhD; Anderson, David PhD; Williams, David EdD The Impact of a Worksite health Promotion Program. Journal of Occupational & Environmental Medicine: January 2001, Volume 43, Issue 1, pp. 25-29.

6   Stewart WF, Ricci JA, Chee E, Morganstein D. Lost productive work time costs from health conditions in the United States: results from the American productivity audit. J Occup Environ Med. 2003;45(12):1234-1246.

7   http://www.forbes.com/2010/03/25/why-people-go-bankrupt-personal-finance-bankruptcy.html

Catherine A. Heaney and Ron Z. Goetzel (1997) A Review of Health-related Outcomes of Multi-component Worksite Health Promotion Programs. American Journal of Health Promotion: March/April 1997, Vol. 11, No. 4, pp. 290-307.

http://www.cdc.gov/workplacehealthpromotion/index.htm

Key Ideas

- Out of the hundreds of medical tests available, the 10 medical tests can provide targeted insight into your employees' current medical state and serve as a baseline against which future health can be measured.

- Cardiovascular disease is the leading cause of the death in the United States and one in three deaths is due to heart disease and stroke, accounting for 2,200 deaths per day.

- Corporations can review their health insurance claims to determine which types of conditions employees are seeking treatment for or review an in-depth, aggregate report derived from a company-wide baseline health screening program.

- While it is frequently difficult to determine the exact Return on Investment (ROI) for wellness programs because they vary so significantly from company to company, the evidence points to risk reduction based on identifying high-risk individuals as a critical factor in the clinical and cost success of a health program.

- The leading cause of personal bankruptcy in the United States are outstanding medical bills.

Questions

1. The leading cause of bankruptcy in the United States is home foreclosure.

    a. True

    b. False

2. How many deaths a day does heart disease account for?

    a. 2,200

    b. 220

    c. 22

    d. 4,400

Case Study: Biometrics at Work
By Renée-Marie Stephano

Introduction and Background
This is a case study from an employer who wishes to remain anonymous. This study shows the benefits of engaging in a dedicated long term biometric screening program. The employer is located across the United States, and has 40,000 employees eligible for the program. The program began in 2010 to add to their portfolio of benefits. The employees received incentives based on performance in four levels, with a 10 percent discount for attainment of all four levels. These levels are: be tobacco free, have a BMI lower than 24, have cholesterol levels below 150 mg/dl, and have a blood pressure of 110/70. These metrics may be high for most employers, but this employer knew that their workforce was relatively young and thus set the bar high.

The Program
The difficulty lies in the dispersion of the workforce at more than 300 locations. The employer hired Optum to administer the testing. Of the 40,000 eligible employees 13,000 participated in the program in 2011, with 65 percent of them earning an incentive of some kind. The metrics measured were a full lipid panel and fasting glucose screening, cotinine (nicotine) testing, waist-height ratio (WHR) or body mass index, and blood pressure.

The Results
Between 2010 and 2011:
- Average total cholesterol dropped 5 percent

- Average ratio of total cholesterol to high-density cholesterol dropped 16 percent

- Average glucose was down 9 percent

- Average BMI was down 7 percent

- Triglycerides were down 30 percent

After the initial year, participation rose 76 percent. This coincides with an advent of coaching into the program. It is believed that this increase is a result of the attention the biometric screening brought to the employee's health risks.

Improvements Made to Screening

Between 2010 and 2011 a number of changes were made to the screening process. The first was a switch from a finger stick to a venous blood draw for the lipid panel. The next is venous blood draw to determine tobacco use, which replaced an unpopular saliva test. They moved to a WHR or BMI measurement from a solely BMI measurement to accommodate people with high BMI but in good health. The window for testing was moved from 3 months to 5 months and was morning so people could fast for a glucose test. Finally, the insurer mailed all of the result privately to the participants increasing understand of where they were.

CHAPTER 5
The C-Suite

Healthy Leaders Lead by Example
By: Mark Anderson

Healthcare costs consume a large portion of a company's overall budget, and with these costs on the rise many recognize the benefit of healthy employees. It can be a challenge to motivate the lower-level employees toward a healthier lifestyle and even harder when the leadership team is not leading by example. When wellness starts at the top, it is often contagious. This article focuses on the best ways that executives can motivate and lead their company to a better, healthier tomorrow. With leaders focused on health, everybody wins.

Employer-sponsored health insurance premiums have more than doubled in the last nine years, at a rate three times faster than cumulative wage increases.[1] There are many diseases and disorders that cost companies thousands, or even millions, of dollars that could be diminished, if not eliminated, if the employee population adopted an attitude of wellness and personal responsibility. This is quite the task when change means undoing years of bad habits.

According to MetLife's 9th annual employee benefits trend survey, about three-quarters of American companies that have between 500-10,000 employees have initiated wellness programs.[2] Often, companies put wellness programs in place, but the lack of enthusiasm to participate decreases the benefits they were hoping to achieve. Executives have the power to not only lead the company to higher profits through production; they can change an entire culture by setting a good example. Wellness and good health among employees is more easily achieved when the leadership team is fit and conscious of their own health goals.

Health Pitfalls for Executives

Long hours, extensive travel, and high stress take its toll on top talent. At no other time in our history has so much been asked of individuals. Our global economy has opened up a whole new set of health challenges for executives. Overcoming the health pitfalls that those challenges present is the first step in growing an overall healthier company.

The best way to get the attention of executives is to speak to them in their language. By offering an executive physical program, each member of the leadership team will be able to have a full assessment of their health and learn the areas in which they can improve. It's hard to argue with facts, and a good program will give well-organized data, including charts and graphics, outlining the overall health of the individual. In order to improve one must first know what needs improvement.

Since travel schedules make it tough for many executives to focus on their health, an executive program that forges a relationship with a personal physician is best. The physician can help hold the executive to his or her health goals, and the executive will have someone to call when on the road and in need of immediate medical advice.

Leadership Involvement

Employees are more likely to take health advice from a leader who is in good shape, or at least working toward the same goal. Encourage executives to share their own personal goals with other employees. They can even create a competition between different departments and the executive leadership team on improving overall health. Using metrics like blood pressure, BMI (body mass index), and cholesterol results as the markers for improvement, people will strive for results that are measurable and definitive.

Encouraging employees to stop smoking and reduce their alcohol intake will also help create an atmosphere of health consciousness. Offering programs during lunch and after hours to assist with these challenges can improve compliance. Some insurance companies also offer a discount when companies incorporate such benefits into their wellness programs. Of course, these same health goals should be set and encouraged among the executive team.

Creating a wellness bond that spans all the ranks of a company is ideal. When executives reach out to other employees and become vested in the interests of individuals it creates a sense of corporate caring. This allows everyone to lift each other up through encouragement and positive interaction. Not only will employees be happier at work, but their health will improve, which in turn makes them more productive.

The Big Three

Cardiovascular disease, cancer and diabetes plague the current generations, robbing them and the companies that supply them healthcare coverage of billions of dollars. The American Heart Association reports that cardiovascular diseases were projected to cost $444.2 billion in 2010, including healthcare services, medications and lost productivity. A close second is cancer which, according to the National Institutes of Health, has an estimated cost of $263.8 billion. Diabetes, a growing problem in America, also has a growing price tag that exceeds $174 billion.

One thing that all of these diseases have in common is that they are preventable, or if found early, manageable at much lower costs. Changes in daily habits can increase the chances for a longer life and lower medical expenses. Things like exercise, increased nutrition value, and less stress play a large role in disease prevention. Couple this with regular health screenings for health management and the net result is healthier and happier people. From a financial point of view, it also results in a healthier bottom line for the company.

Why Companies Must Improve Wellness

Healthcare costs add $1,525 to the price of every General Motors vehicle. The company spent $4.6 billion on healthcare in 2007, more than the cost of steel.[3] This example is a familiar woe among most of corporate America. Companies may find themselves priced right out of the market, since healthcare costs are driving the price of their products up. Consumers have become much more cost conscious since the dip in the economy and will wait longer to spend money on big-ticket items. Therefore, it's in everyone's best interest to keep healthcare costs down and product pricing competitive and desirable to the end user.

References

1   Kaiser Family Foundation & Health Research and Educational Trust, Employer Health Benefits 2008 Annual Survey. (Menlo Park, CA: Kaiser Family Foundation, 2008). http://ehbs.kff.org/?page=abstract&id=1

2   Metlife, 10th Annual Study of Employee Benefits Trends 2012 http://www.metlife.com/assets/institutional/services/insights-and-tools/ebts/ml-10-Annual-EBTS.pdf

3   R. Wagoner, Testimony before the House Financial Services Committee, December 5, 2008. http://thinkprogress.org/2008/12/05/gm-health-care-reform/

Key Ideas

- Wellness and good health among employees is more easily achieved when the leadership team is fit and conscious of their own health goals.

- The best way to get the attention of executives is to speak to them in their language. By offering an executive physical program, each member of the leadership team will be able to have a full assessment of their health and learn the areas in which they can improve.

- The Big Three

  - Cardiovascular disease

  - Cancer

  - Diabetes

Questions

1. Wellness and health among employees is easily achieved when the leadership is taking part in the program

   a. True

   b. False

2. What is the best way to get executives to pay attention?

   a. Speak to them in their own language

   b. Have all of the employees confront them

   c. Give them special executive privileges

   d. Executives do not need to be a part of a wellness program

3. What is missing from the following list of the "Big three diseases": Heart disease, Cancer, and _____?

   a. Phenomena

   b. Diabetes

   c. HIV/AIDS

   d. Dementia

Organizational Health Leadership Engagement Innovations
By Les C. Meyer

Aligning workforce wellbeing with strategic business objectives is the basis for organizational leadership, which requires vision and innovative methods to engage employee populations with the right incentives in a meaningful pursuit of healthy living and working. The task at hand comes with mounting pressure on the C-Suite to more aggressively manage escalating employee medical claims, one of the biggest costs of doing business, through a metrics-based, scorecard-driven approach with an emphasis on "value realization." Other keys to understanding this new thinking involve the deployment of "disruptive innovation," which serves as the bedrock of strategic business process improvement, and establishment of a "culture of health" to help employers achieve the profound change that's needed. Adopting these approaches will invariably help improve clinical outcomes, increase employee satisfaction, "bend the trend" on rising medical costs, boost productivity and give employers a competitive leg up. Performance-focused organizational health strategies lay the groundwork for a wiser investment in human capital. When employees feel better, they perform better, and when they perform better, there is a positive impact on the bottom line.

Creating Productive Advantage Through Healthy People
Visionary leaders drive organizational health as a strategic imperative and meaningful economic strategy. They're savvy enough to recognize that people are a company's only natural resource and most valuable asset, which is burnished when healthy employees perform at their peak. These leaders also are able to decode the complexities of leadership in order to achieve organizational health. As such, visionary leaders are reengineering their fundamental way of doing business and adopting a nimble approach to boost growth. They are creating a productive advantage through healthy people and adopting meaningful advantageous communication channels among all company leaders, associates and customers to sustain revenue streams. In short, this formula will serve as the key to success for Corporate America in the 21st century.

Every investment that leaders make begins with the promise to improve employee productivity. An environment that evolves, achieves and thrives on organizational health achievement executes key population health promotion methods and high-value workforce wellbeing innovations. They include efforts that strategically align business objectives while creating a lifelong capacity for people to learn and keep changing, and concurrently engaging employees to nurture their individual health and wellbeing achievements. This is the basis for vigorous organizational health, profitable customer exchanges and improved functionality at every level to shape and mold the company's future more quickly and better than the competition.

Leaders at the top demand the best. CEOs are driving a framework for accountability in the C-Suite to create healthy organizations and achieve business results. CEOs know that the best way to drive value creation in the C-Suite is to focus on the root cause of escalating costs by enabling a metrics-based, scorecard-driven alignment system approach that supports the well-known "triple aim" of achieving population health promotion: better care for individuals, better health for populations and lower per capita costs. This effort includes three key stakeholders: the employer, employee and provider—with fully engaged employees serving as the conduit to a turbo-charged, full-bodied individual productive advantage realization progression and robust strategic continuous organizational health systems improvement process.

Change Agent Leaders Understand Organizational Health
If there is one quality leaders seek for themselves and their employees; it is sustained high performance in the face of ever-increasing economic pressure and rapid change in a global economy. As all leaders are aware, past performance is no guarantee of future success. Effective leaders drive results.

Leaders change their companies for the better to achieve the sustainability imperative by focusing on long-term health, even as they execute their strategic action plans for higher performance straight away.

Since maximizing resources for enhancing worker capacity and sustaining a competitive edge is more important than ever before, leaders must be capable of aligning the workforce with key business objectives featuring healthy organizational strategies.

One critical mission is to tame runaway employee healthcare costs, but industry practitioners have found that current methods no longer work. The next generation of solutions can be found in the notion of "value realization." Success depends on an accountability-based organizational health leadership, insightful decision-making and problem-solving, as well as an intuitive ability to lead their strategic business unit to create self-sustaining environments.

Robert W. Suttles, vice president at Health First, believes that "true leaders are able to envision a compelling future, something that causes people to want to be a part of and see the value of helping to create productive change. Everything we do should be focused on or designed to positively impact the performance of any associate we deal with or to possibly impact the contribution that any team of associates can make together."

Leaders have a unique definition of value, which they consider the glue that galvanizes the workforce. In their view, value better aligns the interests of each organization's leadership with employees to maximize individual peak performance for results that collectively improve a company's bottom line. The cutting edge of this thinking can be found in the C-Suite emergence of "disruptive innovation" (DI), a business term used to describe how a more nimble or entrepreneurial approach to creating value via individual productive advantage realization and sustaining a competitive edge in the enterprise quest disrupts certain markets.

The critical ingredient to realizing short-term savings, as well as a lasting return on investment (ROI) is the leader's track record for achieving enterprise-wide performance improvement goals and a strong return on enhancing individual productive advantage work capacity achievements.

A new IBM study of more than 1,700 chief executive officers from 64 countries and 18 industries reveals tremendous insight. To wit: that leaders are changing the nature of work by adding a powerful dose of openness, transparency and employee empowerment to the command-and-control ethos that has characterized the modern corporation for more than a century.

The advantages of this fast-moving trend are clear. Companies that outperform their peers are 30 percent more likely to identify openness—often characterized by a greater use of social media as a key enabler of collaboration and innovation—as a key influence on their organization. Outperformers are embracing new models of working that tap into the collective intelligence of an organization and its networks to devise new ideas and solutions for increased profitability and growth. [2]

Recent "strengths-based leadership" (i.e., Q12 Leadership) research by Gallup and others also shows that unified engaged leaders and employees create a unique productive advantage healthiness in a global economy. "They are more profitable, more customer-focused, safer and more likely to withstand temptations to leave," Suttles explained. "The best-performing companies know that an employee engagement improvement strategy linked to the achievement of corporate leadership engagement business goals will help them win in the global marketplace."

Highly effective leaders empower people to act within an agreed-upon vision and build for the future. Their task is to design high-impact business goals to attain organizational health and achieve enduring high-performance objectives. This means that sharp intellect, strategic adaptability, fierce resolve, teamwork, vitality, resiliency and precision are essential. Adaptive leaders understand the power and potential of creative execution and DI. The DI mindset can be used to evaluate the street value of population health "bend the trend" index systems and create "People Innovation Centers." These components will serve as an organizational health dashboard information system and leadership key performance indicator clearinghouse for benchmarking the business of sustainability.

Leadership Strategy by Design Works Here

Leadership is about nurturing progressive human relationships and tapping the power of social intelligence to achieve meaningful productive interactions. Personalized experiences tend to influence strategic business plans and the convergence of productive-advantage key performance indicators that benefits business team members and the firm's valuable customers.

Leaders need to learn to think like a designer when creating an organizational health strategy in order to do a better job of developing, communicating and directing action toward designed business results. "Design is the fundamental soul of a man-made creation. It's not just what it looks like and feels like. Design is how it works," said Steve Jobs, technology innovator and Apple genius. Advanced leadership engagement innovations were designed to include an intensity of adaptability, involvement, insightfulness, interaction, connectedness, influence and degree of execution a leader has with its people over time. Leaders should bring clarity to organizational health expectations; it should be a road sign for showing people where you, as their leader, are taking them—and what they need to do to get there.

No more business as usual. There is no such thing as "substandard leadership"—just disengaged leadership and ineffective strategic business process improvement systems, enterprise-wide technologies and flawed ideas created in intellectual isolation in the C-Suite. Such thinking is cut off from valuable, real-world insight and frontline leadership know-how. It is also out of tune with seismic shifts in the new-world market—devoid of any focus on organizational health, effective execution and robust financial performance. Each of these elements is essential for having a clear pathway to improved economic wellbeing and quality of life for employers, employees and community providers. Those misaligned leadership missteps are over. As rising leaders learn to reap the benefits of leadership engagement innovations, so will their company's bottom line.

The world's top-performing enterprises understand that leadership engagement is a force that drives bottom-line performance achievement outcomes. In the best companies to work for, it is more than a human resources initiative—it is a leadership attitude to organizational health for the way they do business.

Leadership Engagement Continuous Improvement Transforms Organizational Health
DI is the bedrock of strategic business process improvement (SBPI), an effective continuous improvement organizational health approach to align processes with disciplined execution of an organization's strategic goals. This will optimize underlying systems and structures to transform focused program integration convergence to achieve more efficient business results.

DI is a remarkable idea that was insightful (and strategically) designed to transform existing markets or create a new market through the continuous use of critical thinking behaviors: adaptability, simplicity, convenience, accessibility or affordability to transform organizational health business results.

DI is about profound change in the C-Suite. It is not just the magnitude of the advance. If it works to sustain the status quo, it is not disruptive. The key is a change in approach to one that better addresses critical business issues in the C-Suite and the demands to create and sustain "customer value."

What's different about DI leadership is that it moves from being an occasional episodic management by objective shortcoming to a breakthrough balanced measurement system achievement. It paves the way for the leader to create C-Suite and frontline solidarity, as well as a united culture of innovation mindset and far-reaching organizational health effectiveness attitude adjustment in the company.

Leaders judiciously converge on C-Suite leadership engagement techniques and incentive-alignment SBPI action plans to precisely execute optimal measurement systems designed to determine gaps. This information is prioritized for a guided program planning and evaluation strategic roadmap to instate a sense of balance and achieve leading-edge best practices.

A balanced view of the business requires continuous predictive data analytics for insight. Value realization of corporate benefits administration reporting in the C-Suite has not been meaningful, far-reaching or productive. Legacy benefits administration reporting is "aggregated" but not "integrated" and includes "data" versus actionable "information." It also is not intelligible, accessible, consistent, precise, or reliable to the C-Suite.

Susan R. Meisinger, former president and CEO of the Society for Human Resource Management and a board director for the National Academy of Human Resources, recently wondered: "Is it possible that we think we're playing an important role in driving innovation in our organizations just because of how hard we're working and not because we have any data to support that conclusion? Perhaps."

The time has come for a major paradigm shift that enables pioneering employers to simultaneously realize greater employee trust, talent engagement and customer value realization, as well as prevent spiraling healthcare costs and actually bend the trend.

According to Kathleen Yeager, a senior professional human resources (SPHR) specialist and leading strategist on chief organizational effectiveness: "SBPI and DI spotlight creative execution and encourage organizations to focus on critical talent management [people] challenges and related 'customer value realization' issues. These concepts also begin to embrace proactive constructive change in the HR operating model."

Profound change will not happen without constructive conflict. "The new value-centric HR professional who has a DI mindset would be an ideal role model and business leader in the C-Suite to promote the meaningful use of HR systematic performance improvement processes and best practices," Yeager continued.

It is clear that C-Suite distinctive competency discussions, recommendations and value realization optimization barriers cannot be tackled or resolved if there are no solid metrics to analyze and compare valuable employee engagement investments alongside comprehensive organizational health programs that emphasize high-value workforce wellbeing.

Strategic productive advantage from comprehensive organizational health, high-value workforce wellbeing improvements can be achieved only if understood and embraced at the C-Suite level. To realize optimal engagement, leaders have created next-generation SBPI C-Suite level benefits administration reporting dashboards and scorecards. Value realization materializes when action is taken on SBPI measurement insights.

Cracking the Code of Critical Thinking Behaviors in the C-Suite

An organizational health innovation trumps everything else in business. Many ideas aimed at improving organizational health, high-value workforce wellbeing fail to deal with DI and improving the business value of health and how leaders drive organizational health in the C-Suite.

More than a decade of research and frontline experiences lead insightful leaders to believe strongly that health synergizes high-value workforce wellbeing performance—and that, in fact, at least 50 percent of any organization's long-term success is driven by its health. [3]

Achieving measurable value realization directly addresses the core drivers of process optimization/ continuous improvement ("lean") as pursued by senior leaders and frontline decision makers. Savvy leaders understand the inner workings of leadership's critical thinking behaviors and linkage between employees, customers and profits. How so? Simple: by isolating perceptions and attitudes of organizational health investments and the business value of workforce wellbeing dividends that drive strategic SBPI business plans.

Savvy leaders are engaging DI methods and executing best-in-class C-Suite Active Engagement™ innovation tools, techniques and best practices with team leaders and frontline managers to deploy employee-centric, value-based purchasing and advanced value-based insurance design strategic business process improvement systems that include **five key leadership engagement innovations:**

1) **Create Health**—*Necessity Prompts Strategic Adaptation*

2) **Assess/Reassess**—*Cracking the Code*

3) **Plan Design**—*The Sustainability Factor*

4) **Execution**—*Critical Thinking in the C-Suite*

5) **Evaluation**—*Putting Health to Work™ Bend the Trend Index (See Figure 1)*

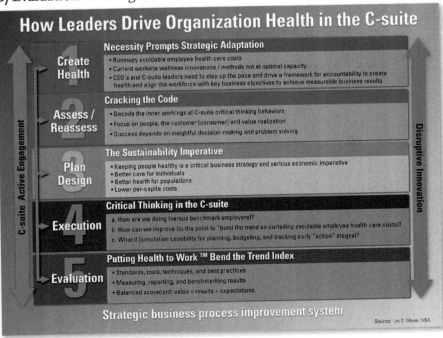

Value realization encompasses several areas and requires relevant onsite, corporate level and company-wide reporting as defined by C-Suite leaders and frontline managers. What gets measured gets improved. The role of a leader is to determine what is important for the company to measure. The undertaking is intended to rapidly shape the SBPI process created to help pioneering employers answer:

1. How are we doing?

2. How can we make it better?

3. What if: simulations to find specific and optimum opportunities for interventions and that will define measures of success?

Leadership engagement innovations comprises core organizational health competencies and systematic enterprise capabilities, such as leadership, strategic planning, customer focus, measurement, analysis, as well as knowledge management, workforce focus and operations focus that conventional metrics don't capture in C-Suite performance or frontline corporate performance (or individual) achievement reviews.

For example, leadership is evaluated by a number of measures that include annual budgeted revenue growth, net operating profit before tax, annual health insurance claims paid, total healthcare cost budget annual comparison, average days without injury and annual disability incidence rate. Others examine the impact of direct and indirect healthcare costs on profits or how the workplace environment affects employee healthcare costs, return on capital employed, and total returns to shareholders. Organizational health is defined as the ability of an organization to identify, engage, establish, elevate, achieve, and renew itself faster than the competition to sustain stellar business performance over time. **(See Figure 2)**

Streetwise leadership change agents realize that organizational health and performance improvement is not designed to be an annual independent study or self-administered "worksite wellness checklist" fire drill—but rather, a rigorous SBPI leadership process. This strategy is designed to promote and achieve organizational health transformation by converting valuable workforce investments into individual productive advantage achievements. It is all made possible with the convergence of meaningful productive interactions and personalized experiences of valuable people with loyal customers, which translates into lifetime corporate profits.

What Does Success Look Like for a Leader?

Imagine a workplace where all teams of employees are committed to the company, fully engaged in what they do for customers, excited about work, accountable for their health and wellbeing, and accept responsibility for worksite performance achievement. Imagine a workforce connected to the vision of organization health, looking forward to healthy living and healthy working, and actually wanting to create meaningful productive interactions along with personalized customer experiences.

"There are four keys to success for next-generation corporate leaders," according to R. Dixon Thayer, senior fellow Jefferson School of Population Health, as well as co-founder and CEO of HealthNEXT. They include:

1) Providing a "clinical effectiveness" balance to the current "benefits efficiency" focus

2) High-touch engagement, retention and behavior change systems and processes

3) Reducing the "random access to care" and the "medically homeless" covered lives

4) Sincere advocacy and champions in the C-Suite... "living the vision"

Imagine the Unimaginable
The power of good health is far reaching. Healthy people are at work for longer periods of time and can accomplish more on the job than unhealthy people. The more they can do of their job, the more it affects the employer's bottom line—and when employee achievement and corporate performance is tied to healthy employees, everyone benefits. Jobs stay in America. The economy flourishes. And exorbitant healthcare costs are avoided. Keeping people healthy is crucial to how well business succeeds today and in the future.

"Nearly two years after the passage of the Affordable Care Act, we are starting to see significant changes in the way healthcare is delivered and received," states David B. Nash, M.D., MBA, Dean, Jefferson School of Population Health, Thomas Jefferson University. Population health promotion, prevention, care coordination and high-value workforce wellbeing are at the forefront of healthcare— and employee-centric, value-based insurance design is here to stay. Nash told the Twelfth Population Health and Care Coordination Colloquium at Thomas Jefferson University: "Employers, payers, purchasers, clinicians and academia are working more collaboratively toward the common goal of implementing meaningful changes to the delivery of healthcare that will improve the health of the population."

Healthy living and healthy working, coupled with flexible, full employee engagement and job satisfaction, have become the new imperative for employers. Working around the clock to improve employee health (regardless of personal health status or multiple risk factors), the objective is to execute healthy living and healthy working strategies and standards of practice to attain healthy employee achievement and business performance.

Donald Berwick, M.D., MPP, former administrator, Centers for Medicare & Medicaid Services, as well as former president and CEO of Institute for Healthcare Improvement (IHI), recently stated on IHI's **WIHI** audio broadcast network that healthcare improvement leaders need to both improve quality and achieve costs savings in order to fulfill obligation to patients. "Similar to the challenges of addressing climate change, the answer is… there is no single way to do it. The only way we can do it is to do, not one thing, but everything," he said. Without a doubt, there is *also* a social imperative to demonstrate that better care equals lower costs.

"Three decades ago, we thought that education was enough," states Michael P. O'Donnell, Ph.D., MPH, MBA, editor-in-chief, *American Journal of Health Promotion*. "We thought all we had to do was help people understand the health risks of tobacco, junk food, alcohol and drugs, and the health benefits of exercise, nutritious foods, stress management and proactive medical self-care. We thought people would use this knowledge to transform their lives. Three decades of research and practical experience have shown us that education is not enough, in fact, it may not be very important at all."

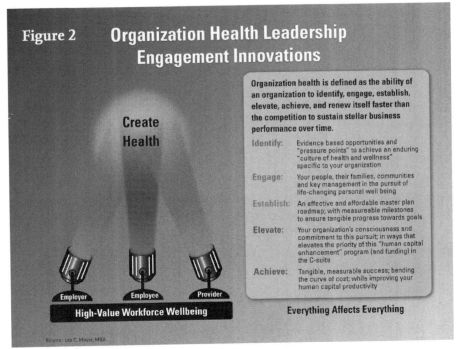

Figure 2   Organization Health Leadership Engagement Innovations

Create Health

Organization health is defined as the ability of an organization to identify, engage, establish, elevate, achieve, and renew itself faster than the competition to sustain stellar business performance over time.

Identify: Evidence based opportunities and "pressure points" to achieve an enduring "culture of health and wellness" specific to your organization

Engage: Your people, their families, communities and key management in the pursuit of life-changing personal well being

Establish: An effective and affordable master plan roadmap; with measureable milestones to ensure tangible progress towards goals

Elevate: Your organization's consciousness and commitment to this pursuit; in ways that elevates the priority of this "human capital enhancement" program (and funding) in the C-suite

Achieve: Tangible, measurable success; bending the curve of cost; while improving your human capital productivity

Employer   Employee   Provider

High-Value Workforce Wellbeing   Everything Affects Everything

Source: Les C. Meyer, MBA

It's time employers protect, sustain and promote the health and wellbeing of their employees—and align incentives and rewards for healthy and productive behaviors. But they also must consistently take care of their people, knowing that healthy living and healthy working lead to healthy corporate performance and improved revenue streams for the employer and its community health system. Employer leadership engagement at its best entails turning an agenda into action

The Making of a Corporate Leader

In order to achieve a productive advantage, leaders need to develop an integrative "healthy organizational roadmap" to support the learning and leadership development initiatives in their companies that are critical for sustaining organizational health.

Leaders realize that engaging, deploying and optimizing a fluid company-wide organizational health systems improvement initiative requires hard work. More importantly, the final step is to prepare a "culture of health" business plan that reinforces the company's focus on DI and doing whatever is needed to satisfy employees, caregivers, providers and community stakeholders. Leaders know that critical thinking is not driven by answers but by questions. The driving force in the leaders' mindset is the critical thinking process and profound questions.

Leaders demand that executives optimize the total economic impact of employee health to maximize an individual's health achievement potential and job satisfaction expectations through personal and organizational performance results.

Their population health framework focuses on leadership engagement innovations involving better care for individuals, improved health for populations and lower growth in expenditures. As part of this equation, total-rewards initiatives will help employees achieve greater satisfaction on the job and optimize their personal lives, (i.e., physical, social and financial), enabling them to define their own needs and expectations as distinct choices.

All Aboard

In order to yield hard returns on employee and family population health programs and bend the healthcare cost curve, true leaders must lead by example and steer cross-functional work teams toward relentlessly fostering a value-centric organizational health culture. This produces a self-perpetuating productive advantage and competitive edge. It is accomplished by motivating disengaged leaders and employees, embracing meaningful use of population health achievement benchmarks and metrics, as well as creating C-Suite leadership visibility for innovative organizational health and wellbeing indices. Other strategies include raising the bar on individual productive advantage and financial security aspirations, aligning meaningful incentives and generally helping people get the best out of life.

Next-generation organizational health initiatives require a collaborative effort that includes an employer-employee partnership, array of providers, value-focused vendors and community resource groups. The role of the employee is vital in terms of creating individual productive advantage and health achievement, as well as performance-based talent management programs, since these are the very people who need to be engaged in order to live healthier and perform at optimal levels at work and home.

The key to success in an increasingly competitive global economy will be integrating a model with performance-focused organizational health strategies that lay the groundwork for a wiser investment in human capital. What attracts employees to jobs and keeps them from looking elsewhere also results in improved health outcomes and optimized job performance. It's more than healthy people equating to healthy bottom lines. It's recognizing that people should be paid for better performance. And when they feel better, they perform better. When they perform better, everybody wins.

How can current worksite wellness programs be retooled to inspire healthier living and peak performance to yield both personal and corporate gain? It is not easy to change organizational cultures and to achieve sustainable health improvement. The time has come, however, to acknowledge that organizational health achievement may very well be the silver bullet that has been sought all along. Visionary leaders view the meaningful use of organizational health improvement as a strategic imperative and meaningful economic strategy. It will take a nation to raise population health to the next level.

Key Ideas

- Aligning workforce wellbeing with strategic business objectives is the basis for organizational leadership, which requires vision and innovative methods to engage employee populations with the right incentives in a meaningful pursuit of healthy living and working.

- Visionary leaders drive organizational health as a strategic imperative and meaningful economic strategy. They're savvy enough to recognize that people are a company's only natural resource and most valuable asset.

- CEOs know that the best way to drive value creation in the C-Suite is to focus on the root cause of escalating costs by enabling a metrics-based, scorecard-driven alignment system approach that supports the well-known "triple aim" of achieving population health promotion: better care for individuals, better health for populations and lower per capita costs.

- This effort includes three key stakeholders: the employer, employee and provider.

- Leaders should bring clarity to organizational health expectations; it should be a road sign for showing people where you, as their leader, are taking them—and what they need to do to get there.

- In order to yield hard returns on employee and family population health programs and bend the healthcare cost curve, true leaders must lead by example and steer cross-functional work teams toward relentlessly fostering a value-centric organizational health culture.

Questions

1. What is missing from the "triple aim" of population health promotion: better care for individuals, better health for populations and_____?

   a. High ROI

   b. Lower per capita costs.

   c. Decrease of absenteeism

   d. More productive C-Suite

2. Who is missing from the three stakeholders of the "triple aim": The employer, employee, and _____?

   a. Provider

   b. TPA

   c. C-Suite

   d. CEO

3. Savvy leaders recognize that _____ are a company's only natural resource and most valuable asset.

   a. Profits

   b. Salaries

   c. Materials

   d. People

CHAPTER 6
Onsite Clinics

Population Risk Management and Workplace Health Centers

By David M. Demers and Richard Pinckney

Introduction

Onsite health in the context of the employer-employee relationship is nothing new; its American roots can be traced back at least as far as the turn of the century.[22] What has changed over time is the impetus for providing care at the worksite. In the mid-19th century, basic access to care was the driving force; throughout much of the 20th century, the focus was on occupational health and safety,[23] compliance and productivity. Moving into the 21st century, with the rapidly rising costs of healthcare and declining population health, employers are looking to onsite care to improve and manage worker health and improve productivity.

Approximately 25-30 percent of companies now provide onsite health services to their employees, up about 50 percent since 2000.[24] In onsite centers opened since 2000, the three most cited reasons for implementing onsite health services were to reduce medical costs, enhance productivity and improve access to care. As further evidence that the focus of onsite clinics has shifted to wellness and health management, clinics opened since 2000 were wellness-based vs. occupational-based by a 2:1 margin. The most common services provided in these clinics are immunizations, preventive screenings, acute care, providing medications, and chronic care management. Approximately 35 percent of onsite clinics also provide care to spouses and dependants.

Onsite health is now gaining momentum as a business strategy to manage population health and productivity.[25] Mounting data suggests that onsite delivery can be an effective way to manage health and the costs of care.[26-27] This chapter explores the central concepts supporting onsite health and the characteristics of a well-managed population.

Population risk management – the missing piece of the healthcare puzzle

Over the course of time, science has given us many simple equations that are useful in day-to-day life. Remember the Pythagorean

Theorem? The sum of the squared legs on a right triangle equals the square of the hypotenuse ($a^2 + b^2 = c^2$).[28] That equation is very useful when you attempt to build a deck in the backyard. Healthcare actuaries know of another simple equation: total spending = utilization x unit cost ($s = u \times c$).[29] That is to say, total healthcare spending is the product of how often you use the system (doctor's visits, hospital admissions, etc.) and how much it costs each time you use it. Efforts to reign in healthcare spending over the past 40 years have largely focused on reducing the factors of this simple equation.

In the 1980s, the Federal Government took aim at unit costs. Medicare's prospective payment system (PPS), which had its origins in the 1972 Social Security Amendments, and first applied to hospitals in 1983, focused on controlling unit cost by pre-determining a set payment for treating patients with particular conditions.[30] No longer could hospitals charge by the day, or according to the number or type of tests performed. For Medicare patients, the total amount to be reimbursed would be determined prospectively and be a fixed amount.

In the 1990s the managed care industry took aim at utilization.[31] Primary care physicians began to function as gatekeepers controlling access to specialists and hospitals.[32] Limits were placed on the use of certain services such as behavioral health and rehabilitation.[33] More recent efforts to affect utilization and unit costs have included buying coalitions, payer consolidation, cost shifting, greater regulation at the state and federal level, and asking employees to assume a greater share of the healthcare premium.[34]

Why, then, with all this effort, are healthcare costs still out of control? It is as if someone built the deck in the backyard using the Pythagorean Theorem, but the corner came out crooked. Part of the problem is that *the formula is flawed*. The healthcare spending equation needs revision. Specifically, it needs a little calculus. A revised view of healthcare as a system is that utilization is a function of risk management ($u = (f)$ rm). Population risk management includes genetic predisposition to disease, environmental conditions such as the quality of the air and water, and, in particular, lifestyle risk such as tobacco use, alcohol and substance abuse, eating habits and levels of physical activity. Population risk management also embodies whether people with chronic conditions such as diabetes and asthma are able to manage their condition and are at the standard of care, an important factor in preventing serious complications.

Onsite healthcare for optimal population risk management

With this revised view of the formula $(u = (f)\ rm)$ necessary for improved health system performance, we can now change how the elements of our delivery system work to produce the results we are trying to achieve. Employers can and should begin looking at their healthcare costs as the end product of a system absolutely within their control. Healthcare should be thought of in the same way as production, distribution and other business systems. That is, a set of interdependent parts that can be measured, benchmarked and improved. The employer's healthcare system includes the employee delivery infrastructure, health plan design and incentives; information systems, and the provider network.

An integrated onsite program of population health management improves the employer's healthcare delivery system by:

Placing clinics onsite. This is a simple case of accessibility. Placing a clinic in close proximity to the workplace of those being served increases the emphasis on preventative and primary care while offering services at a lower unit cost than the average community-based physician practice, with no apparent adverse effect on the quality of care.[35] This is because most onsite clinics rely on mid-level practitioners and otherwise eliminate the high overhead of the physician's office.

Employee incentives. Changing health plan design such that employees have greater control and accountability for their healthcare is vital. Specifically, to be effective plan design should provide payment for screening, engagement and outcomes.[36] By law, employers can and should offer 20 percent of total health plan premiums for these factors.[37] This can be done in the form of deductible credits, payments into a health reimbursement or savings account, or straight cash payments. A research team lead by Dr. Michael Taitel found that total payments of as little as $150 produced as much as 70 percent participation in screening when coupled with an effective program of corporate communications and visible managerial support.[38]

Provide information tools. It's important to equip employees with the information tools needed to select treatment options for acute care, risk reduction, chronic condition management and "shopping" for specialty and hospital care when necessary.[39] Information tools should also provide an integrated personal health record and electronic medical record that contains the employee's health information, complete problem list, risk profile, personal care plan, goals and objectives, and progress notes.[40] Finally, information tools should help the employee research medical content, schedule appointments, communicate securely with members of their healthcare team and, if desired, participate in a social support network.

Emphasize core clinician competencies. Selecting, training and placing clinicians who have the core competencies and core behaviors necessary to function effectively as healthcare coaches is imperative. In our revised healthcare delivery system, front-line clinicians for primary and preventive care should have clinical skills *as a minimum requirement only.*[41] The key to helping the individual assume greater responsibility and accountability for their own health is the ability of the healthcare professional to function as a coach. Health coaching requires knowledge of how humans approach, experiment with and adopt lifestyle change.[42] Techniques such as motivational interviewing and rapid cycle improvement are essential.[43] Core competencies and core behaviors include approachability, compassion and listening; interpersonal savvy and managing diversity; negotiating and motivating others; organizing, priority setting and planning; analytical skills, problem-solving and decision quality; being action-oriented and driving for results.[44]

Integrating acute care with health coaching. As employees present for acute care, such as an ear infection or cellulitis, many will be diagnosed with underlying risk factors (obesity, hypertension, tobacco use, etc.) and/or chronic conditions (diabetes, asthma, etc.). This presents an opportunity for both clinician and patient to work together to create a health improvement plan fashioned by the employee and supported by the coach-clinician through an ongoing relationship based on trust. An onsite clinic and information technology provide the proximal resources necessary to achieve meaningful, long-lasting health improvement.

Slowing down throughput. In traditional primary care practices, clinicians see between 20-30 patients per day, sometimes more. Patient encounters are very brief, with emphasis on diagnosis and treatment. Physicians do not have the time, training or incentive to work with patients on health improvement in any structured or consistent way. Typically a diagnosis is made, treatment prescribed and a brief explanation offered. Perhaps the patient is given a brochure or verbal instructions on the prescribed treatment. Rarely completed however, is the challenging work of involving the patient in a dialogue about their overall health status and how he or she might take action to improve it. This work requires time and a different interactive style. It requires the collection of a comprehensive data set on the patient's health, examining the range of evidence-based management options for addressing underlying risk, exploring the patient's readiness to change and engaging the patient in selecting health improvement goals that go beyond the treatment of the immediate acute symptom being treated.[45] Integrating acute care with health coaching requires slowing the process down so that this work can be completed. Rather than 10-15 minutes, sessions may run anywhere from 20-40 minutes, and in some cases take as much as one hour. This means the coach-clinician may see only 10-15 patients a day.

Providing ongoing feedback and support. In traditional primary care practices the patient may be asked to return for another visit in a week or two, primarily to assure the acute symptoms have been successfully treated. This concludes the process until the underlying root-cause manifests itself again in another symptomatic episode. In a model where the coach-clinician is working with the patient to achieve long-lasting health improvement, ongoing feedback and support becomes a critical part of success.[46] For patients with serious underlying risk factors (obesity, hypertension, tobacco use, etc.) or chronic conditions (diabetes, asthma, depression, addiction etc.) the coach-clinician should plan on spending an average of four sessions within the first six months.[47] In addition, the coach-clinician should expect to check in with their patient by telephone and through secure messaging regularly. Some patients will require less support, some more. In all cases the goal is to move the patient along a continuum of small-step, rapid-cycle change while building self-efficacy and confidence, all in keeping with an approach set by the patient with the guidance of the coach-clinician.[48] The patient's personal health record provides tracking tools and monitors progress on goals, actions taken and outcomes achieved.

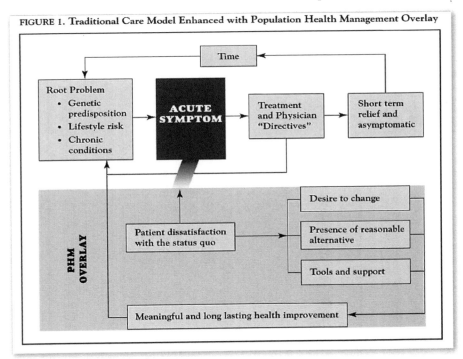

FIGURE 1. Traditional Care Model Enhanced with Population Health Management Overlay

Measuring the impact of population risk management

If population risk management has been successfully managed through onsite clinics, we would expect a variety of health-related measures to show improvements; including costs, quality of care and burden of illness. Risk management metrics should include the percentage of the population being screened for genetic predisposition to disease and/or lifestyle risk, the percentage of the at-risk population engaged with one or more health professionals to address their risks and the percentage of the population with chronic conditions who are able to manage their condition and are at the standard of care.[49] These key measures drive subsequent utilization of primary, secondary and tertiary healthcare resources.[50, 51, 52] Any system that does an inadequate job of identifying and managing risk will have members who have higher rates of disease and higher subsequent utilization of resources.[53]

Key utilization measures include primary care and specialty care utilization[54], expressed as visits per person per year; hospital admissions, expressed as admissions per 1,000 population[55]; emergency department visits, expressed as visits per 1,000 population[56]; and ancillary utilization such as lab and pharmacy, expressed as tests and prescriptions per person per year. Key unit cost measures include the amount paid for each of the utilization measures.[57]

FIGURE 2. Characteristics of an Unmanaged Population.

CATEGORY	MEASURE	LOOSELY MANAGED	MODERATELY MANAGED	WELL MANAGED
Risk Management	HRA completion rate	<20%	40%	80%
	Biometric screening rate	<20%	40%	80%
	Percent at risk engaged	<20%	40%	70%
	Diabetics at standard of care	<20%	35% 40%	60%
	Asthmatics at standard of care	<20%	40% 45%	60%
	CHD at standard of care	<20%	32% 40%	60%
Utilization	Office visits PMPY primary	1.0 1.2	1.8	2.5
	Office visits PMPY specialty	2.3 2.0	1.5	1.0
	Hospital adms per 1,000 pop	90	75 70	50
	ED visits per 1,000 pop	250	200 190	150
X	Lab services PMPY	8	7.1 6.5	5
	Rx scripts PMPY	11.5	9.5 8.9	7.5
Unit Cost	Primary care	$150	$101	$75 $67
	Specialty care	$225	$175	$130 $125
	Hospital admission cost	$11,500	$8,199 $7,500	$5,000
=	ER visit cost	$1,000	$750 $660	$500
	Rx cost	$81 $75	$50	$30
	Lab cost	$50	$35 $31	$25
Total Spend	PMPM Medical & Rx	$326.63 $300.85	$263.97	$201.30

For example, in the utilization category, a loosely managed system would have an average of 250 visits or greater to the emergency department per 1,000 members.[58] A well-managed system would have an average of 150 visits or less.[59] In this example the population under study has 190 visits, placing their performance in the moderately managed category.

Leverage is greatest in the risk management category and, with few exceptions, lowest in the unit cost category. That is to say, it is hardest to move the needle on unit cost, easiest on risk management. This contrasts with where business, government and the healthcare industry itself currently expend energy. Sadly, unit cost forms the current focal point for healthcare reform. Any and all reform policies are destined to fail until the upstream metrics related to risk identification and management are addressed.

Integrated onsite population risk management provides a basis for achieving long-lasting health improvement. We would anticipate that population risk management would result in significant changes in our health metrics:

1. **Screening penetration:** Seventy-percent or greater of the employer population would complete annual biometric screening and a health risk appraisal.[60] This means that the many undiagnosed cases of hypertension, hyperlipidemia, diabetes and other serious conditions could be detected.

2. **Coaching contact:** Seventy-percent or greater of those identified with underlying chronic conditions or serious lifestyle risk factors would engage with an onsite coach-clinician.[61] This would involve the review of a comprehensive health history and the creation of a complete problem list. The coach-clinician would guide the employee in selecting health improvement goals and support them with small-step improvements that, over time, are sustained and built upon.[62]

3. **Chronic care utilization:** Greater than 75 percent of employees with chronic conditions such as diabetes and asthma would be working closely with their primary care physicians and/or onsite coach-clinician to maintain the standard of care for their condition. [63]

4. **Specialty care utilization:** Employees would increase their utilization of preventive and primary care and depend less on downstream utilization of specialty care and emergency care. Improved health, greater self-efficacy skills and better access to front-end components of the delivery system infrastructure would facilitate these changes.

5. **Pharmaceutical costs:** There would be decreased dependence on pharmacotherapy as the primary treatment modality for chronic and lifestyle- related conditions. Accordingly, a patient with hypertension who adopts a modest program of physical activity finds they can go from two medications to one.[64]

6. **Hospital utilization:** Hospital admissions for preventable conditions would decrease as patients with chronic conditions improve their health status and serious consequences are reduced.[44,45,46]

7. **Total costs:** Finally, as personal engagement increased, utilization would be altered and unit cost reduced, with total system spending reduced accordingly.[65]

The resulting metrics profile for a well-managed population can be seen on figure 3.

These changes would take time, potentially a number of years.[66] This is because the phases of population health management include risk identification, outreach and engagement and the establishment of a trusting relationship with accessible coach-clinicians supported by technology. However, the gains achieved are long-term and the product of systemic improvements rather than short-term treatment of acute symptoms.

FIGURE 3. Characteristics of a Well Managed Population.

CATEGORY	MEASURE	LOOSELY MANAGED	MODERATELY MANAGED	WELL MANAGED
Risk Management	HRA completion rate	<20%	40%	60%
	Biometric screening rate	<20%	40%	60%
	Percent at risk engaged	<20%	40%	60%
	Diabetics at standard of care	<20%	40%	60%
	Asthmatics at standard of care	<20%	40%	60%
	CHD at standard of care	<20%	40%	60%
Utilization	Office visits PMPY primary	1.0	1.8	2.5
	Office visits PMPY specialty	2.0	1.5	1.0
	Hospital adms per 1,000 pop	90	70	50
	ED visits per 1,000 pop	250	200	150
	Lab services PMPY	8	6.5	5
	Rx scripts PMPY	11.5	9.5	7.5
Unit Cost	Primary care	$150	$101	$75
	Specialty care	$225	$175	$125
	Hospital admission cost	$11,500	$7,500	$5,000
	ER visit cost	$1,000	$750	$500
	Rx cost	$75	$50	$30
	Lab cost	$50	$35	$25
Total Spend	PMPM Medical & Rx	$326.63	$263.97	$201.30

Practical Considerations with Implementing Onsite Health

There are a number of key questions in deciding whether onsite health is right for an organization, the answers to which will determine whether this initiative is a success both financially and in the eyes of the company's stakeholders.

Committed Senior Management

First, is there a strong spirit of commitment by senior management for improving employee health, or is this just a thin veneer for saving money? Employees should be allowed to access the clinic *during paid hours*. This will be one of senior management's more visible forms of support. The success or failure of onsite health will be largely driven by whether employees use the clinic, and they will only use the clinic if they feel a genuine commitment toward quality patient care; if there is a friendly, top-notch professional staff; if the clinic uses the latest technology and equipment and the facilities are pleasant; and if the care is more convenient than on the outside. These "preconditions" for utilization will rarely be fulfilled if the end-game is just saving money and senior management doesn't visibly support the program. The best testimony for senior support is their actual use of the program.

Marketing and Communications

There needs to be a coherent, comprehensive and ongoing marketing and communications plan for the onsite health program. The key elements of this plan include: clear communications about why the company is investing in employee health, naming productivity and cost savings as driving forces; a description of how incentives work and what the employee needs to do to receive those incentives; how others are using the services with specific examples of success, specifying that all personal health information is strictly confidential and available only to the patient and designated healthcare providers, and general information about clinic hours, how to schedule appointments and how to contact the onsite providers. The clinic should be the "centerpiece" of the company's culture of health, not a distant appendage with limited application.

Financial Due Diligence

In today's challenging economic environment, financial due diligence is absolutely critical to get the health center off the ground and keep it growing to meet ever-changing needs. It is essential to analyze the underlying demographics as well as medical and pharmacy claim data for the population/location in question to determine whether an onsite health center is viable and sustainable, and how to scope and focus the program. From an economic point of view, the most important factors in evaluating return on investment for a given situation are: expected annual onsite office visits and related penetration, average market cost of an office visit in the network (including exam and related services), expected reduction in specialist visits and related lab and imaging; expected reduction in ER urgent care and retail acute visits; expected reduction in short-stay inpatient admissions, and expected reduction in workers' compensation visits. Generally speaking a well-scoped onsite clinic should be able to produce annual net savings of about

4-6 percent after accounting for all costs of operating the clinic and amortization of build-out and equipment.[67] ROI models should also factor in an additional average net savings of 3-5 percent per year as the result of health risk reduction, plus 5-10 percent per year for productivity improvement depending on the nature of the industry, wage rates, work rules, time off policies and the like.

Onsite Health Management Support

While most companies decide to outsource the management of wellness or acute-based onsite clinics to specialty providers, regardless of the ultimate answer, there are a number of decisions and resource needs that must be fulfilled for the clinic to be successful in today's complex environment. Specialized requirements in running an onsite health center include: access to an electronic medical record for the clinicians and mirror image personal health record for the patient integrated with evidenced-based decision support software to guide treatment options; a clear quality assurance process to track efficacy and continually make adjustments, provider review and referral relationships, interfaces with vendors for claim processing and reporting; organization and staffing with respect to internal and external supervision, peer review, absence backfill and ongoing training for the clinical team.

Compliance Issues

Numerous compliance issues associated with operating onsite health centers exist. The major compliance considerations are as follows: 1) Onsite clinics may be subject to ERISA[68] and the provisions of COBRA[69]. 2) If the company has a health savings account (HSA) plan and those members can use the onsite clinic, it will be necessary to establish and charge a "fair market value" for the onsite acute care services against the deductible , 3) In many states, there are "corporate practice of medicine" restrictions which prevent a company from directly employing physicians and sometimes nursing staff, 4) HIPAA provisions apply and the onsite program must assure that all personal health information is treated securely and confidentially.

Summary and Conclusions

Workplace health centers offer employers an effective way to provide access to high-quality, low-cost healthcare at the place of work. They increase access to preventive and primary care services while decreasing dependence on expensive healthcare services such as specialty and emergency department care. Onsite clinicians offer a better method to engage members with chronic disease or who are at risk of developing disease. Engagement rates and efficacy rates are typically threefold of the industry standard telephonic model for risk reduction and disease management. This results in higher employee productivity, lower medical spending and strong customer satisfaction.

Key Ideas

- Moving into the 21st century, with the rapidly rising costs of healthcare and declining population health, employers are looking to onsite care to improve and manage worker health and improve productivity

- Approximately 25-30 percent of companies now provide onsite health services to their employees, up about 50 percent since 2000

- Clinics opened since 2000 were wellness-based vs. occupational-based by a 2:1 margin

- Approximately 35 percent of onsite clinics also provide care to spouses and dependents.

- To be effective, plan design should provide payment for screening, engagement and outcomes. By law, employers can and should offer 20 percent of total health plan premiums for these factors.

- In our revised healthcare delivery system, front-line clinicians for primary and preventive care should have clinical skills as a minimum requirement only.

- The key to helping the individual assume greater responsibility and accountability for their own health is the ability of the healthcare professional to function as a coach.

- Employees should be allowed to access the clinic during paid hours. This will be one of senior management's more visible forms of support.

- The best testimony for senior support is their actual use of the program.

- There needs to be a coherent, comprehensive and ongoing marketing/communications plan for the onsite health program

- The clinic should be the "centerpiece" of the company's culture of health, not a distant appendage with limited application
- (Workplace health centers) increase access to preventive and primary care services while decreasing dependence on expensive healthcare services such as specialty and emergency department care

Questions

1. The best testimony for senior support of onsite health clinics is:

   a. Funding the clinic 100 percent

   b. Email from senior leaders recommending the clinic

   c. Actual use of the clinic

   d. None of the above

2. An effective plan for wellness clinics designs to use what percent of total health plan premiums to pay for screening, engagement, and outcomes?

   a. 50 percent

   b. 10 percent

   c. 20 percent

   d. 35 percent

3. Employees should not be allowed assess to the clinic during paid hours

   a. True

   b. False

4. Fill in the blanks: Workplace health centers _____ access to preventive and primary care services; while _____ dependence on expensive healthcare services such as specialty and emergency care.

   a. Increase, Increasing

   b. Decrease, Decreasing

   c. Decrease, Increasing

   d. Increase, Decreasing

Worksite Clinics – The Next Generation
By Jonathan Spero, M.D.CEO, InHouse Physicians

A recent survey from Mercer found that work site clinics are becoming an increasingly popular way to control healthcare spending and even enhance employee productivity.

Until recently, work site clinics were largely popular only at Fortune 500 companies, however the trend is now spreading to local governments and mid-size companies of 250 or more employees.

Generally, the care received at the clinic is free to the member and there is an added convenience factor for employees. Work site clinics to date have primarily experienced their return on investment for the employer by providing more efficient care at the worksite clinic rather than paying claims from community physicians. However, the next generation of clinics are in the process of being rolled out and offers a more compelling value proposition and much greater associated healthcare savings.

The rest of this article will focus on the key concepts of this next generation of worksite clinics and how they will drive significant reductions in healthcare costs for employers.

Concept #1: At Risk Model

Worksite vendors are more increasingly willing to deliver these services with some portion of the compensation being at risk. The greater the savings to the employer, the greater the potential bonus for the vendor. In this model both the client and vendor have incentives that are congruent.

How these vendors are measuring savings or return on investment varies. The most accurate way to determine the saving generated from the onsite clinic is to compare the annual cost of healthcare (pmpy) for members eligible to use the clinic ("study group") vs. members who are not eligible to use the clinic ("control group"). This provides the employer with a direct comparison of the two groups' costs and a direct measurement of the savings.

Concept #2: Gaps In Care Analysis

Before the clinic even is launched, the employer benefits from powerful analytic software tools that can filter through the previous year's claims data to determine gaps in care for individuals and identify "high risk" members that require additional intervention. These high-risk members can be invited to visit the clinic and enroll in onsite programs designed to ensure quality care and improved outcomes.

Concept #3: Patient Centered Medical Home

The clinicians at the worksite clinic can build a medical home model program. The medical home model understands that chronic diseases require input from multiple providers and specialists and are often difficult to manage for providers as well as the patient. The worksite clinician can act as a coordinator of care ensuring quality, cost effective, evidence based medicine is delivered. In addition to educating the patient on their condition, the "coordinator" communicates to all physicians involved in the care of the patient. This program acts as a very effective disease management program with member engagement levels routinely above 80 percent. The worksite clinic enrolls members who are at high risk based on the analysis of gaps in care mentioned above. Common diseases that are coordinated include diabetes, heart disease, asthma, arthritis, and chronic pain.

Concept #4: Clinical Engineering

Traditionally employers have relied solely on the carriers to negotiate agreements with providers. However, these agreements are not necessarily in the best interest of the employer or the patient. Not only can more favorable pricing be negotiated from quality providers but also the agreements have no quality guarantees associated with them. Worksite vendors have a unique opportunity to identify high cost procedures and hospitalizations and negotiate case rates directly with providers and hospitals with built in quality performance guarantees. Significant savings for employers and members as well as improved patient outcomes are the results of these arrangements.

Concept #5: Price Transparency and Patient Advocacy

Worksite clinicians, now armed with comprehensive pricing and quality metrics, can effectively act as patient advocates assisting members with making informed medial decisions. Patients, with the assistance of the worksite clinic, can comfortably choose a cost saving option for a diagnostic or clinical procedure knowing that they are receiving quality healthcare for the right price.

Concept #6: Predictive Modeling

Worksite clinics have the ability to attach current member health risks to future costs allowing the clinics to develop targeted wellness programs that zero in on future cost drivers. In addition, the clinic can provide useful healthcare budget estimates to the employer's benefits department when planning for next year.

Concept #7: Telemedicine

The worksite clinic is often not available for remote employees and dependents. Telemedicine, quickly becoming a mainstream method of care delivery, can address this issue. Telemedicine, via telephonic and two-way video communication, can allow patients to receive medical evaluation and treatment. Not only can this be offered to members that do not have access to the onsite clinic, but also members with access to the clinic have a resource for after hours care.

Concept #8: Wellness

The clinic offers year round, onsite, integrated wellness programs that cannot only drive participation, but are very effective in modifying healthy lifestyle behaviors amongst members. Clinicians are being cross-trained as certified health coaches and up to 15 percent of the visits to the clinic are being utilized as purely health coaching sessions.

In summary, employers are looking for employee health solutions that offer a one-stop shop for effective healthcare cost containment. The next generation of worksite clinics promises to offer just this. The onsite clinic builds trust and relationships with members, which facilitates engagement in wellness, disease management, and patient advocacy programs driving improved outcomes and lower costs.

Questions

1. Which concept has the incentives of client and vendor congruent?

   a. At Risk Model

   b. Clinical Engineering

   c. Wellness

   d. Gaps in care analysis

2. Which concept has the worksite clinician act as a coordinator of care?

   a. At Risk Model

   b. Patient Centered Medical Home

   c. Wellness

   d. Gaps in care analysis

3. Which concept has the clinician act as a patient advocate?

   a. At risk model

   b. Patient Centered Medical Home

   c. Wellness

   d. Price Transparency and Patient Advocacy

Case Study: Hog Slat Health and Wellness Program
By Renée-Marie Stephano

Introduction and Background

Hog Slat, Inc. is a family-owned business engaged in many aspects of hog and poultry production. They are involved in turnkey construction of confinement type and hog and poultry units, the manufacture and distribution of hog and poultry equipment, and the production of live hogs. The company is the largest contractor and manufacturer of hog equipment in the United States with approximately 1,000 people directly employed and an additional 1,400 subcontractors working on the company's construction projects. Hog Slat / Georgia Poultry has constructed turnkey units for both family farms and large corporate farm units in the United States. Hog Slat / Georgia Poultry also sells equipment packages to customers who choose to construct their own facilities, both domestically and internationally. Their 1000 employees are in 70 locations in four countries. 80 percent of their workforce are men and 20 percent are women. Their program is self-funded and administered by a third party administratior.

The Problem

Between 2000 and 2008 Hog Slat experienced a significant increase in medical trend. This increase was making it difficult to price their product competitively. Their medical trend in this period was between 15 and 20 percent, and this is coupled with a 15 to 20 percent annual increase in healthcare costs. The health issues they faced were primarily heart disease and strokes caused by high blood pressure, high cholesterol and a largely non-active workforce. Also, a high percentage of smokers and employees with high glucose were issues.

The Solution

Hog Slat employed a year by year plan for their wellness program:

- Year 1: Focus on culture change, participation, and obtaining baseline metrics. Biometrics screenings, health risk assessment, and fitness program introduction. Premium reduction incentives and fitness reimbursements

- Year 2: Focus on increasing participation, expand program to spouses, require annual physical for program expansion of fitness and weight program. Expanded premium reduction incentives to be tied to exercise program participation.

- Year 3: Focus on outcomes. Bring back requirement of physical. Portion of premium reduction tied to outcomes. Add differential premium for smokers.

- Year 4: Continue to focus on outcomes. Begin looking at health improvements of those in fitness programs to justify continuation of programs.

There were many resources required for this endeavor. Support from the C-Suite was essential to getting the entire program off the ground. Money was needed to fund gift cards for incentives, and for the premium reductions. An Access database was used to track programs and activities. Forms for employees to track doctor's visits, exercise times and other elements as well as a legal review of these forms and the tobacco affidavit were needed. A wellness director was also required to pull everything together and oversee it all. Hog Slat was fortunate because the management was already committed to creating and rewarding a culture of health. Hiring a wellness professional to create, maintain, and evaluate their program was natural.

The goals of the programs were many. Hog Slat wanted to obtain and then maintain employee participation of at least 70 percent. Reduction of obese BMI values, percentage of employees with high blood pressure, high cholesterol and high glucose levels. A major goal was reduction of healthcare cost trend and to show ROI within three to five years. They also wanted to provide for their employees access to fitness centers, weight management programs, and free preventive care.

In order to meet these goals Hog Slat began to reduce the cost of generic drugs for their employees and educating their employees about them. This was coupled with change in the benefit plan so annual physicals and preventive were covered 100 percent. Employees were also given paid time off of up to four hours a week for doctors' visits for them, their spouses, and their children and elderly parents. Hog Slat also negotiated lower fees at gyms near their production locations, and paid for memberships for Weight Watchers for their employees. This was coupled with an increase in premiums for employees who used tobacco.

The Results

Results were found using a self-reported health risk assessment with biometric screening. A claims analysis and financial analysis was done to determine healthcare cost improvements. Below is a basic overview of the results:

Medical cost trend of per employee health-care spending		-19.78 %	-8.82 %	7.77 %	PENDING
Claims over 30k			22	17	PENDING
Wellness program participation (insured)	78.4 %	77.5 %	83.0 %	82.3 %	PENDING
Percent of participants with high blood pressure	26.9 %	29.4 %	15.5 %	14.9 %	10.2 %
Percent of participants with high total cholesterol	45.2 %	38.6 %	37.8 %	35.2 %	34.3 %
Percent of participants with high glucose:	NA	NA	31.8 %	12.8 %	17.7 %
Percent of participants who have lost weight	NA	NA	NA	45.0 %	33.0 %

These results made both the management and employees happy. The management saw the above results, with a reduction of medical trend and claims over $30,000. Employees became healthier, happier and had affordable access to gyms and lower premiums. Hog slat is currently in the process of examining their program to what works and what does not.

Denise Holland Director of Benefits and Employee Healthcare at Hog Slat has word of advice for other wellness programs. First, be sure that your benefits encourage healthy behavior as strongly as your wellness program does. Next, ask your employees about the sort of incentives that they would like to see implemented. Don't assume you know what they would want. While cash is king, other items can be cheaper and just as effective. Finally, do not skimp on biometric screenings. If you forego anything, forego the health risk assessment. There is more value in real, measureable data than there is in self-reported experiences, behaviors, and opinions on employee health.

CHAPTER 7
Creating a Culture of Health

A Culture of Health: Solving the Healthcare Crisis
By Raymond J. Fabius, MD

Introduction

Corporate culture can serve as a powerful agent of change that helps stem the tide of rising healthcare costs and alarming clinical outcomes associated with preventable diseases. Forward-thinking employers have established a "culture of health" to "bend the trend" on escalating employee medical costs—an effort that has evolved from the experimentation stage to a tangible, benchmarked solution and best hope for curing the nation's healthcare crisis. A growing body of evidence shows that healthy workers are more productive. However, before any substantive change can occur within organizations, it is critical for employers to carefully brand and promote a culture of health and provide the right environment for it to flourish. For example, cafeterias will need to favor healthy food and beverage choices, exercise should be encouraged and smoking banned. This new culture also must tie into employee benefits design, with both preventative and advanced consumer-centric care coordination services that make care more accessible. Finally, there needs to be a system of measurement in place to help advance the business case for such an effort. The best quantitative efforts use appraisal and claims data, while the best qualitative efforts identify gaps from benchmarks that help identify and prioritize key steps.

Cultural change is possible in companies, organizations, communities and nations. In the 1970s, large employers such as Alcoa realized that workplace injuries were not necessary and the culture of safety movement began. With the elimination of polio, the March of Dimes found a new purpose. The association between secondhand smoke and illness has changed our nation's view and tolerance of it in public places.

The speed with which these campaigns have succeeded has depended on such influences as leadership endorsement, management participation and employee engagement. The sustainability of these efforts has its basis on measurement, feedback and quality improvement.

Where do You Start?

Building a culture of health is no longer an exercise in experimentation. Early pioneer organizations made many missteps along their way.

Today we can study the processes of benchmark companies and follow their lead. We know that data collection and integration into a warehouse is associated with top performance. Attending to the needs of all segments of the population is required. This includes keeping well people well, reducing the risk factors of those on the path toward illness, managing chronic conditions and providing the best that healthcare has to offer to the catastrophically ill.

Keeping Well People Well

Wellness is not the absence of illness but rather the holistic pursuit of physical, mental, spiritual and intellectual wellbeing. It is the pursuit of maximal functionality and personal achievement. Of course, it is in the best interest of companies, communities and nations to encourage and support the achievement and extension of wellness.

Reducing Health Risks

The traditional healthcare system focuses on making patients better after the onset of illness. This is curious in the face of much evidence that prevention offers better results. Medical science has uncovered the key risk factors responsible for chronic illness. Sedentary lifestyles, obesity, poor nutritional habits and stress are all examples. Cultures of health provide environments, tools and services conducive to reducing these risk factors.

Managing Chronic Conditions

The disease management movement is predicated on the three "I's" - Identification, Intervention and Impact. First, find people with chronic conditions to help. Then provide evidence-based solutions to mitigate the consequences of their disease. Finally, measure to see if you have produced an improvement in the illness burden of this cohort.

Special Services for the Catastrophic

A culture of health needs to be responsive to organizational members who are stricken with severe medical problems. On the front end, this may require centers of excellence, intensive care management and rehabilitation services. On the back end, this may call for compassionate care, pain management and hospice. Humane approaches to these situations yield better outcomes for patients and their loved ones.

The Connection Between Health and Productivity / Performance

The literature is replete with evidence that healthy workers are more productive. In fact, studies show that for every dollar spent on healthcare, two or three dollars are gained due to increased productivity. It is logical to realize that healthy people perform better in all facets of life. Not only did I lose my father at a young age to morbid obesity, but during the last few years of his life his condition limited him from doing many things fathers do with their sons.

Moreover, it is also interesting to note the correlation between the states with the highest life expectancy and those with the highest mean income. Health produces wealth.

Organizational Pillars

Branding and marketing a culture of health is essential. Establishing a brand is paramount. During my tenure as GE Global Medical Leader we used a brand called - Health by Numbers - the 0, 5, 10, 25 program. This stood for zero tobacco use, five daily fruits and vegetables, ten thousands steps a day and maintaining a normal body mass index of 25. With a brand you can embark on a multimedia marketing approach leveraging print, web, video and promotional events.

The environment should be complementary to your culture of health efforts. Cafeterias need to favor healthy food choices and catering policies need to eliminate unhealthy options. On-campus exercise should be endorsed by investing in walking trails, fitness centers and gym memberships. Smoking must be banned on campus.

Companies need to tie their benefit design plan to a culture of health. Preventative services and smoking cessation programs should be covered completely. Disease and complex case management services should be provided without a charge. Those covered who can demonstrate that they are taking optimal care of themselves should earn higher levels of benefits.

Everyone should be required to establish a connection with a trusted primary care provider and encouraged to pick ones who function within certified medical homes. Employers should reach out to community providers to align them with their other culture of health activities.

Those employers who have high concentrations of employees should strongly consider full-service workplace primary care centers such as the ones my former company, CHD Meridian, built for Toyota and Disney.

Health appraisal with biometric screening is a hallmark of most benchmark culture of health companies. Crucial to this success is the application of behavioral change theory and follow-up with trusted clinicians and health coaches.

Assessing Progress

Best quantitative efforts utilize appraisal and claims data. Best qualitative efforts identify gaps from benchmark and can help companies identify and prioritize next steps.

Concluding Remarks

We are experiencing a new era. Benchmark employers are publicly declaring that they have successfully bent the curve, markedly decreasing their medical inflation rate. Some are even seeing their costs go down. Since the larger ones are self-insured, these savings drop directly to the bottom line. The smaller companies are experiencing moderation of their healthcare premiums. It looks like building a culture of health may be the best solution to our nation's healthcare crisis. I encourage you to build one where you work and live.

Building a Culture of Health, Productivity and Wellbeing
By Colleen Reilly

Today, corporate wellness solutions are focused on employee health, but lack a focus on overall wellbeing and productivity. If integrated, all three elements can be a better predictor of productivity than health alone.[70] Relying on "drag-and-drop" solutions, does not take the wellness needs of the whole person under consideration, result in wellness programs that are ineffective and, financially and mentally draining. Most solutions today do not take a holistic wellness approach that incorporates the physical, financial, personal and professional aspects of employee wellbeing. In this chapter, readers will learn how to take a refreshing wellbeing approach to building a performance-based wellness culture within an organization that results in healthy, productive and well people.

Building a Performance-Based Wellness Culture: Keys to Success
To truly build a sustainable culture of wellness, four key success factors are essential:

Success Factor #1: Integrate wellness goals with corporate goals to drive results and sustainability.
Performance-based corporate wellness is the total integration of wellness strategy into business strategy. This means that, just like any other business initiative, corporate wellness must be a completely integrated solution with a long-term strategy and the technology to support it in place. This integrated solution is the only way to get results.

If you don't have the support of senior leadership, a wellness champion team in place and an operational plan mapped out, it is vital that you take a step back and get these foundational pieces in place. Start small and take the time needed to grow the program in a strategic, purposeful way. Hiring key consultants and account managers can also be an effective way to help you build the team and get it done more quickly and without setbacks.

Just like any other business process, such as a Lean Process or Six Sigma, you must create and implement strategies that align with your corporate goals, match your governance practices and build an ongoing analysis of outcomes. Then, continually tweak the program to maximize results.

Success Factor #2: Empower leaders to be visible, healthy role models in order to maximize culture change.

Leaders have vision. They also realize that if they want to make a difference within their organizations, they must connect their vision to the business strategy.

This also holds true when companies want to build a culture of health and wellbeing. There is a big difference between wanting a culture shift and committing to a culture change. Commitment – at all levels – is essential.

Not only must leadership provide adequate resources but, more importantly, they must also commit to communicating the values of wellbeing to employees and act as an organizational role-model. Leaders are not dummies. They realize that they need to be engaged, visible and committed participants; but they often need to be provided with some instructions on how to do so.

For example, in a larger organization that I worked with, Nelnet Inc., we created four different leadership groups to ensure that communication was clearly disseminated, buy-in was created and engagement was happening at all different levels, and visible support was implemented across the organization. A Leadership Steering Committee, made up of the CFO, CEO, President and EVP of Organizational Effectiveness, provided guidance and oversight for programs. A Director-Level Wellness Advisory Committee provided checks and balances on steering committee decisions. Finally, regional wellness leaders and local champions disseminated messages to regional and local offices.

While all of these committees were comprised of volunteers, they were very respected among their peer groups. Often, being a part of the company's cultural transformation was a more motivating experience for employees than was their annual bonus payout for meeting their normal job functions. These people were changing a culture, and more importantly, they were changing people's lives, their families' lives and the lives of people within the communities in which they lived and played. That is rewarding!

Success Factor #3: Deploy a multi-modal communication strategy to influence behavior change and keep messaging and programs relevant.
Life is busy. With everything that is already on our plates, including the demands of work and family, creating accountability for health and wellbeing can seem like a chore – particularly to an already overwhelmed wellness coordinator. However strategic, purposeful communication can help to cut through the noise. A thoughtful communication strategy can influence peoples' lifestyle choices if the communication is frequent, regularly timed, consistent in messaging and relevant to the participants' situations, timing and priorities. So what does that mean? Tailored emails to every age bracket, gender and salary range? Well, not exactly.

Communications need to happen at least seven times in three different modes (such as email, print and word of mouth) for people to notice and understand the message. Employees need to have wellness information presented in a clean, clear way that drives positive action. They need to feel empowered to direct themselves to resources or have resources strategically placed so they can find them quickly when they are ready. In addition, people need to feel in charge of their own self-improvement rather than feeling like the company is telling them exactly what to do.

Most importantly, your wellness strategy must be simple and communicated regularly through corporate communications as well as grass roots and viral methods.

Success Factor #4: Develop key metrics for optimal impact.
My company, Total Wellbeing, has helped companies save 9 to 15 percent on healthcare costs. How can you do this? Simply follow these steps:

> **Step 1:** Get 80 percent of your population to take a health risk assessment and biometric screening.

> **Step 2:** Get 50 to 75 percent of your population engaged in your wellness programs and challenges and earning wellness points.

> **Step 3:** Reward improvements in biometrics and REAL results.

As you read the three simple steps, you may think this process looks too easy to be true. The truth of the matter is that it is not easy, but it is true. There is an art and science to behavior change. With the right process in place, you can get people engaged for the long run and inspire them to actually make healthier choices that result in improved biometrics, fewer healthcare claims and overall less productivity loss. It all starts with visible senior-leadership support, culture support policies, environmental change and the right mix of intrinsic and extrinsic incentives.

Sample Case Study: Company X has 2,500 employees in the financial industry

Total Wellbeing started working with Company X in 2006. The first step we took was to closely tie benefits eligibility with the wellness program. All employees are required to complete a Health Screening and Health Assessment for benefits eligibility. Employees were originally resentful, but with solid communications and incentives of up to $1,200 deposited into their Health Savings Accounts for regular wellness engagement, employees shifted their opinion of the program. They began registering positive results and solid engagement.

Refreshing the initiative

As with most things, the novelty wore off after the first three years, and employees began simply checking the wellness box and earning their wellness points without doing anything. Employee engagement and motivation fell flat. After three years, the "engagement" was high, but the biometric results were starting to lag.

To combat this lag in employee interest, we started a REFRESH campaign and created an initiative that inspired, engaged and motivated employees and their families to get involved and get results.

Based on this we redirected our energy toward each one. In this process we pinpointed three priorities:

1. *Sustain engagement*

   To sustain engagement, we started to evaluate health, productivity and wellbeing. We implemented a three-tiered wellness strategy that allowed individuals to work on their own personal wellness goals, participate and challenge each other in peer-to-peer challenges and engage in corporate-wide wellness campaigns and programs. We found that by helping people work on what was relevant to them and providing them with a support structure, engagement increased.

2. *Increase intrinsic motivation*

   Company X's increase in engagement was purely tied to employees who were more intrinsically motivated. They no longer felt that the company was telling them which program to participate in; they felt like they were in the driver's seat. People like to be in control; they don't like to be told what to do.

3. *Reduce risks*

   After many years of running a participation-based program, we moved to tying the premium discount to improvement of biometrics. With frequent and consistent communications, we transitioned to a results-based program and all the employees were thrilled to have goals to strive for.

Seeing Results

In our first year of implementing a performance-based corporate wellness solution for Company X, assessment and biometrics participation skyrocketed to 88 percent, and over 78 percent of consumer-driven health plan participants engaged in quarterly challenges. Biometrics improved as well.

-73 percent decrease in Tobacco Use

-58 percent decrease in Poor Nutrition

-36 percent decrease in Lack of Physical Activity

-32 percent decrease in Triglycerides

-16 percent decrease in Blood Pressure

-16 percent decrease in Cholesterol

The participants in the wellness program maintained their weight. Employees started asking how they could get their spouses and dependants involved. There was tremendous enthusiasm, active support and real participation. Behavior change started occurring.

The organization was communicating better, being smarter about catering programs to employee wants and needs, and making it simple and easy for employees to track their progress through smartphone technology, mobile apps and onsite check-ins.

This new approach was focused on helping people achieve personal goals that were relevant to them. The by-product of this strategy was increased employee engagement, which ultimately supported the organizational mission of building a culture of healthy, productive and well people.

By focusing on health, wellbeing and productivity, wellness became relevant and important to all employees and their families. Wellness participants were starting to thrive and they had the ability to respond to changing demands, given the increasing pace and unpredictable nature of work. They also adjusted more aptly to the normal setbacks of life. Actual resiliency increased and people were able to bounce back to optimal "wellbeing" and performance without incurring severe functional decrement. Even when leaving the organization, employees stated their favorite part of working at the organization was the culture – the culture of healthy, happy and high-performing people.

Performance Matters in the Long Run

To truly create a culture of health, productivity and wellbeing, it is vital to take the time to develop a performance-based solution that strongly integrates wellness strategies into business strategies. Shortcuts lead to an apathetic employee base, a waste of company funds and an unhappy C-suite. With a strategy in place, an engaged leadership team on board, a multi-modal communications strategy established and a focus on metrics and results in mind, you will create an engaging and cohesive experience that will get results.

Key Ideas:

- Performance-based corporate wellness is the total integration of wellness strategy into business strategy.

- There is a big difference between wanting a culture shift and committing to a culture change. Commitment – at all levels – is essential.

- Communications need to happen at least seven times in three different modes (such as email, print and word of mouth) for people to notice and understand the message.

- Your wellness strategy must be simple and communicated regularly through corporate communications as well as grass roots and viral methods.

Questions:

1. Performance based Wellness is the total integration of wellness and business strategy.

   a. True

   b. False

2. How many modes of communication are needed for people to notice and understand the message?

   a. One

   b. Three

   c. Five

   d. Seven

3. How times must a message be sent for it to be noticed and understood?

   a. One

   b. Three

   c. Five

   d. Seven

Population Health Management and a Healthy Workplace Culture: A Primer

By Dr. Nico Pronk

Introduction

Efforts to create and sustain a healthy work culture that reflects "the way things are done around here" and results in healthy, productive and resilient workers is a goal many companies strive to achieve. First and foremost, it appears that companies that benefit from such healthy workplace cultures also seem to have healthcare cost trends below average, consistently generate savings due to lower absenteeism and disability, generate higher revenues and total shareholder returns and are recognized in the community for being good community partners (Baicker 2010; Berry 2010; NBGH 2011/2012). Perhaps even more importantly, the shared experiences that result from the wide array of health management programs at the worksite affects how employees feel about their company, the pride they feel in the work they do and their genuine interest in the wellbeing of themselves, their families and their colleagues. As such, workplace health management programs represent an important community-based health improvement model that influences a variety of other sectors and settings.

What if a company was to provide all of its employees with direct, onsite access to medical care providers, prescription medications, wellness coaches, prevention programs and the like, and not a single employee showed up? Were this to happen, one might think that the company's solution to health-related problems and the culture of the employee population were so incompatible that nobody would use the resources. Obviously, this could be related to a host of issues, including such factors as lack of trust, lack of leadership engagement and concerns about data privacy, among many others. While it is highly unlikely that such a scenario would actually occur, it does highlight the fact that workplace culture matters. The normative values and beliefs of employees, that is, "the way things are done around here," may be regarded a powerful determinant of success in worksite health programs. In fact, when considering the literature on best practices of worksite health promotion programs, factors associated with the notion of a healthy workplace culture are among the most often cited key variables for success (Pronk 2009).

Obviously, every workplace has a culture of some kind. One way or another, health is represented in the culture; however it may not necessarily be a "healthy workplace culture." It is intuitively clear that culture matters when it comes to the health of employees—what people believe, think, do, and hold each other accountable for is certainly related to the overall health of the population.

It is the purpose of this chapter to explore several definitions so it is possible to consider what is meant by "population health management" and a "healthy workplace culture," how those two relate to each other, how such a culture may be enabled and to consider the important role played by company leaders in shaping and sustaining population health management programs and a healthy workplace culture.

Definitions Matter

Previously, population health management, when applied to the workplace setting, has been defined as "the strategic and operational processes used to generate the health outcomes of a defined group of individuals collectively associated with a company's health improvement efforts," (Pronk 2009a). This high-level definition is supported by the identification of best practices that help define what the important design principles that ensure positive outcomes of such programs may be. A review of the literature on best practices produces a relatively short list of key design principles that should inform program design and development. Reports by O'Donnell and colleagues (1997), Goetzel and co-workers (1998; 2007), Chapman (2004), Pronk (2009), Berry and colleagues (2010) and NIOSH (2008) provide many overlapping factors that relate to successful programs. As a result, characteristics that relate to successful population health management programs may be gleaned from a summary overview of those factors, and such an overview is presented in Figure 1.

Figure 6.1. Population Health Management Best Practice Design Principles

Leadership and Strategy	•Organizational commitment •Participatory processes to include employees •Wellness champions •Connection to business goals •Supportive environment (physical, psychosocial, policy)
Operations	•Implementation plan •Communications •Easy access for all employees •Assessments of health risk with feedback •Effective interventions and Incentives
Integration	•Integration across corporate functions and departments •Integrated data systems •Protection of privacy and confidentiality
Evaluation	•Program measurement, evaluation and reporting

Note: Adapted from Pronk, 2009.

It is important to consider how population health management programs may influence the shared experiences among employees in the context of the existing workplace culture and the impact of the program on a potential shift in the culture of the group. The formation of culture among people may be considered a striving toward satisfying the need for stability, consistency and meaning common among people in general, and, employees more specifically. It is based on the accumulation of knowledge among members of the group. Schein (2004, p. 17) presents the notion of culture as accumulated shared learning of a given group that includes behavioral, emotional and cognitive elements. He also argues that for shared learnings to occur there must be a history of shared experiences that imply some level of stability of membership in the group. The emergence of culture represents a pattern of shared elements formed as a result of the group's need for consistency, stability and meaning. Behavior is a result, an offshoot, or derivative of the culture of the group—it is determined by the perceptions, thoughts, feelings and context in which people find themselves. As a result, Schein defines "culture" as "a pattern of shared basic assumptions that was learned by a group as it solved its problems of external adaptation and internal integration, that has worked well enough to be considered valid and therefore is to be taught to new members as the correct way to perceive, think, and feel in relation to those problems."

Others have applied this notion of culture more specifically to health. From a medical, anthropological and sociological perspective, the following definition of "health culture" brings us closer to the application of culture to health. As forwarded by Weidman (1977, p. 25), a health culture refers to:

All the phenomena associated with the maintenance of wellbeing and problems of sickness with which people cope in traditional ways within their own social networks. It is a general term that includes both the cognitive and social aspects of [health traditions]. The cognitive dimension involves values and beliefs, the blueprints for health action, disease etiology, prevention, diagnosis, treatment and cure. The social system dimension refers to the organization of healthcare or the healthcare delivery system. It requires understanding of the structure and functioning of an organized set of health-related social roles and behaviors.

However, it may be argued that added to this should be the consideration of geographic spaces and places; health cultures may vary from region to region, depending on how some places treat illness in comparison to others and how culture may interact with specific environments such as the workplace for example.

Specific definitions of "a healthy workplace culture" are relatively hard to find. Often, the culture of health at the workplace is described in a variety of terms and factors, but lacks clear definition. A clear definition, however, is important because it will allow for a much more meaningful manner in which to express metrics and measures for tracking and improvement. Considering the two definitions presented above, a definition of a healthy workplace culture ought to include not only factors that promote healthy lifestyle choices for employees (Aldana 2012), but also the context in which such factors operate (Pronk 2012). In this case the context is related to the workplace setting and, as such, the company's wellbeing is directly related to the stability of the group, i.e., the sustainability of the business is related to the success of the company in the marketplace. As such a healthy workplace culture is also related to how well a company performs in the market with the products and services it provides for its customer base. Therefore, the formal definition of a healthy workplace culture used for purposes of discussion here is one which includes individual and shared experiences as well as the health of the company itself.

A healthy workplace culture may be defined as a workplace ecology in which the dynamic relationship between human beings and their work environment nurtures personal and organizational values that support the achievement of a person's best self while generating exceptional business performance (Pronk, Allen 2009, p. 224).

Enabling a Healthy Workplace Culture

To enable a healthy workplace culture is to single out and draw attention to health-relevant aspects of the larger organizational culture, and to create a context that makes it possible for people to translate these aspects into meaningful activities in their local health and wellbeing routines. To effectively consolidate, elucidate and direct features of an organization's culture that pertain directly or indirectly to employee health, a set of actions that support this enabling of a healthy culture need to be identified and presented. Such features and factors are not limited to the promotion of healthy lifestyle choices. Health encompasses a broader set of characteristics and dimensions than healthy lifestyle choices and behavior alone. When considering existing definitions of health, such as the one introduced by the World Health Organization in 1946 (WHO 1948), health is more than the absence of disease and includes social, physical and emotional dimensions and environments.

Features and Factors to Focus On

A healthy workplace culture may be enabled by factors related to the psychosocial, physical and socioeconomic environment. Table 1 outlines several examples in each of these categories. Factors like physical activity, nutrition, sleep, abstaining from tobacco and responsible alcohol use certainly promote healthy lifestyles. However, they also shape psychological effects such as mood states and feelings, happiness, a general sense of wellbeing, a sense of belonging and ownership, social cohesion and positivity.

Table 1. Examples of Organizational Factors that Enable a Healthy Workplace Culture

Psychosocial environment	Physical environment	Socioeconomic environment
Company mission includes health	Ergonomically-designed workspaces	Payment scales commensurate with the market

Respect—a respectful work environment	Physical-activity friendly workplace	Team-based incentives for employee health and wellbeing participation
Trust—the degree to which employees can trust what executives and managers tell them	Accessible stairs that have good lighting and are designed as an "inviting" space (e.g., painted, art displays, music, etc.)	Meaningful company-wide charitable giving campaigns
Transparency—staff is aware of the company's direction	Safe work spaces	Individual-level incentives for program participation
Merit—the idea that the individual worker's ideas are judged based on their merit rather than on the employee's status within the organization	Access to microwave, refrigerator at work	Option to participate in automatic payroll deduction for retirement savings (401K-type programs)

The Role of Leadership

Strong leadership at all levels of the company is paramount in adopting and maintaining a healthy workplace culture. Leadership needs to occur at the executive level, at the managerial and supervisorial levels, and at the frontline of the company. Executive-level leadership is needed to ensure a vision consistent with company mission and vision. Managerial and supervisorial-level leadership is necessary in order to integrate the enabling factors and employee experiences into the daily routines and workflows so that individual employees and work teams feel supported in their efforts to optimize health throughout the workday. The frontline leadership is needed to ensure that initiatives are implemented and employees engage throughout the organization. In a sense, executive leadership sets the vision and the field, managers and supervisors take the program broadly across the company, and the frontline leaders drive it deep into every nook and cranny of the organization.

However, leadership for health is not necessarily associated with employment status within a given company. It is entirely possible that leaders emerge within an organization based on their energy, enthusiasm or interest in health. Leadership may emerge as a result of grassroots efforts and activities and, over time, include upper-level management more explicitly. Regardless, whether it's top-down, or bottom-up, visible leadership for health initiatives is a necessary component of any program to assure participation, engagement, scalability, sustainability and overall program success.

Leaders play important roles in the company. Table 2 outlines several examples of appropriate leadership roles. When summarizing these examples, they ensure that leadership is visible, actively involved, supportive on resource needs in context of good stewardship, and connecting departmental health objectives to overall company direction.

Table 2. Leadership Tasks Supporting a Healthy Workplace Culture

Design	Design the governing ideas of purpose and vision and design the core values for the program. Few acts of leadership have more enduring effects on an organization than building a foundation of purpose and core values.
Teach and mentor	Help everyone in the organization, self included, to gain more insightful views of the vision of a healthy company.
Be a good steward	Let your sense of stewardship operate at two levels: stewardship for the people being led and stewardship for the larger purpose or mission that underlies the enterprise. Stewardship interacts directly with the teacher and mentor tasks, the responsible use of allocated resources, the design of the program's vision, and the communication of this vision on a daily basis.
Lead by example	Don't delegate being an example of an active participant. There is no message as strong as actually demonstrating the point.

Be visible	Use every opportunity to reinforce healthy messaging by connecting the message with the leader—in person, on the Intranet, in the newsletter, and so on.
Communicate	Make sure to talk in a variety of ways to all employees. Use written, verbal, and visual methods to communicate, and do it often. Communicate, communicate, communicate!
Report	Let employees and specific stakeholder groups know how the program is doing. When reports become available, use them to identify messages appropriate for such audiences, and remember to put them in a positive light.
Celebrate	Celebrate at any chance you get. Celebrations are great opportunities to relate fun and a sense of accomplishment to the program's experiences. People want to be associated with such feelings.

Note: From Pronk (2007), reprinted with permission.

Measuring a Healthy Workplace Culture

When do you know you have arrived at a healthy workplace culture? How do you know that you may have made a positive difference following a series of program implementations? If you know it when you experience it, how can you leverage it to get even better results out of your health management program? Measurement can help you get there. However, how does one measure a healthy workplace culture?

Considering a multi-dimensional construct that includes health as one dimension of overall wellbeing is important. As such, dimensions such as social, career, financial, physical, emotional and community may all be considered as part of the measurement strategy. Rath and Harter (2010) have used this approach as part of their work at Gallup and present a comprehensive view of wellbeing at the worksite. Crimmins and Halberg (2009) describe the healthy workplace culture at General Mills using employee questionnaires that included a core set of health value questions alongside demographics and open comments. Golaszewski and colleagues (2008) report on the results of an organizational health culture audit and show acceptable reliability and validity, similar to the results of Rath and Harter (2010). Finally, Aldana and co-workers (2012) report on aspects of a healthy worksite culture based on results of the HERO Scorecard. Therefore, several different approaches to measuring a healthy workplace culture exist.

Closing Thoughts

The purpose of this chapter was to briefly introduce the notion of population health management and its relationship to creating and sustaining a healthy workplace culture. Using a set of explicit definitions and considering the important principles of successful program design, it is argued that existing workplace culture shapes the behavior of employees as it relates to their willingness to participate in population health management programs via the worksite and that population health management programs will impact shared experiences that may ultimately steer the culture towards a healthier one. Enabling a healthy workplace culture to emerge is likely to involve a variety of strategies and tactics and is clearly linked to overarching issues, such as trust and respect, among all employees. Leadership is broadly recognized as a key ingredient but this leadership needs to come from multiple levels and sources—executive, middle-management, frontline, champions and others. Finally, early measurement approaches are encouraging and are successful at connecting a broader workplace context to more specific health-related factors.

At a time when healthcare costs have reached unsustainable levels for employers and individual employees are increasingly faced with added healthcare cost pressures, the role of being or becoming healthy cannot be understated. Ensuring that such efforts at the individual level are supported by a culture at the workplace that will steer people in the direction of the "better-for-you" choices will likely have a profound impact on the overall health and wellbeing of employees and their families.

References

Aldana SG, Anderson DR, Adams TB, Whitmer W, Merrill RM, George V, Noyce J. A review of the knowledge base on healthy worksite culture. *Journal of Occupational and Environmental Medicine.* 2012;54(4):414-419.

Baicker K, Cutler D, Song Z. Workplace wellness programs can generate savings. *Health Affairs.* 2010;29(2): doi: 10.1377/hlthaff.2009.0626.

Berry LL, Mirabito AM, Baun WB. What's the hard return on employee wellness programs? Harvard Business Review 2010; Dec. www.hbr.org.

Chapman L. Expert opinions on "best practices" in worksite health promotion (WHP). *The Art of Health Promotion.* 2004;July/August:1-6.

Crimmins TJ, Halberg J. Measuring success in creating a "culture of health". *J Occup Environ Med* 2009;51:351-355.

Goetzel RZ, Guindon A, Humphries L, et al. Health and productivity management: Consortium benchmarking study best practice report. Houston: American Productivity and Quality Center International Benchmarking Clearinghouse; 1998. www.apqc.org.

Goetzel RZ, Shechter D, Ozminkowski RJ, Marmot PF, Tabrizi MJ, Roemer EC. Promising practices in employer health and productivity management efforts: Findings from a benchmarking study. *Journal of Occupational and Environmental Medicine*. 2007;49:111-30.

Golaszewski T, Hoebbel C, Crossley J, Foley G, Dorn J. The reliability and validity of an organizational health culture audit. *Am J Health Studies* 2008;23(3):116-123.

National Business Group on Health and Towers Watson. Pathway to health and productivity report. 2011/2012 Staying@Work Survey Report. See: http://www.towerswatson.com/assets/pdf/6031/Towers-Watson-Staying-at-Work-Report.pdf (Accessed April 4, 2012).

NIOSH Essential Elements List. See: http://www.cdc.gov/niosh/docs/2010-140/ (Accessed April 4, 2012).

O'Donnell M, Bishop C, Kaplan K. Benchmarking best practices in workplace health promotion. *The Art of Health Promotion*. 1997;1(1):12.

Pronk, N.P. Leadership for worksite health promotion. *ACSM's Health & Fitness Journal*, 2007, 11(5), 40-42.

Pronk NP. Population health management at the worksite. In: Pronk NP (Ed.) *ACSM's Worksite Health Handbook, 2nd Ed.* Champaign, IL: Human Kinetics, Inc., 2009. p. 2.

Pronk NP, Allen CU. A culture of health: Creating and sustaining supportive organizational environments for health. In: Pronk NP (Ed.) *ACSM's Worksite Health Handbook, 2nd Ed.* Champaign, IL: Human Kinetics, Inc., 2009. p. 224.

Pronk, NP. The power of context: Moving from information and knowledge to practical wisdom for improving physical activity and dietary behaviors. *American Journal of Preventive Medicine*. 2012;42(1):103-104.

Rath T, Harter J. Wellbeing: The five essential elements. New York, NY: Gallup Press, 2010.

Schein E. *Organizational Culture and Leadership* (3rd Ed.). San Francisco, CA: Jossey-Bass, 2004. p. 17.

Weidman H. On Mitchell's changing others. *Medical Anthropology Newsletter.* 1977;8(14):25.

World Health Organization. Preamble to the Constitution of the World Health Organization as adopted by the International Health Conference, New York, 19-22 June, 1946; signed on 22 July 1946 by the representatives of 61 States (Official Records of the World Health Organization, no. 2, p. 100) and entered into force on 7 April 1948. See: http://www.who.int/about/definition/en/print.html . (Accessed April 4, 2012)

Key Ideas:

- The shared experiences that result from the wide array of health management programs at the worksite affects how employees feel about their company, the pride they feel in the work they do and their genuine interest in the wellbeing of themselves, their families and their colleagues. As such, workplace health management programs represent an important community-based health improvement model that influences a variety of other sectors and settings.

- Previously, population health management, when applied to the workplace setting, has been defined as "the strategic and operational processes used to generate the health outcomes of a defined group of individuals collectively associated with a company's health improvement efforts,"

- The formation of culture among people may be considered a striving toward satisfying the need for stability, consistency and meaning common among people in general, and, more specifically, employees. It is based on the accumulation of knowledge among members of the group

- Behavior is a result, an offshoot, or derivative of the culture of the group—it is determined by the perceptions, thoughts, feelings and context in which people find themselves

- Schein defines "culture" as "a pattern of shared basic assumptions that was learned by a group as it solved its problems of external adaptation and internal integration, that has worked well enough to be considered valid and, therefore, is to be taught to new members as the correct way to perceive, think, and feel in relation to those problems."

- Executive-level leadership is needed to ensure a vision consistent with company mission and vision. Managerial and supervisorial-level leadership is necessary in order to integrate the enabling factors and employee experiences into the daily routines and workflows so that individual employees and work teams feel supported in their efforts to optimize health throughout the workday. The frontline leadership is needed to ensure that initiatives are implemented and employees engage throughout the organization.

- In a sense, executive leadership sets the vision and the field, managers and supervisors take the program broadly across the company, and the frontline leaders drive it deep into every nook and cranny of the organization.

Questions:

1. What is missing from the characteristics that relate to successful population health management program: Leadership and Strategy,_____, Integration, Evaluation?

   a. Executive action

   b. Operation

   c. Maintenance

   d. Behavior Assessment

2. Behavior is determined by the perceptions, thoughts, feelings and context in which people find themselves.

   a. True

   b. False

3. Why is executive-level leadership needed?

    a. sets the vision and the field

    b. Proves commitment

    c. Creates a buzz

    d. Inspires other do act

4. Why is Managerial and Supervisorial-level leadership needed?

    a. To be a reminder of the healthy behavior

    b. To enforce compliance

    c. To take the program broadly across the company

    d. Because managers often do not participate.

5. Why is frontline leadership needed?

    a. To drive it into the company

    b. Because they comprise most of the company

    c. Because they are often the ones who do not participate

    d. To create a buzz

Case Study: Sustaining a Culture of Health at Johnson and Johnson

By Renée-Marie Stephano

Background and Introduction:

Fik Isaac, the Vice President, Global Health Services and Chief Medical Officer at Johnson and Johnson detailed the scope and breadth their of wellness programs which are over 30 years old. To understand why this program has lasted as long as it did, shedding some light about the history of the company is necessary. In 1978 then CEO James E. Burke wanted to form "the healthiest work force in the world." He believed that this would create an environment of health; in which employees would be responsible for their own wellbeing. This would lead to better productivity and lower costs. This is a clear indication that interest from leaders within the company is essential to a successful and sustainable program.

Facts about the program:

Johnson and Johnson is a big and easily recognizable brand. In 2011 their total sales were approximately $65 billion. Couple this with the 116,000 to 117,000 employees in 70 countries; it becomes clear that they are a large program with a multistate and multinational presence. The employee population is divided equally between men and women with the median age of employees being 48 years old. Furthermore, the benefits program is self-funded, as most of the large corporate programs are, and is administered by a Third Party Administrator. Some of the health problems faced by Johnson and Johnson employees were cardiovascular, mental health, and mostly represented in what is called non-communicable disease (NDC). As a part of the company credo, there is a section detailing the commitment to health, not just to the community but to the employees as well. In order to address population health and be able to assist employees in improving their health, they offer Health Risk Assessment and make biometrics available to those who want to participate.

The Health & Wellness programs at Johnson & Johnson evolved over the past 30 years and are described as a journey to a sustained culture of health that is becoming part of the fabric of day to day operations. As the caring company, it is part of the value system "the credo".

The Solution:

Plotting steps of the implementation of the program is difficult because of the how long it has been around, and how the company operates in many states and nations. This decentralization caused them to look into the viability of putting the entire wellness program into one roof for US employees. This strategy was executed in 1995. In order to drive participation into the newly consolidated program the company decided on a new approach, tying an upfront discount on their medical plan for participation in the wellness program. Although this form of incentive is not new today, in 1995 this was a bold and innovative at its time.

In order to get the program off the ground it required the expertise and hard work of many people. They began by taking a detailed analysis and inventory of the program to see what was working prior to integrating and what was not. This also required a team of experts in occupational medicine, wellness, health promotion, and mental health to get the program on its feet and to utilize the services that already existed to its full potential.

Fast forward to today, the focus of the program is no longer driving participation and analyzing its effectiveness; now the goal is sustainability and improving health outcomes. Every three to five years they examine their goals, strategies and approach. The current set of sustainability goals is called Healthy Future 2015 there are three health goals for the

Johnson and Johnson program:

- 90 percent of employees have access to "culture of health" programs

- 80 percent of employees have completed a health risk profile and know their key health indicators

- 80 percent of measured population health risk will be characterized as low health risk

These goals are intended "to promote and sustain a culture of health through leadership commitment to offering among many others, access to what we call the culture of health components, this means leadership commitment in their various programs such as:

- Tobacco Cessation
- HIV/AIDS Policy
- Health Profile
- Medical Surveillance
- Promoting Physical Activity
- Employee Assistance Programs
- General Health Promotion
- Promoting Healthy Eating
- Cancer Awareness
- Stress Management
- Access to Travel Health
- Modified Duties

They also established their health champions which are "leaders within the organization that really work as ambassadors to support health initiatives, sustainability, health programs and efforts..."

The strategies they employ have been mentioned already but there are some which have not been discussed. They use tool kits, which detail the "how" within their health guidelines and standards but allow some degree of customization depending on the location's needs. Another is the use of incentives within their benefits design. They were one of the first large company to utilize incentives, and they continue to use them. In addition to a medical contribution discount of $500 for participating in the health profile and health advising if employees are at risk, employees get rewards deposited in their health reimbursement account. For example; an employee who gets a colonoscopy gets a monetary reward for taking this preventative screening test.

The Results:
Johnson and Johnson has concluded that investing in wellness and prevention does have a positive return, not only in improving health risks, but also reducing the rise in healthcare costs, with an average return of $1.88 to $3.92 for each dollar invested . They attribute

this to the nursing of their culture of health, continued employee engagement and management support.

Not only does Johnson and Johnson measure their program internally, they have published the findings of their program in the Harvard Business Review, Health Affairs, Journal of Occupational Medicine, to list a few. This allows for peer review and a scientific examination of the results of their program.

The on going review process also identifies some of the aspects of the program which were not well utilized. An example is one of their telephonic services, a nurse line. A key learning through this review process was as you put these programs in the work place you need to ensure the offering of multimodality approaches to employees and their families (from face to face, to telephonic, to web based).

There are four words of advice which Dr. Isaac has for other wellness programs. The first and most important is leadership commitment; the support for a program must come from upper and middle management. The second is to meet people needs as they are, and not where you want them to be. Next is to make sure that the people running the program and the people using the program are engaged; as if they are not involved and not using the program it will not be successful no matter how great the quality of the services are. Finally, the management of the program must be outcomes and results oriented, and must have a strategy to succeed for the long term.

CHAPTER 8
Measuring Program Success

Tell the Right Story with Your Program Reporting Processes

By Ronald J. Ozminkowski and Seth Serxner

Introduction

The secret to success in reporting is to tell a credible story about the value of health promotion programs to senior management and other key stakeholders.

In 2011 GfK, a leading independent research firm, surveyed benefits decision makers about what they expect from their health promotion programs.[71] GfK collected web-based survey responses from 403 people working at companies with at least 3,000 employees. These employers offered disease-management programs for asthma, diabetes, coronary artery disease, or other chronic conditions. They also provided wellness programs including health risk appraisal surveys, biometric screening to gather information about body mass, blood pressure, lipid levels, or blood sugar levels and health coaching programs to help deal with problems in these areas.

About 87 percent of the survey respondents said it was important to offer a wide range of health-promotion benefits, and 89 percent said one of their key objectives in doing so was to maximize the productivity of their workforce. Over 80 percent said their major objectives were to reduce health risks, improve quality of life, and reduce healthcare costs. However, more than half said they did not trust the reporting they obtained about these factors.

In addition to the trust issue, over 60 percent of the respondents said getting timely information about program impact on employee health, healthcare costs, and productivity was a major challenge.

The GfK study made it abundantly clear that employers have difficult objectives to achieve and are unsure about the validity of the measurement strategies their program partners are using to monitor progress. With this in mind, we present an approach to ensure stakeholders have the right information to improve the health and productivity of today's workforce.

A Solid Reporting Process

The ability to manage the health and productivity of the workforce requires information about eight issues:

1. Who You Serve: Major characteristics of the workforce influence health status, healthcare utilization, quality of life, and productivity. These characteristics include age, gender, worksite location, job type, full-time or part-time status, union and management status, and the types of health plans that are being utilized.

2. The Health Risks They Have: Health risk appraisal (HRA) surveys and biometric tests can provide an understanding of which behavioral health risks are most important. Linking these survey and test results to information about Who You Serve will show how these risks vary for subgroups of employees. This in turn will influence the variety of strategies that may be needed to improve health and productivity for different groups. Important behavioral health risks include eating, exercise, smoking, drinking, and sleep habits. Key biometric information includes measures of body mass or body fat, blood pressure, blood sugar, and cholesterol levels. This information provides important clues about risks for diabetes, heart disease, stroke, and other major killers.

3. The Health Conditions They Have: Healthcare claims can provide information about the top 10 physical and mental health problems that reduce healthcare productivity and quality of life, and associated costs.[72] The HRA can provide information about history with these conditions, effects on productivity, treatments that might not be found via analyses of claims, and respondents' willingness to better manage these conditions.

4. Operating Metrics for the Programs Used to Manage These Risks and Conditions: Examples of key program operational metrics include:

    a. *Engagement rates*: How many and what percent of employees qualify for each program? How many of these are contacted about it, and how many of those who are contacted actively participate in each program feature? How do these engagement metrics vary according to the

Who You Serve and What Conditions They Have metrics noted above?

b. *Methods of engagement:* What exactly does engagement entail? Are people engaged via face-to-face contacts, telephone calls, or mailed materials? Are email and text messaging used? What about online services? What triggers these and how often are they used? What operational hiccups occur that might cause unexpected spikes or declines in the use of these technologies? What happens behind the scenes – are frequent referrals to medical doctors, social workers, employee assistance programs, nutritionists, or other professionals required and used?

c. *The gaps addressed:* It is not possible to address all health risks or manage every chronic condition. Most program providers prioritize these. Which particular risks and issues most heavily influence health and productivity in your population? What is the relationship between methods of engagement and resolution of these, and how do risks and issues change over time? Your reporting should tell you this.

d. *When engagement ends, and why:* Some people engage until all of their major needs are met, but more likely engagement wanes over time. Some people drop out before reducing all their health risks or closing all relevant care management gaps. Review reasons for case closure and then discuss how to maximize the percentage of people who engage until all major gaps are closed.

5. Quality of Care: Reporting should note what percentages of employees use services in accordance with clinical practice guidelines put forth by the US Preventive Services Task Force[73] and major specialty societies. Reports should note how such utilization varies for similar program participants and non-participants, so that stakeholders can estimate the impact of participation on key quality-of-care metrics.

6. Healthcare Utilization and Expenditures: Most care management programs save money by eliminating unnecessary services or reducing risks so that fewer members need emergency room or inpatient services. Also, better

management of chronic conditions will increase some types of physician visits and pharmaceutical services but reduce other types, so reporting on inpatient, outpatient, emergency room, pharmacy, and ancillary services should track how these are used and the actual payments to providers for them.

7. Productivity-Related Utilization and Expenditures: Research suggests that the largest savings result from program impacts on the productivity of the workforce.2 Let the reporting entity have access to data about absenteeism, short-term disability program services, or other personal-time-off metrics. Allow these data to be linked to metrics from the Who You Serve, Engagement, Quality of Care, and other sections noted above, so differences in productivity-related services can be tracked periodically for varying levels of program engagement and non-engagement. Also, include presenteeism questions on your health risk appraisal survey, and then link the HRA data to program engagement data, so the reporting strategy can help estimate program impact on productivity at work as well.

8. Access to Care, Health Status, and Program Satisfaction: Supplement the metrics above with periodic surveys about health status, access to program services and providers, and satisfaction with their services. Some of these survey questions will pertain to just the programs and cannot be asked of non-participants, but most questions should be worded in a manner that is pertinent to and identical for people who engage in each health promotion program and similar people who do not. Data for both groups of people allows comparisons to be made, providing information about the relative contribution of program activities to these key outcomes.

How Often Reporting Should Be Conducted

Almost half of the respondents to the GfK survey said they did not receive reporting on medical cost savings and productivity improvements often enough. The appropriate time to report the eight categories of information noted above varies by dimension. Information about Who You Serve and The Health Risks and Conditions They Have can usefully be reported annually. These dimensions will not change much unless your workforce is changing due to frequent mergers or reductions in staff or frequent re-organizations. Quarterly reporting, for a year or two, might be useful if you frequently change program vendors or as program utilization grows over time, because different vendors may focus on different subsets of the population and different programs appeal to different types of people.

Information about Operating Metrics should be reviewed at least quarterly, as should most of the Quality of Care, Utilization, Expenditure, and Productivity metrics. Presenteeism metrics can be reviewed annually, as the HRA survey data are reported. Similarly, information about Access to Care, Health Status and Satisfaction can be reported annually.

Transparency, Accuracy, Credibility, and Brevity
Telling the reporting story in a cohesive and credible way is the single most important issue to confront. It will not matter how well programs work if key stakeholders do not believe the reported results. Disbelief will lead to lower funding, less frequent communication, reduced engagement, and lower effectiveness.

Credibility can be enhanced by transparency, accuracy, and collaboration with all major stakeholders. Finding out which metrics are most important to stakeholders is an early key to success. Agreement on metric definitions, followed by open and periodic reviews of computer code, can assure transparency, consistency and accuracy in reporting.

Next, the amount of information needed will depend on the stakeholder. A full examination of all eight areas mentioned above could easily result in hundreds of metrics. Those who manage the health and productivity of the workforce on a day-to-day basis will need all of these metrics at various times during the year. Those in the C-Suite and on the Board of Directors will have much less time for reporting reviews, however, requiring just a five- or ten-minute overview.

To provide that five- or ten-minute overview, a one-page Key Indicator Report or "dashboard" can be generated which includes just the top three or so metrics from each of the eight areas mentioned above. These metrics can be provided for the major groups and programs of interest. Color coding can be used to let stakeholders know if these metrics are within expectation, not within expectation but close, or widely out of the norm. Metrics that are well out of the norm can then be briefly explained.

Finally, notions about norms and expectations imply that stakeholders must collaborate to define normality and discuss their expectations. Some metrics may be deemed so important as to have targets associated with metric values, and contractual performance guarantees that accord with the targets. Other metrics can be tracked over time and discussed as need be, without firm targets or performance guarantees.

Concluding Comments

Best in class reporting about the health and productivity of your workforce should be timely, accurate, credible, and user-friendly. Focusing on the eight areas mentioned here will provide a complete story about the health and productivity levels and needs of the workforce. Frequent, ongoing collaborations between employer staff, other key stakeholders, program vendors, and reporting entities will be required to make sure data are accurate and useful. When that happens, the story that unfolds about the utility of your health and productivity management programs will catch no one by surprise and help you continually enhance the lives of everyone affected.

Key Ideas:

- Employers have difficult objectives to achieve and are unsure about the validity of the measurement strategies their program partners are using to monitor progress

- The ability to manage the health and productivity of the workforce requires information about eight issues:

  - Who you serve (characteristics of he workforce)

  - Their health risks (HRA)

  - Their health conditions (healthcare claims)

  - Operating Metrics

  - Quality of care

  - Health Utilization/Expenditures

  - Productivity-Related Utilization

  - Access to care

- Almost half of the respondents to the GfK survey said they did not receive reporting on medical cost savings and productivity improvements often enough

- Information about Who You Serve and The Health Risks and Conditions They Have can usefully be reported annually

- Quarterly reporting, for a year or two, might be useful if you frequently change program vendors or as program utilization grows over time, because different vendors may focus on different subsets of the population and different programs appeal to different types of people.

- Finding out which metrics are most important to stakeholders is an early key to success. Agreement on metric definitions, followed by open and periodic reviews of computer code, can assure transparency, consistency and accuracy in reporting.

Questions

1. Which of the following is **not** one of the eight information requirements?

   a. Health Risks

   b. Operating metrics

   c. Quality of Care

   d. ROI

2. Finding out the factors stakeholders find important is an early key to success

   a. True

   b. False

3. Agreement on metric definitions will not help in transparency.

   a. True

   b. False

Benchmarking Wellness Programs: How Does Your Program Measure Up?

By Shirley Musich, Ron Ozminkowski, and Frank Bottone, Jr

What is benchmarking?

Benchmarking is a widely used business term describing research that compares one company's business processes to those of other similar or leading companies in the industry. For health management programs, benchmarking may be used to compare program implementation, operations, and outcome metrics. Benchmarking promotes learning from the experiences of others and can help you identify potential areas of concern in your own workforce.

The most desirable benchmarking practices involve comparisons to a recognized industry leader. Leading visionary corporate health management approaches are those taken by Bank of America, Dow Chemical Company, Johnson & Johnson, Union Pacific Railroad, and the California Public Employees Retirement System. Their experiences have been described in several studies. More broadly speaking, benchmark information may be found in the 2004 National Worksite Health Promotion Survey data.[74]

Programs evolve rapidly over time and information that is more than just a few years old may have less value than information obtained more recently. We use an ever-evolving dataset for such comparisons. Metrics obtained from these data may help you focus on changes needed to improve your program early on, saving time and resources.

Which programs are most amenable to benchmarking?

One of the reasons benchmarking is such a common and useful practice is that virtually any business process or performance metric is amenable to benchmarking. If leading companies or existing survey data are less compelling for your particular use, benchmarking with reference to similar companies can help to reduce the number of potentially confounding variables that might influence health or productivity outcomes of interest. Those confounding variables might include industry type, size of the organization, geographic location of the employees, demographic characteristics, and so on. By holding these relatively constant, comparisons of program participation rates, changes in health risks and healthcare expenditures over time, and comparisons of productivity-related metrics can be made with a fair degree of confidence.

Some of the more common health management program components amenable to benchmarking include health risk appraisal (HRA) survey programs and telephone-based lifestyle coaching and disease management programs. These programs are typically contracted to external vendors who may serve many of your benchmarking peers. Benchmarking your experiences to those of other companies can help determine if your communication processes, program participation rates, health risk patterns, and health and productivity outcomes seem in line with your peers.

Where can you find benchmarks?

Recent information about what to expect from health management programs is not always readily available. One may query program vendors for information about their books of business, but vendors have a strong financial incentive to provide information from the more positive side of their experiences.

The scientific literature can provide another source of information about program designs and effectiveness. For example, reviews of return on investment from wellness and disease management programs have been published by Chapman[75] and Goetzel et al.,[76] respectively. Baicker et al.[77] offer a more recent review of corporate wellness programs. These reviews are likely to represent the best experiences observed in the industry, however, and the authors have acknowledged that less positive findings are less likely to be published. Exemplary programs may show returns of three or more dollars saved per dollar spent on health management. If there is a strong desire to learn which returns are typical rather than exemplary, published studies may be of less interest.

Third-party evaluators may have access to book-of-business benchmarks that show a broader range of experiences. We have analyzed a variety of health management programs for ten employer clients in the last two years. These clients work in the energy, health, technology, transportation, and financial services industries. They range in size from roughly 9,000 to 120,000 employees, with a median of about 21,000 workers. These clients range from 24 percent to 85 percent male employees, with a median age of about 42 years. Five of these clients implemented their programs for the first time in 2005, and 89 percent of the programs we studied were offered to employees and their spouses.

Our clients also vary according to the number of risk assessment, coaching, and disease management program components they offer. Most include HRA, lifestyle coaching, and disease management programs, but only a few have onsite fitness centers or medical clinics. With their permission, we present information on their health management program participation rates, changes in health risks over time, changes in healthcare expenditures associated with changes in risk, and return on investment in their wellness and disease management programs.

Participation rates and incentives

Information about program participation rates provides an early indicator of how a health management program is functioning. Participation rates depend on marketing and communication strategies, ease of access to program services, and the use of incentives to motivate participation. Incentives can be structured as cash or other payouts, free or reduced prices for merchandise, prizes for competitions designed to increase participation, reductions in healthcare premiums or other out of pocket requirements, or in other ways. Incentives can help increase participation in health management programs if sustained year over year. If incentives are withdrawn, however, participation rates may drop precipitously.

Companies differ in their thoughts about using incentives. Some use incentives frequently, while others do not use them at all. When used, incentives most often target programs that every employee can use (for example, the HRA survey that is designed to find candidates for other wellness, coaching, or disease management programs). Among our ten clients, incentives range from $50 to $100, payable upon documented participation. Participation rates for their HRA programs varied from 12 percent to 81 percent of eligible employees or spouses. When installed for the first time, incentives were associated with participation rates that grew from about 10 percent to 20 percent to about 50 percent to 80 percent.

In contrast to HRA programs which are designed for entire working populations, lifestyle coaching programs typically target high risk individuals such as smokers, heavy drinkers, poor exercisers, those with nutrition problems, and those who are overweight or obese. Disease management programs are typically limited to those with selected chronic conditions such as diabetes, coronary artery disease, congestive heart failure, depression, or musculoskeletal (back) problems. Among our clients, incentives to encourage enrollment or to complete programs were used less often for these programs. Participation rates among those eligible for lifestyle coaching and disease management programs range from 8 percent to 81 percent, with medians of 41 percent for lifestyle coaching and 30 percent for disease management programs.

What about health outcomes?

Health outcomes are typically measured via the health risk appraisal survey and/or biometric testing of blood pressure, blood sugar levels, cholesterol levels, and body mass index (BMI). Different HRAs may target different sets of health risks, but health risks known to be disease predictors are measured on almost all HRAs. These include physical inactivity, stress, blood pressure, cholesterol, smoking, and BMI. Other risks that are commonly measured relate to poor eating habits, depression, safety belt use, and measures of job or life satisfaction.

The scientific literature shows a strong positive relationship between the number of risks that are observed and medical and pharmaceutical expenditures. Examples include studies by Musich and Edington.[78,79] Our clients vary on how they characterize their populations in terms of these risks. For example, some consider those with 0 or 1 risk to be at low overall risk, while others consider those with 0 to 2 risks to be at low overall risk. In our benchmarking database, roughly one-fifth of the HRA participants are at low overall risk, about two-fifths are at medium overall risk (i.e., they had 2, 3, or 4 individual risk factors), and the remaining two-fifths are considered to be high overall risks because they have more than 4 or 5 individual health risks.

Changes in the prevalence of individual health risks and health status can be documented using repeat HRA participation. In our experience, about half of those who complete a baseline HRA opt to complete another one a year or so later. Stronger incentive structures can drive repeat percentages up to 60 percent to 80 percent. Higher participation in baseline and repeat HRAs provides more information on the target population. Within one year, there should be evidence that selected health risks have begun to improve. Poor nutrition and physical inactivity are examples of health risks that can demonstrate significant improvements in a relatively short time, especially with risk-specific programming and communication strategies.

The ultimate goal of health management programs is to enable participants to maintain or improve their health and productivity. Low risk individuals typically have the lowest medical and productivity-related costs. They also have the lowest probability of developing chronic diseases and enjoy the highest quality of life. Unfortunately, achieving decreases in risk over time is difficult and more people tend to increase rather than reduce health risks as they age. The programs we analyzed showed minimal long-term risk improvement. However, for many people even maintaining risk status over time can be considered positive.

Cost outcomes or return on investment?

The scientific literature indicates that changes in medical and productivity costs can follow changes in health risks: costs are observed to decrease when risks decrease and to increase when risks increase.[6,80] Maximizing cost savings thus requires risk reduction strategies (to reduce costs as risk are reduced) and risk maintenance strategies (to prevent cost increases by preventing risk increases).

Comprehensive health management programs start with the HRA and biometric screening to assess risks, then offer easy access to fitness centers or other exercise opportunities and lifestyle coaching to manage health risks. Comprehensive programs will also offer disease management programs for selected chronic conditions. In our experience applying rigorous statistical analyses to estimate return on investment (ROI) for these programs, ROI estimates have remained remarkably consistent for well-managed programs. Such programs yielded savings of about $2 for every dollar invested. Generally, however, ROI estimates were not positive in the first program year and sometimes not even in the second year.

HRA surveys are relatively inexpensive to apply, so efforts devoted to these tend to break even more quickly. Lifestyle coaching and disease management programs require more sophisticated expertise and are more costly to apply. Among our clients, lifestyle coaching and disease management programs generally did not offer a positive ROI until at least the second or third year; others have found this as well.[3] A key challenge is to make programming attractive enough and to maintain motivation long enough to keep people enrolled. So far sustaining enrollment has been difficult; very few people remained in these programs for longer than a year or two.

Conclusions

A review of key benchmarks can be used by employers to set expectations for their health management programs. The earlier in the process this is done, the better-informed program managers will be. To ensure the most comprehensive and valid comparisons, key metrics to be tracked include participation rates, health risks, changes in health risks over time, medical and productivity-related expenditures, and return on investment. Knowing these will make it easier to present the business case for health management to senior executives year after year. The business case can be greatly facilitated by incorporating benchmarks from leading companies or others one wishes to emulate.

The search for benchmarks is a fluid process. The scientific literature is helpful in establishing benchmarks from visionary employers who have used sophisticated design, development, marketing, communication, implementation, and evaluation strategies to apply leading programs. The information to be obtained from the published literature is not typical though, because there is little incentive to publish poor results. The ten-client benchmarks noted herein are admittedly a small slice of a big industry pie, but they are timely and probably more typical than can easily be found from other publicly available sources. To help others evaluate their wellness programs, we encourage you to make your findings public. As employers increasingly disseminate and discuss their findings, the knowledge required to improve program outcomes will grow for everyone, and the health and productivity of the U.S. workforce will improve along the way.

Key Ideas

- Benchmarking is a widely used business term describing research that compares one company's business processes to those of other similar or leading companies in the industry.

- Some of the more common health management program

components amenable to benchmarking include health risk appraisal (HRA) survey programs and telephone-based lifestyle coaching and disease management programs. These programs are typically contracted to external vendors who may serve many of your benchmarking peers.

- Information about program participation rates provides an early indicator of how a health management program is functioning

- A review of key benchmarks can be used by employers to set expectations for their health management programs. The earlier in the process this is done, the better-informed program managers will be.

Questions

1. How does benchmarking work?

    a. One company adopts the procedures of a more successful company

    b. One company compares their program to similar or company in the industry

    c. One company compares their program to company with a similar size in another industry

    d. None of the above

2. What is a good early indicator of a how a health management program is functioning?

    a. Weight Loss

    b. HRA responses

    c. Participation rates

    d. ROI

3. A review of key benchmarks can be used by employers to set expectations for their health management programs. The earlier in the process this is done, the better-informed program managers will be.

    a. True

    b. False

The Value of Happiness: The Invisible Benchmarking Metric

By Les C. Meyer

Overview

Benchmarking thought leaders are taking aim at the value of happiness. Better health outcomes are well within reach based on a few favorable developments, but the results won't be truly meaningful unless there's a greater realization of the indisputable linkages between a healthy work force, the value of happiness and a healthy bottom line.

Understanding the value of happiness through traditional benchmarking systems is a challenge. It's hard enough to manage people you can see, visualizing and managing workforce happiness metrics invisible to the eye can seem like an unachievable benchmarking task.

There's no disputing the street value of organization (workplace) health "bend-the-trend" benchmarking systems or unique dashboarding capabilities that represent the next frontier in helping employers identify performance effectiveness metrics aimed to significantly improve clinical outcomes and workforce wellbeing. These metrics include overall labor costs, new (and retained) business revenue stream overflows, and employee and customer satisfaction leading to significantly better business results. Be that as it may, business leaders around the globe are creating a new economic paradigm based on happiness and wellbeing in their quest to make the invisible, visible in next generation of benchmarking systems designed to continuously transform their business models to create customer value, improve the bottom line and the way adaptive leaders' measure happiness as a metric for better workforce living and corporate wellbeing.

It is the purpose of this chapter to provide a context for "the value of happiness" and a central tenet related to workforce wellbeing program value and what's important to workers: better health, financial security and life fulfillment. We will profile global research interests in the value of happiness and wellbeing. In addition, the chapter will explore several relevant interconnected definitions of "health, health promotion and happiness" and better understand how the three may relate to each other. The chapter will then focus on recent evidence-based "happiness" research and lessons learned related to the value of happiness in life. Finally, the chapter will end detailing the key elements of "happiness test" and then discuss the challenge and reality of the invisible (happiness) benchmarking metric designed to create thriving wellbeing people and improve the global economic wellbeing and quality of life of stakeholders.

The Value of Happiness at Work

Value is the glue that galvanizes the workforce and better aligns the interests of each organization's leadership with its employees. The central tenet of a robust organization (workplace) health and advanced workforce wellbeing program is value. The receivers (employees) of the organization's health promotion, workforce wellbeing program must value what they expect to get in exchange to do the work. Most savvy employees expect continuous value realization from their employer though a team-based, i.e., mutually beneficial workplace experience that helps their company's employees to achieve: better health, financial security and life fulfillment.[1, 2]

Are "happy" workforces in fact more productive? Emerging research from neuroscience, psychology, and economics clearly establishes a distinct link between thriving workforce wellbeing and better business performance. The value of happiness is a key driver for sustaining workforce living achievements and corporate wellbeing results. Research shows that happy employees are more motivated, loyal and engaged at work.[3] Happy employees have, on average, 31 percent higher productivity; their sales are 37 percent higher; their creativity is three times higher.[4]

Employees are vital human capital assets of every organization. Across industries and job types, research also shows that people who fit our description of thriving demonstrated 16 percent better overall performance (as reported by their managers) and 125 percent less burnout (self-reported) than their peers. They were 32 percent more committed to the organization and 46 percent more satisfied with their jobs. They also missed much less work and reported significantly fewer doctor visits, which meant healthcare savings and less lost time for the company.[5] "Happiness can have an impact at both the company and the country level. And the movement to measure national wellbeing on factors other than GDP could be game changing: As we know, what gets measured gets managed. We've learned a lot about how to make people happy. We'd be stupid not to use that knowledge." [6]

The value of happiness and wellbeing is also taking on new meaning around the world.[7] The United Nations recently met and held a high level meeting for **"Wellbeing and Happiness: Defining a New Economic Paradigm."** Global leaders want wellbeing — not gross national product — to guide economic decisions. The recent UN meeting began with an address by Prime Minister Jigmi Thinley of Bhutan, where the government tracks the nation's **"Gross National Happiness."** [8] The Gross National Happiness Index (GNHI) was designed in an attempt to define an indicator about happy people that measures quality of life or social progress in more holistic and psychological terms than only the economic indicator of gross domestic product (GDP). The concept of GNHI has often been explained and classified into nine domains in order to create widespread understanding of GNHI and to reflect the holistic range of GNHI values. The nine domains are: psychological wellbeing, health, education, time use, cultural diversity and resilience, good governance, community vitality, ecological diversity and resilience, and living standards.[9]

"Imagine you open the paper tomorrow, and the headlines are not about the "sluggish economy," but our nation's quality of life. You turn to the business section, and find not just information about a certain company's profitability, but also about its impact on community health and employee wellbeing," states BZ Riger, Staff Writer, The 2012 Scenario.

Absent from the UN meeting were officials from the United States. But that does not reflect that nothing is happening in the USA. The Department of Health and Human Services also recently convened a panel of experts in psychology and economics to determine relevant ways to reliably measure subjective wellbeing — a move toward government tracking and analysis of happiness statistics. However, some U.S. cities are beat HHS officials to the punch, using a survey instrument developed by **"The Happiness Initiative,"** a U.S.-based nonprofit, which offers a subjective metric for happiness that can be used at a personal or neighborhood level.[10]

In Nevada City, CA, the city council members are using the happiness index to gather data about citizen's needs and preferences for a potential land development project. In Eau Claire, WI, the city's government leaders are working with a local chamber of commerce, state university, boys and girls club, library, and other organizations to gather information and convene town hall meetings where citizens can explore ways to promote individual happiness and quality of life.

In St. Paul, MN, **LaborCare Health and Benefits Fair** is an annual free event for families that features engaging activities and information that helps union members and attendees learn about and embrace lifestyle choices that will help them live healthier and more satisfying lives. It is the largest labor health fair in the United States. The LaborCare Health and Benefits Fair is a collaborative effort of Medica and six Taft-Hartley Health and Welfare Funds, including Minnesota Laborers Health and Welfare Fund, Twin City Pipe Trades Service Association, Minnesota and North Dakota Bricklayers and Allied Craft Workers Health Fund, Minnesota Cement Masons Health and Welfare Fund, Rochester Plumbers and Steamfitters Local 6 Health and Welfare Fund, and The St. Paul Electrical Workers. The Minnesota heath and benefits fair appears to raise the bar on community-based, collective impact initiatives designed to sustain health promotion goals, inspire total wellbeing (happiness) objectives and support quality of life activities for union workers and their family members.

Dan Buettner, founder and Chief Executive Officer of **Blue Zones, LLC** in Minneapolis, MN has launched "the best happiness test on the Internet," created **"Blue Zone Cities"** in California and Minnesota and continues to work with **Gallup, The World Values Survey and the World Data Base on Happiness.** Mr. Buettner has traveled the globe as a *National Geographic* writer to uncover the best strategies for longevity and happiness. Mr. Buettner's book **Blue Zones —** identifies places where people have the greatest life expectancy and where more people reach age 100 than anywhere else.[11] In the book **Thrive: Unlocking the Secrets of Happiness** — Mr. Buettner outlines how science shows that where we live – not education, marital status or wealth – is the biggest, controllable factor that determines our happiness.[12]

Definitions of Health, Health Promotion and Happiness

It's no secret that happiness is not just about wellbeing, being wealthy or successful. Nor is it confined to the concept of physical health, health promotion or wellness. **The fact of the matter is that happiness entails an interdependent approach to work-life wellbeing achievement:** training the mind in the course of creative imagination expression, and continuation of positive thoughts, and the synergistic transforming of one's self whereby: "the whole is greater than the sum of its parts" to achieve self-connection.

1. Definition of Health

The Institute of Medicine of the National Academies, State of the USA Health Indicators, Letter Report, Committee on the State of the USA Health Indicators embraces a broad definition of health as that proposed by the **World Health Organization** (WHO): "Health is the state of complete physical, mental and social wellbeing and not merely the absence of disease or infirmity" and the "extent to which an individual or group is able to realize aspirations and satisfy needs, and to change or cope with the environment. **Health is a resource for everyday life, not the objective of living; it is a positive concept, emphasizing social and personal resources as well as physical capabilities"** [13]

2. Definition of Health Promotion

Health Promotion is **the art and science of helping people discover the synergies between their core passions and optimal health, enhancing their motivation to strive for optimal health, and supporting them in changing their lifestyle to move toward a state of optimal health.** Optimal health is a dynamic balance of physical, emotional, social, spiritual, and intellectual health. Lifestyle change can be facilitated through a combination of learning experiences that enhance awareness, increase motivation, and build skills and, most important, through the creation of opportunities that open access to environments that make positive health practices the easiest choice. [14]

In addition, health promotion has been defined by the WHO as "the process of enabling people to increase control over their health and its determinants, and thereby improve their health". [15]

3. Definition of Happiness

The value of happiness in the workplace is based on creating synergistic systems that build, organize, inspire, deploy, enable, measure and reward people who maximize their skills and ability to thrive.

"**Happiness** is a mental or emotional state of wellbeing character-ized by positive or pleasant emotions ranging from contentment to intense joy. A variety of biological, psychological, religious, and philosophical approaches have striven to define happiness and identify its sources. Various research groups, including Positive psychology, endeavor to apply the scientific method to answer questions about what "happiness" is, and how we might attain it," according to Wikipedia. [16]

"To transform the conversation one needs to redefine health from seeing health as not only the absence of disease but to a more inclu-sive concept of health as vitality, energy and positive thoughts," states Dee W. Edington, Ph.D, Founder, Edington Associates LLC In the past decades we have focused too much on the cost containment of healthcare. Collective impact initiative leaders now need to broaden their focus also to include the happiness of the individual and total value of a healthy person. "Health is more than just the health of an individual but also the health of the population and more than just getting individual participation in healthy behaviors but also in engaging populations in total positive engagement. Finally we must enhance our focus from individual behavioral change to popula-tion health within a culture where healthy wellbeing is held in high esteem," further states Edington.

Happiness is a result of our actions. "It is the human mind that translates the outer conditions into either genuine happiness or discontent. It is the mind that we deal with from morning until evening; it is the mind that can be our best friend, our worst enemy; so we should not underestimate the power of mind to conjure happi-ness or suffering. This is not just a luxury; this is not just happiness 'lite' – this is the quality of every moment of our life," according to Buddhist monk Matthieu Ricard and author of the book **Happiness: A Guide to Developing Life's Most Important Skill.** [17]

Wellbeing is a deep sense of personal serenity and fulfillment. In a recent talk at **Ted.com,** Ricard stated that instead of trying to define happiness, we should call it wellbeing — not merely a pleasurable sensation, rather a deep sense of serenity and fulfillment. When taken literally, wellbeing is actually a state of being, not just a fleet-ing emotion. [18]

Ricard further stated, "that very often in our quest for happiness, we look outside. We think that if we could gather this and that - if we could have everything that we need to be happy - then we would be happy. However, our control over the outer world is limited, temporary, and often illusory. So what if one of the things we think we need in order to be happy is missing? Then it all collapses."

"It appears that true happiness is a measurement of two different types of happiness: **Remembered happiness** and **experienced happiness**," further states Buettner. **1) Remembered happiness** is how we think about ourselves overall. It's how we answer the question, "Am I happy in life?" It's how we remember our vacations, our years in high school, holidays with the family, or the early years of life with kids, our divorce, or our work history. It's more of a "big picture" perspective on our state of happiness. **2) Experienced happiness** is very different, but equally important. Imagine someone asks you randomly throughout the day what you're doing and how happy you are at that second. Experienced happiness is the moments of joy, bliss, relief, laughter you have throughout the day. [19]

Lessons Learned: The Value of Happiness
Cracking the code on the value of happiness requires a basic understanding of what inspires, motivates, retains and sustains people to better understand their barriers to happiness and optimal health. The key for team leaders is taking personal responsibility for maintaining one's health, as well as embracing healthy attitudes and a culture of health achievement with their associates.

According to the January-February 2012 issue in *Harvard Business Review* entitled: **The Value of Happiness,** outlined below is a synopsis of the lessons learned that will help innovative organizations focus on better ways to fine-tune their approaches to identify high-value workforce wellbeing performance effectiveness metrics within existing benchmarking and dashboarding systems aimed to significantly improve clinical outcomes, workforce wellbeing and achieve better business results: [20, 21]

1. Much of the research confirms things we've always suspected. For example, in general people who are in good romantic relationships are happier than those who aren't. Healthy people are happier than sick people. People who participate

in their churches are happier than those who don't. Rich people are happier than poor people. And so on.

2. Why do events have such a fleeting effect on happiness? One reason is that people are good at synthesizing happiness—at finding silver linings. As a result, they usually end up happier than they expect after almost any kind of trauma or tragedy.

    a. One of the most reliable findings of the happiness studies is that we do not have to go running to a therapist every time our shoelaces break. We have a remarkable ability to make the best of things. Most people are more resilient than they realize.

3. Aren't they deluding themselves? Isn't real happiness better than synthetic happiness?

    a. Let's be careful with terms. Nylon is real; it's just not natural. Synthetic happiness is perfectly real; it's just man-made. Synthetic happiness is what we produce when we don't get what we want, and natural happiness is what we experience when we do. They have different origins, but they are not necessarily different in terms of how they feel. One is not obviously better than the other.

4. Is being happy always desirable? Look at all the unhappy creative geniuses—Beethoven, van Gogh, Hemingway. Doesn't a certain amount of unhappiness spur good performance?

    a. Nonsense! Everyone can think of a historical example of someone who was both miserable and creative, but that doesn't mean misery generally promotes creativity

5. Many managers would say that contented people aren't the most productive employees, so you want to keep people a little uncomfortable, maybe a little anxious, about their jobs.

    a. Managers who collect data instead of relying on intuition don't say that. I know of no data showing that anxious, fearful employees are more creative or productive

6. So challenge makes people happy. What else do we know now about the sources of happiness?

    If I had to summarize all the scientific literature on the causes of human happiness in one word, that word would be "social."

We are by far the most social species on Earth. Even ants have nothing on us. If I wanted to predict your happiness, and I could know only one thing about you, I wouldn't want to know your gender, religion, health, or income. I'd want to know about your social network—about your friends and family and the strength of your bonds with them.

7. Beyond having rich networks, what makes us happy day today?

    a. The psychologist Ed Diener had a key finding. He essentially shows that the frequency of your positive experiences is a much better predictor of your happiness than is the intensity of your positive experiences. When we think about what would make us happy, we tend to think of intense events—going on a date with a movie star, winning a Pulitzer, buying a yacht.

8. What are those little things we can do to increase our happiness?

    a. They won't surprise you any more than "eat less and exercise more" does. The main things are to commit to some simple behaviors—meditating, exercising, getting enough sleep—and to practice altruism. One of the most selfish things you can do is help others.

9. If there's no secret, what's left to study?

    a. There's no shortage of questions. For decades psychologists and economists have been asking, "Who's happy? The rich? The poor? The young? The old?" The best we could do was divide people into groups, survey them once or maybe twice, and try to determine if the people in one group were, on average, happier than those in the others. The tools we used were pretty blunt instruments. But now millions of people are carrying little computers in their pockets—smartphones—and this allows us to collect data in real time from huge numbers of people about what they are doing and feeling from moment to moment. That's never been possible before.

10. During the research, Matt Killingsworth, built an experience-sampling application called "Track Your Happiness." He

follows more than 15,000 people by iPhone, querying them several times a day about their activities and emotional states. Are they at home? On a bus? Watching television? Praying? How are they feeling? What are they thinking about? With this technology, Matt's beginning to answer a much better question than the one we've been asking for decades. Instead of asking who is happy, he can ask when they are happy. He doesn't get the answer by asking, "When are you happy?" — Because frankly, people don't know. He gets it by tracking people over days, months, and years and measuring what they are doing and how happy they are while they are doing it. I think this kind of technology is about to revolutionize our understanding of daily emotions and human wellbeing.

Happiness — The Reality of The Invisible Benchmarking Metric

Corporate profits are essential. But for measuring the value of happiness in current benchmarking systems business tools is a challenge. As everyone in business knows, you manage what you measure.

So although the creation of the invisible value of happiness metric may seem a little airy, the thought is growing credibility in important business circles and could give it a real impact on boosting growth, productivity, profits and competitive advantage. And the happiness effort in some C-Suites is gaining momentum. So it's worth exploring where movement is coming from and where it might be headed.

Nonetheless, human performance thought leaders and behaviorists maintain their views on the "science of high performance" and the inextricable link to health, health promotion, happiness, workforce performance and the interconnectedness to high-value workforce wellbeing. "In a corporate environment that is changing at warp speed, performing consistently at high levels is more difficult and more necessary than ever. Narrow interventions simply aren't sufficient anymore. Companies can't afford to address their employees' cognitive capacities while ignoring their physical, emotional, and spiritual wellbeing," state Jim Loehr and Tony Schwartz, co-authors, "The Making of a Corporate Athlete."[22]

So what might a reasonable individual "happiness" benchmarking metric look like? For simplicity sake, and a starting point for business executives to begin to explore the potential creation of "happiness" benchmarking methods and innovations, we suggest benchmarking and dashboarding specialists take on the **Blue Zones True Happiness® Test** online as a starting point of reference. **The True Happiness® Test** will cover: **A.** How you remember your life; **B.** How you experience your life; and **C.** The effect of your environment.[23] Listed below are the happiness test question areas of concentration **1) Your Background; 2) Life Satisfaction; 3) Remembered Self-Image; 4) Experienced Emotion and 5) Circumstances & Environment.** To access and complete the **True Happiness® Test** and compile and obtain your confidential results via the Internet by going to: http://apps.bluezones.com/happiness/compass.php

The only way for employees to become world-class performers who provide a clear productive advantage for their organization's is if they're able to function at their highest possible level while sustaining their lifetime personal goals for better health, happiness, financial security and life fulfillment.

"On the playing field or in the boardroom, high performance depends as much on how people renew and recover energy as on how they expend it, on how they manage their lives as much as on how they manage their work. When people feel strong and resilient – physically, mentally, emotionally, and spiritually – they perform better, with more passion, for longer. They win, their families win, and the corporations that employ them win," further state Loehr and Schwartz.

A healthier, happier workforce will eventually lead to a healthier bottom line at a time when employee healthcare benefits represent one of the biggest costs of doing business. Savvy benchmarking thought leaders understand and appreciate the value of happiness. Better health outcomes are indeed within reach but the results won't be truly meaningful unless there's a greater realization amongst business leaders of the indisputable linkages between a healthy work force, the value of happiness and a healthy bottom line. Measuring the value of happiness makes sense. Let's roll-up our sleeves and go to work!

References

1   Meyer L. Editor's inbox: Reader offers three-pronged strategy to improving health. Employee Benefit Adviser, February 2010.

2   Yeager K, Meyer L, The Link Between Employee Engagement Plus Health-Care Cost Savings, WorkSpan Magazine,

July 2010

3   Amabile T, Kramer S, Do Happier People Work Harder? New York Times, September 3, 2011

4   Schulte E, The Weigh-In: What's The Best Way To Motivate Your Employees? Fast Company, January 24, 2012

5   Spreitzer G, Porath C, Creating Sustainable Performance, The Value of Happiness, Harvard Business Review, Jan-Feb, 2012

6   Ignatius A, Spotlight: The Happiness Factor, The Value of Happiness, Harvard Business Review, Jan-Feb, 2012

7   Thinley J, Happiness and wellbeing: Defining a new economic paradigm, United Nations Development Programme, April 2, 2012

8   Ura K, Alkire S, Zangmo T, Wangdi K, A Short Guide to Gross National Happiness Index, The Centre for Bhutan Studies, February 2012,

9   http://www.grossnationalhappiness.com/9-domains/ (accessed August 1, 2012)

10   http://www.happycounts.org/ (accessed August 15, 2012)

11   Buettner D, The Blue Zones: Lessons for Living Longer from the People Who've Lived the Longest, Amazon, April 21, 2009

12   Buettner D, Thrive: Finding Happiness The Blue Zones Way, Amazon, October 19, 2010

13   IOM (Institute of Medicine). 2009. State of the USA Health Indicators: Letter Report. Washington, DC: The National Academies Press.

14   http://www.healthpromotionjournal.com/ (accessed August 1, 2012)

15   http://en.wikipedia.org/wiki/Health_promotion (accessed August 15, 2012)

16   http://en.wikipedia.org/wiki/Happiness (accessed September 1, 2012)

17   Ricard M, Happiness: A Guide to Developing Life's Most Important Skill, Amazon, April 12, 2006

18   http://www.ted.com/talks/matthieu_ricard_on_the_habits_of_happiness.html (accessed September 3, 2012)

19   http://www.bluezones.com/live-happier/true-happiness/ (accessed August 15, 2012)

20   Gilbert D, Morse M, The Science Behind the Smile, The Value of Happiness, Harvard Business Review, Jan-Feb, 2012

21   Fox J, The Economics of Wellbeing, The Value of Happiness, Harvard Business Review, Jan-Feb, 2012

22   Loehr J, Schwartz T, The Making of a Corporate Athlete, Harvard Business Review, Jan 2001; pp. 120-128

23   http://apps.bluezones.com/happiness/ (accessed September 3, 2012)

Key Ideas

- The value of happiness is a key driver for sustaining workforce living achievements and corporate wellbeing results. Research shows that happy employees are more motivated, loyal and engaged at work. Happy employees have, on average, 31 percent higher productivity; their sales are 37 percent higher; their creativity is three times higher.

- Most savvy employees expect continuous value realization from their employer though a team-based, i.e., mutually beneficial workplace experience that helps their company's employees to achieve: better health, financial security and life fulfillment.

- It's no secret that happiness is not just about wellbeing, being wealthy or successful. Nor is it confined to the concept of physical health, health promotion or wellness. The fact of the matter is that happiness entails an interdependent approach to work-life wellbeing achievement: training the mind in the course of creative imagination expression, and continuation of positive thoughts, and the synergistic transforming of one's self whereby: "the whole is greater than the sum of its parts" to achieve self-connection.

- Value is the glue that galvanizes the workforce and better aligns the interests of each organization's leadership with its employees. The central tenet of a robust organization (workplace) health and advanced workforce wellbeing program is value.

Questions:

1. Research shows that "happy" employees achieve:

   A. 31 percent higher productivity

   B. Sales are 37 percent higher

   C. 125 percent less burnout than their peers

   D. Creativity is three time higher

   E. 46 percent more satisfied with their jobs

   F. All of the above

2. What do employees expect to receive in exchange for the work they do?

   A. Better health,

   B. Financial security

   C. Life fulfillment

   D. All off the above

   E. None of the above

3. There are three relevant interconnected definitions discussed in the chapter that clearly relate to each other. Select the three:

   A. Health

   B. Health Promotion

   C. Disease Management

D. Happiness

E. Chronic Care Management

4. The central tenet of a robust organization (workplace) health and advanced workforce wellbeing program is "value."

A. True

B. False

5. Happiness entails an interdependent approach to work-life wellbeing achievement: training the mind in the course of creative imagination expression, and continuation of positive thoughts, and the synergistic transforming of one's self whereby: "the whole is greater than the sum of its parts" to achieve self-connection.

A. True

B. False

A Discussion of ROI
By Mark Bloomberg

1. Introduction

No employer can afford to spend their limited funds on programs that do not result in a positive return on investment (ROI). Yet when it comes to expenditures for healthcare-related programs, most employers have little insight as to how an accurate ROI should be structured. This is due to a lack of understanding of the many varied and disparate components of a company's medical costs and how such programs fit, or do not fit, into a broad strategic approach to controlling these expenses.

2. Definition of ROI

The ROI is a calculation that looks at what a specific activity or set of activities actually costs to produce and compares that to the benefits achieved from those activities. An ROI is normally expressed in terms of the ratio of the dollars saved or earned as compared to those spent to achieve the savings or earnings. It is important to remember to deduct the actual costs of the program itself from the dollars saved or earned. For example, if an employer spends $500,000 on a new program that saves the firm $1,500,000, then the program netted $1,000,000 ($1,500,000 minus the program costs of $500,000). Dividing that net of $1,000,000 by the program costs of $500,000 yields an ROI of 2:1, or $2 saved/earned for every $1 spent.

While the formula to calculate an ROI may be straightforward, how to determine what elements to include in cost assessments can be quite challenging. Depending on one's point of view, some elements may be critical to include in the ROI calculation while others may be less so. This flexibility in selecting the cost elements to include in an ROI calculation has a potential downside as it can be manipulated to suit the user's purpose, often creating different results. When evaluating an ROI, make sure you understand what inputs were used and why they were selected.

For example, if a firm spends $250,000 for a disease management program to address the needs of diabetic employees, how should it measure the benefits of that program? Within the arena of assessing medical costs, there is often the limitation of the inability to calculate a "non-event." In the diabetic disease management program above, how does one account for the fact that a diabetic may have a bad year and incur serious medical costs that were not going to be repeated the following year no matter what was done? Are such "savings" to be considered benefits of the program?

3. Using an Improved Definition of ROI

While the actual costs of medical care can usually be quantified, a valid ROI calculation needs to include many elements that can easily be overlooked and may be less readily available. Serious consideration must be given to what elements are included in the ROI formula and will have a potentially large impact on how management can assess the value to be gained of the required investment.

Dollars expended to provide a program are not the only consideration when calculating an ROI for that program. It is also important to consider the time it takes to accomplish one's goals, as well as the risks of not achieving those goals. This is especially critical in the area of medical costs because there is ample evidence that prevention does pay itself back many times over when looked at over a term of several or more years.

4. Impact of Population Health Interventions

American consumers typically only receive about half of recommended medical care processes.[81]

Addressing the health of your work force can have a very substantial impact on disease progression and reduction in morbidity/mortality over the long term. Every one of your employees will at any point in time fall into one of these five population health buckets: The Well; The At Risk; The Acutely Ill; The Chronically Ill; and The Catastrophically Ill.

The long-term results and accumulated benefits from a population health approach accrue in the retention of employees within, or their movement back toward, the healthier buckets; i.e. keeping people well, reducing their risk and preventing their advancement to the presence of chronic disease or catastrophic illness. While this can be accomplished, and indeed has been shown to work well in those employers who have succeeded in doing so[82,83,84], it requires a long-term, strategic focus and is not achieved by the usual limited and short-term approaches taken by most employers. What is missing is the leadership commitment and knowledge to transform a piece-meal mix of wellness services to an integrated development of a culture of health within the work environment.

5. Impact of Culture of Health on HC costs

An organizational culture consists of shared fundamental assumptions and a common ideology that explains why the members of a group think, feel and behave as they do. A culture of health is therefore how a group collectively thinks, feels and behaves about health and not just their own health, but that of the entire group. Group members sincerely care about and work to promote the health of their colleagues. In this way, a culture of health is directly analogous to a work place culture of safety. When a culture of safety is in place, workers look out for each other and are constantly aware of the impact specific actions taken by them and/or their co-workers may have on the overall safety of the work force. A worker will quickly step up and point out a potential safety issue, e.g.: "Sue, you forgot to put on your eye protection." Similarly, when a culture of health is in place, workers look out for each other and are constantly aware of the impact specific actions taken by them and/or their co-workers may have on the overall health status of the work force. Co-workers coach and support each other in their efforts to make better choices as regards achieving a healthier lifestyle whether their selection of foods, opportunities to exercise together, attending smoking cessation classes, diabetes educational sessions, etc.

Over several years, a culture of health recruits more and more workers into efforts to stay healthy and/or reduce their existing risk factors. This results in the gradual movement of the work force into those healthier buckets of the population health spectrum. You will never convince every worker to address his health and lifestyle issues, but you do not need to do so to reap substantial benefits from these programs. The result of such movement is overall better health outcomes and these directly impact the usual medical costs, both direct and indirect, incurred by the employer. We will next explore exactly how that happens.

Beyond the dollars spent on medical costs, however, there are other, less tangible benefits to a company when its employees are healthy. Fewer diabetics mean fewer diabetic complications such as blindness, amputations and kidney failure. These create larger societal benefits and, as an important member of the local community, the employer who creates a healthier work force is making a serious contribution to the overall health of that community.

6. Impact on Medical Costs

Direct medical costs, what is paid for actual healthcare services, represent about 24 percent of the health-related costs borne by the typical employer.[85] The fact that this number is so low is often a surprise to management and poses a serious limitation to understanding the potential ROI of efforts to improve the health of the work force. While efforts to improve employees' health do take time and are variably effective on the individual employee, a constant and pervasive program to promote wellness, encourage and reward healthier lifestyle choices and reduce each employee's specific risk factors does result in lower rates of both acute illness and the development of chronic disease. While both of these are important outcomes, it is the reduction in the development of chronic disease that has the greatest impact on the bottom line since 75 percent of direct medical costs result from the treatment of chronic disease. The ability to reduce the incidence of such risk factors as obesity, smoking, elevated cholesterol, elevated blood pressure and high blood sugar provides a solid framework that, over time, causes the overall distribution of the work force across the five population health buckets to shift toward the left. As this occurs, workers will consume less healthcare services individually and the employer will experience a reduction in direct medical costs for that population.

An employer's direct medical costs, however, are actually dwarfed by the indirect medical costs that are usually hidden and upon which we often never focus. While direct medical costs account for 24 percent of overall health-related expenses, there are four other areas of medical costs (collectively called indirect medical costs) that account for the remaining 76 percent. These are absenteeism (6 percent), presenteeism (63 percent), short-term disability (6 percent) and long-term disability (1 percent). A healthier work force will indeed experience less absence from work and the reduction in absenteeism will translate into higher productivity and quality on the shop floor. Of much greater impact however, is the issue of presenteeism. Before you dismiss this as simply an excuse for laziness at work, there is increasing recognition that when an individual is affected by a distraction – be it physical, mental or emotional – it can first affect the individual at work since this is where they must perform. The term presenteeism reflects that although one is present at work, s/he is sufficiently distracted due to pre-occupation or side effects as to diminish his or her work output. Multiple studies have demonstrated the negative impact on productivity of such common ailments as allergies/hay fever, migraine headaches, sleep disturbances, depression, etc. Clearly, the greatest payback to the creation of a culture of health within the work environment relates to reductions in these areas. Any assessment of the ROI of health promotion activities has to contain elements that will reflect the contribution of improvements in productivity. Furthermore, reductions in obesity and better attention to exercise regimens have a very positive impact on the reduction of the musculoskeletal injuries that comprise the majority of such disability. Improvements in employees' overall health result in greater alertness and situational awareness with a positive impact on accident rates and a reduction in their potential for creating additional episodes of short-term disability.

7. Adopting a Strategic Approach to Health

Necessity prompts strategic adaptation. Organizations adopting a strategic approach to health must first ask themselves, "What is our overarching goal?" Thomas H. Lee, MD, professor of medicine at Harvard Medical School and a professor of health policy and management at Harvard School of Public Health recently stated: "The goal must be to improve the value of care as defined according to the patients' (consumers) perspective. To make progress toward that goal, we must understand the outcomes that matter to patients and families and what it costs to achieve them, and we need teams that own the work of defining, measuring, and improving value.[86]

The benefits of a pervasive culture of health therefore extend throughout the full spectrum of both direct and indirect healthcare costs and therein resides the real opportunity[87]. The employer who adopts the development of a pervasive culture of health as a strategic imperative will set the organization on a path that will, for the first time, address healthcare costs as a factor that can be successfully managed and even controlled.

By creating a culture of health and thereby improving the health of their employees, employers can accrue considerable benefits, including lower per capita direct healthcare costs, less absenteeism, less presenteeism and reduced rates of illness and injuries.

This need to raise healthcare cost management to a strategic level holds great opportunity and promise for the Human Resource and Benefits personnel within major employers. Instead of fighting a rear guard action to stem the tide of inexorable rising healthcare costs, an organization-wide effort to create a pervasive culture of health has the capability of transforming top executives' view of HR and Benefits from that of a frustrating cost center to a serious partner in the goal of creating a long- term strategic advantage for the entire company. "This approach is consistent with and supportive of both value based purchasing and insurance design. Effective conduct of these practices will be key competitive differentiators in all types of companies that continue to provide health benefits to their employees and their dependents, as reform unfolds throughout the rest of this decade, and beyond," according to James B. Couch, M.D. who pioneered these practices in Fortune 50 companies during the late 1980s and early 1990s.

8. Potential ROI Dashboard Elements

From the above discussion, it should be clear that simply looking at the costs of mounting a series of wellness programs and seeing whether healthcare costs are reduced for those who participate in those programs is a limited, short-sighted and inevitably flawed approach.

The ROI calculation for healthcare-related interventions must include more global measures that reflect company-wide medical costs, both direct and indirect. All of these areas must be tracked and managed and, since the indirect costs are three times that of the direct costs, it is especially limiting to consider only the direct costs of medical services.

A sample dashboard that reflects both areas would include such items as:

- Total annual direct healthcare costs on a per-capita basis
- Annualized rate of absenteeism
- Annualized rate of long-term disability

- Annualized rate of short-term disability
- Several measures of productivity appropriate to the company's products & services
- The percentage of employees in each of the five population health buckets
- Trend lines for all of the above covering the past three or more years

Trend lines for all of the measures are extremely important for two reasons: 1) developing a culture of health takes several years to effect and only by monitoring overall trends can one see if real impacts are occurring, and 2) the risks of doing little or nothing are very substantial and executives must always consider what their medical costs trend would be absent of any interventions on their part.

Many examples of how to construct such dashboards are available from numerous well-respected sources. The Center for Improving Value in Healthcare, supported by the Colorado Health Institute, has an excellent monograph on this topic.[88] Common elements for effective and meaningful assessment of the full range of healthcare costs include measures in the dimensions of financial impact, program participation, health risks, preventive services, incidence of chronic conditions, utilization of acute healthcare services, loss time from work, and employee engagement.[89]

Notice that what is not here is what the healthcare costs for diabetics was in the past year or how many employees have lost weight. While such measures may be useful in a tactical sense, they have no place in a strategically-focused dashboard used by senior management. Within the framework of controlling medical costs, the entire focus of executives must be on how to create a healthier work force over the long term and this requires them to be looking only at the high-level metrics of medical cost trends and company-wide productivity.

9. Summary

The assessment of the ROI for healthcare related expenditures must focus on the high-level parameters of overall direct medical costs trended over time, appropriate measures of indirect medical costs such as disability, absenteeism, and productivity measures as a proxy for the all-important issue of presenteeism and how successfully you are moving employees into healthier population health categories. Anything less is a short-sighted attempt to justify individual wellness programs that will each only make small contributions to what must be a high-level effort to create a sustainable strategic advantage through the creation of a healthier work force.

Key Ideas

- When it comes to expenditures for healthcare-related programs, most employers have little insight as to how an accurate ROI should be structured. This is due to a lack of understanding of the many varied and disparate components of a company's medical costs and how such programs fit, or do not fit, into a broad strategic approach to controlling these expenses.

- Depending on one's point of view, some elements may be critical to include in the ROI calculation while others may be less so.

- Serious consideration must be given to what elements are included in the ROI formula and will have a potentially large impact on how management can assess the value to be gained of the required investment.

- Dollars expended to provide a program are not the only consideration when calculating an ROI for that program. It is also important to consider the time it takes to accomplish one's goals, as well as the risks of not achieving those goals. This is especially critical in the area of medical costs because there is ample evidence that prevention does pay itself back many times over when looked at over a term of several or more years.

- Group members sincerely care about and work to promote the health of their colleagues. In this way, a culture of health is directly analogous to a work place culture of safety.

- An employer's direct medical costs, however, are actually dwarfed by the indirect medical costs that are usually hidden and upon which we often never focus.

Questions

1. Dollars expended to provide a program are the only consideration when calculating an ROI for that program.

   a. True

   b. False

2. A culture of health is directly analogous to what?

   a. A well-oiled machine

   b. A family

   c. A work culture of safety

   d. An army in the way it is organized

3. An employer's direct medical costs, however, are actually dwarfed by the indirect medical cost.

   a. True

   b. False

The Street Value of Organization Health 'Bend-the-Trend' Benchmarking Systems

By R. Dixon Thayer, James Reynolds and David Kirshenbaum

Abstract

At a time when escalating employee healthcare costs are eroding corporate profits, organization health strategies represent the next frontier in helping employers significantly improve clinical outcomes and workforce wellbeing, as well as bend the trend on medical benefit costs. A tall order? Perhaps. But C-Suite executives are gradually realizing that they cannot under-estimate the tremendous street value of organization health achievements attributable to the inextricable link to organization (workplace) health performance effectiveness metrics. These include overall labor costs, new (and retained) business revenue stream overflows, and employee and customer satisfaction leading to significantly better business results. The key to success lies in evidence-based research of credible benchmark organizations that have achieved real-world success. And as one informed observer Robert M. Fifer, put it: "If ever there was an area that can benefit from benchmarking, it is healthcare." At the end of the day, a healthier workforce whose results are tracked through meaningful measures offers a productive advantage and sustainable competitive edge. If you are committed to decreasing your healthcare costs, and are thinking of adopting a next generation culture of health mentality and executing a robust strategic roadmap, then you need a means to measure it. After all, you can't manage what you can't measure.

Introduction

Organization health is having a workforce and management which are healthy and actively engaged in programs to reduce each employee's risk of disease and disability, supporting their work life goals, while achieving desired business results. Organization health *"performance effectiveness execution"* enables the meaningful use of top-notch organization health assessment tools developed by those who have studied and documented benchmark organizations that have already begun to achieve success.

Organization positioning system (OPS) tracking methods and benchmarking innovations were designed by performance effectiveness experts to transform data to actionable information for sound decision-making. An OPS tool analyzes tracks and monitors tangible, measurable organization health actions, penetration and results and brings to light relevant configured graphics, numbers and words to mindfully guide the execution of desired strategic business plans to achieve a healthy workforce productive advantage and competitive edge in the market.

Addressing organization health by promoting population health improvement trumps everything else in business. Every corporate health promotion investment that CEOs make begins with the premise of achieving the advantage of a healthy productive workforce while avoiding costs. This is accomplished by applying to one's own organization the tools and techniques shown to have been effective through evidence based research of credible benchmark organizations who have achieved real-world success. An environment that sustains organization health excellence and executes practical and reliable organizational health improvement methods and high-value workforce wellbeing innovations by implementing "bend the trend" benchmarking systems will significantly and positively impact bottom line business results.

Given organization health's impact on the value of human capital, it is critical that executives focus on implementing next-generation "best practices" through benchmarking systems of excellence. The key to success is advancing practical ideas and transformative strategies, as well as building game-changing ways of delivering business value to employers, employees and providers.

Robert M. Fifer, a principal with Fifer Associates who helped define benchmarking tools and processes for organization success, notes, "If ever there was an area that can benefit from benchmarking, it is healthcare. There is enormous opportunity for organizations to both lower cost and improve the quality of care through identification of best practices, rigorous measurement of results and key metrics, and continuous improvement through ongoing monitoring and optimization."

Many innovations that improve organization health and workforce wellbeing fall short on benchmarking and proving the business value of health. CEOs must drive organization health from the C-Suite in order to achieve the sustainability imperative. This is done by focusing on long-term organization health and improving quality of care, which will elevate outcomes and productivity—leading to a competitive advantage. They also must simultaneously advance their strategic action plans based on rigorous measurements of results designed to achieve higher levels of performance effectiveness. When linked to a perspective of "sustainability" of results they advance their strategic action plans to achieve higher levels of performance effectiveness.

There is mounting pressure on the C-Suite to maximize resources that enhance workforce productivity and sustain a competitive edge by more aggressively managing escalating employee medical claims, one of the biggest costs of doing business. This is only accomplished through the company-wide adoption and implementation of advanced metrics-based, bend-the-trend benchmarking systems with an emphasis on multi-year organization health achievements.

Fast Forward Best Practices to Next Practices
One critical mission is to tame runaway employee healthcare costs, but industry practitioners have found that current benchmarking methods no longer work. Performance effectiveness leaders are focusing on how to transform current best practices into next practices. The thinking is to deploy innovative benchmarking capabilities that take legacy tracking and monitoring systems to the next level.

C.K. Prahalad, a corporate strategy thought leader from the University of Michigan Business School, is credited with coining the term 'next practice" at a time when most management concepts were still using the term "best practice." Next practices offer a more competitive edge to organizations and the reason is simple. By distinction, best practices are specific to a company. So when executives benchmark best practices from other organizations, executives cannot expect the same level of human capital workforce capacity improvements or multi-year economic impact gains on the business enterprise.

Benchmarking is a term used to measure performance achievement using a specific indicator, such as cost or productivity per unit of measure—resulting in a metric of performance achievement that serves as a basis of comparison. It is a continuous improvement process that measures optimal performance excellence against other organizations within or outside a particular industry through a myriad of meaningful techniques and strategies. It is also a means through which breakthrough ideas are revealed. Areas that are ripe for measurement include strategies, operations and processes.

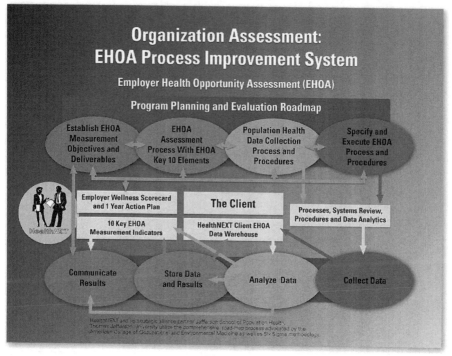

Figure 1

Benchmarking allows an organization to assess its incremental progress and make the necessary critical pathway adjustments to improve organization performance effectiveness. Benchmarking is a practical and reliable way to pinpoint business problems in an organization. In essence, an OPS tool helps executives analyze, track, monitor and guide them toward desired results. This also helps team leaders realize their goal of achieving a healthy workforce productive advantage and gain a competitive edge in the market. In short, benchmarking is a valuable tool in moving beyond national average performance to best-in-class performance achievement excellence. This systematic process is designed to help make corporate organizations evolve, achieve and thrive over time.

Given the strong interest in organization health and the inextricable link between population health and high-impact workforce wellbeing, it makes sense that executives focus on organization health next practices to advance game-changing ways of tracking, monitoring and delivering business value to employers, employees and providers. The key conduit will be through next-generation, bend-the-trend benchmarking systems.

Street Talk on Benchmarking

Benchmarking organization health improvements designed to sustain positive change is a complex undertaking. This is why performance effectiveness experts are advancing evidence-based benchmarking methods and cutting-edge performance effectiveness tracking innovations to determine the real (street) value of organization health bend-the-trend benchmarking systems.

Organization health improvement is the primary objective of benchmarking. This proactive approach seeks to identify the highest standards of excellence for organization health performance effectiveness, as well as multi-year, results-oriented improvements necessary to sustain organization health improvement.

When comparing the best business processes and performance metrics, dimensions typically measured include quality, time and cost. "In the process of benchmarking, management identifies the best firms in their industry, or in another industry where similar processes exist, and compare the results and processes of those studied (the "targets") to one's own results and processes," according to one definition. "In this way, they learn how well the targets perform and, more importantly, the business processes that explain why these firms are successful." [1]

Corporate America's C-Suite executives are advancing organization health best practices that bring together employers, employees and providers. More than a decade of research and frontline experiences have led performance effectiveness specialists to believe strongly that good health synergizes improved workforce capacity for quality improvement—and that, in fact, at least 50 percent of any organization's long-term success is driven by its health.[2] Virgin Health Miles recently predicted the operating profits of companies in major industries such as technology and finance could decline about 25 percent on average in 10 or more years based on chronic disease cost trends from the past decade if organizations cannot increase prices or productivity. And employees feel it, too, paying more out of their pockets for higher premiums.[3] The Institute of Medicine (IOM) 2001 Report "Crossing the Quality Chasm" also identified the healthcare workforce as the health system's most important resource and critical to improving the quality of care.[4] Ironically, despite (or perhaps because of) their close proximity to healthcare delivery, U.S. hospital workers are less healthy, consume more medical services and accrue higher healthcare costs than the U.S. workforce at large.[5]

Corporate America's ability to analyze and track organization health and determine the prevalence of cultures of health realization in U.S. businesses has not improved in recent years. For example, a recent Buck Consultants' survey found only 10 percent of U.S. businesses believed they had fully achieved a "culture of health"—considered the springboard for organization health measurement—while 85 percent intended to pursue one.[6] Organization health execution is uncharted territory for most executives and nearly everyone is clamoring for leadership engagement systems designed to identify, engage, establish, elevate, achieve and renew performance effectiveness best practices faster than the competition to sustain stellar business performance over time.

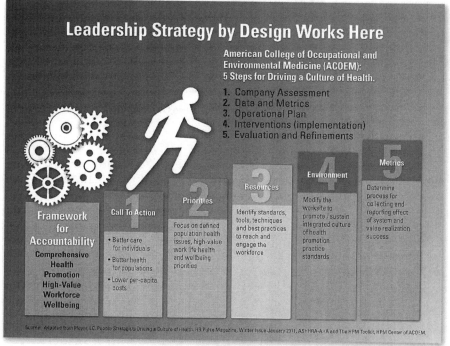

Figure 2

Traditional organization health measurement systems focus on baseline comparisons that generally include leading indicators such as health status and confidence in health-related decision making that may be the cause of trailing indicators such as absence, workers' compensation incidence rates or reduced job performance. These measurement systems are clearly inadequate, but the right resources are now available to achieve ironclad results. Qualitative health and productivity management dashboard trending tools provide great value when it comes to ensuring that health interventions such as chronic care management, health risk management and population health promotion achievements improve workforce capacity output. These dashboard and scorecard resources typically profile detailed information for program evaluation and management that can be rolled up into the high-level summaries necessary for the rapid review, interpretation and action by decision makers.

Long-established population health promotion program benchmarking has provided the best practical information for employers to improve organization health programs, but these checklists may not provide enough valid measures to show evidence of "culture changes" across time. There are many employee health management best-practices yardstick tool options available to companies. They provide no-cost surveys that explain employee health management systems and provide an online "inventory checklist" resource— often including an instant benchmarking assessment of the firm's best practices. Specific benchmarks can provide a set of metrics that define worksite wellness success and measure how companies stack up to others in a results-oriented, national program evaluation scorecard database. These online tools are intended to help guide employers to improve their population health promotion programs and inculcate unique opportunities for systems improvement. As these tools are fine-tuned and intertwined with next-practices scorecard systems, they will create better value for employers, employees and providers, as well as deliver a positive return on investment (ROI).

In addition, there are robust employer health asset management tools and techniques published by well-known business experts, academic leaders and industry trade group leaders. These attempt to:

1. Sketch out worksite culture change systems audits;

2. Determine how employers can introduce cost-effective employee health lifestyle programs;

3. Demonstrate ROI-based analysis techniques of employee wellness programs;

4. Showcase stepwise approaches to building a culture of health model in order to implement a total wellbeing (holistic) worksite wellness program;

5. Advance surveys to examine the business case for being a healthy enterprise, as well as determine whether the nature and scope of these efforts make a difference to their ROI as measured by lower healthcare costs, employee turnover and absence, and;

6. Measure community health plan performance and manage critical processes that control costs, reduce or eliminate waste, ensure patient safety, close gaps in care and improve health status.

Effective application of benchmarking to achieve organization health goals focuses on two different yet symbiotic tools:
The first tool is the strategic business process improvement (SBPI) framework employer health opportunity assessment (EHOA) program. This is a planning and evaluation roadmap that provides real-world, peer-to-peer benchmark comparison of an organization's health. It is designed to establish an evidence-based, multi-year master framework (and baseline) for assessing and tracking an organization's work environment, as well as value-based purchasing and insurance benefit design review. It benchmarks to organizations that have already achieved enduring cultures of health that yield high returns within interconnected metrics based on relative application, resourcing and penetration of programs, actions and benefit design.

The second tool is the change-management framework. This benchmarking tool is designed to engage, direct and benchmark internal progress towards goals on specific initiatives, across internal departments, sites and business units. When combined effectively these two tools establish a powerful continuous improvement process that can yield significant tangible results in one-to-two years.

CEOs understand and already apply this approach to benchmarking other functions and goals in the organization. Using this approach to establish an enduring organization health program will make it more easily embraced at the top of the organization, which achieves a third key element of success: C-suite buy-in and visible support for the program. (See Figure 1 and 2)

Figure 3

Imagine an organization capable of forecasting when the curve would start bending. Depending on the degree of intensity, interactive simulations ("what-if") capability for plan development and plan valuation, it becomes feasible to track progress and forecast when and how the curve will bend, which facilitates troubleshooting and remediation customization. This results in a customized, multiyear planning framework and an early stage progress scorecard (vs. waiting for long-term outcomes to materialize) to assist in first year "on-course/off-course" adjustments. (See Figure 3 and 4).

The future is here. It is clear the street value of workforce health is heightened because of its inextricable link to organization health performance effectiveness metrics. These include overall labor costs, new (and retained) business revenue stream overflows, and employee and customer satisfaction. Another piece of the puzzle involves productive advantage metrics and performance effectiveness indices that need to be tracked, measured and reported using advanced, real-life bend-the-trend benchmarking systems. (See Figure 5)

What if best-in-class benchmarking capabilities could use best-practice healthy worksite culture parameters to create a stand-alone performance effectiveness tool to provide quantitative scoring about organization health? Is it possible for research projects to measure the maturity of an organization's performance effectiveness and link it to the leadership engagement and environmental/policy support systems to help compare performance effectiveness consistency?[7] If shown to be valid, such a benchmarking system tool could be used by organizations to document improvements in organization health culture. This information could be valuable to worksites wondering whether implemented leadership, policy and environmental changes were sufficient to influence worksite culture in a meaningful way. Such a benchmarking tool could also help worksites evaluate the economic impact of corporate culture on organization health, employee health and outcomes.[8]

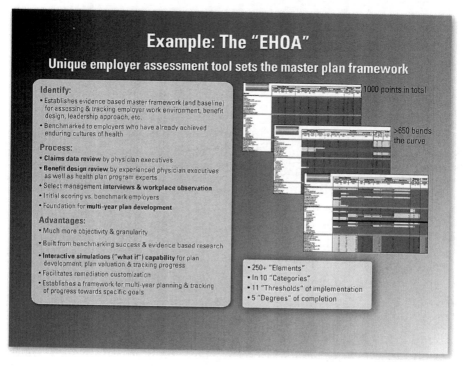

Figure 4

Organization health systems improvement for purchasers, employers and their trusted employees is built around value creation through meaningful productive interactions and the personalized experiences of consumers, providers, purchasers and payers. Adaptive leaders vehemently articulate that maintaining status quo is no longer acceptable. As such, and through the new business and organization health imperatives, the "way things are done" within a company must be reinvented in order to monitor and influence workforce health status.

The Final Frontier: Organization Health Benchmarking Systems
Organization health entails cutting-edge new leadership engagement systems and technology breakthroughs that leverage the success of best-practice organizations. This elite list includes Johnson & Johnson, Dow Chemical, Pitney Bowes and Crown Cork & Seal, all of which have publically declared (and demonstrated) that their healthcare costs are declining while the health status of their workforce is improving.

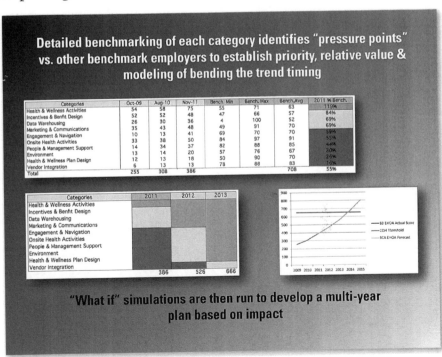

Figure 5

Wellness and disease management companies have been around for 20 years, and the jury is still out on their effectiveness. Recent breakthroughs by corporate benchmark companies have shown that employers can bend the cost curve by having wellness be an essential component of a much bigger and more impactful program. It is clear that checking people's blood and individually coaching them to better habits does not alone produce a sustainable culture of health.

The American workforce, long admired worldwide for setting the gold standard on productivity, is coming apart at the seams. The chief culprit is mounting healthcare costs related to employee lifestyle choices that have undermined efficiency models, which has been exacerbated by a lack of critical thinking in the C-Suite. What's needed are organization health systems-improvement leadership teams and front-line population health strategic plans based on benchmark practices. This formulaic combination will not only bend the healthcare cost curve, but also achieve a healthy productive advantage and sustainable competitive edge.

We are now entering a new era of organization health to advance high-value workforce wellbeing. Strategies that include organization-wide benchmarking systems investment will deliver on the promise to achieve healthy productive workforce advantage, while reducing costs via evidence-based research methods of benchmark companies that have achieved real-world success.

Emerging organization health leadership engagement systems technologies have been built on studying cultures of health to aggressively manage the root causes of poor employee health and lackluster work performance. Another key component is to layer in the latest evidence-based tools and processes developed to help millions of working Americans to improve their health, financial security and achieve work life fulfillment objectives. The best way to drive system progress is through rigorous, disciplined measurement and value improvement, though it remains largely unmeasured and misunderstood in most global companies. The fact is that cutting edge leadership engagement tools, technologies and benchmarking capabilities are transforming the high-value workforce wellbeing.

U.S. healthcare will soon begin transitioning to an advanced framework, accountability model to create healthy communities, improve organization health outcomes and achieve business results. CEOs know that the best way to drive value creation in the C-Suite is to focus on what's causing escalating costs. This is done by enabling a metrics-based, scorecard-driven alignment system approach that supports the well-known "triple aim" of achieving population health promotion: **better care for individuals, better health for populations and lower per capita costs.** There are three key stakeholders: the **employer, employee and provider**, with fully engaged employees serving as the conduit to a multi-year, strategic continuous organization health systems improvement process within the organization. Under this approach, astute organizations will benefit from the right care at the right time, as well as meaningful prevention and treatment strategies that work and cost less.

Beauty is in the Eye of the Beholder

In the eyes of a CEO, businesses create jobs, innovate, manufacture and provide the services that drive economic growth. Yet leadership inertia along the pioneering frontier of organization health is significantly restricting Corporate America's ability to accelerate growth to achieve a sustainable competitive advantage.

Higher profits from a healthier workforce elude most CEOs because they don't have a straightforward C-Suite measurement scorecard to improve their day-to-day worksite wellness tracking and monitoring system to sustain a competitive advantage. The complexity lies in drawing value out of evidence-based approaches to meaningful use of work-life health and wellbeing scorecards, dashboards and cockpits that contend with real-world settings. CEOs are faced with an overabundance of tangible and intangible metrics, as well as distinctive secondary employee benefits data, that challenge health and human capital executives.

Benchmarking is a strong tool for transforming organizational learning when striving for a superior business performance, achievement excellence at work and employer-of-choice productive advantage ratings. Prerequisites for the effective application of engaging bend-the-trend benchmarking index tools include the following components:

- Understanding the guiding principles of population health promotion and high-value workforce wellbeing;

- Using proven employer health opportunity assessment tools and techniques and applying them through leadership active-engagement approaches and benchmarking systems improvement capabilities; and

- Creating strongly engaged frontline management team environments.

Process-focused organization health best practices in benchmarking ensure a concretely business-integrated approach. The most important benchmarking indexing projects are related to redesigning key workforce health business processes, advanced methods and high-impact innovations. The organization health benchmarking index system approach is also is carried out in a strategic business process-like manner.

The focus is on empowering CEOs in elevating their company's economic wellbeing by helping to improve the health and wellbeing of their people—all while improving an individual's productive advantage, which ultimately impacts business capacity in a manner that is both sustainable and measurable.

Value realization encompasses several areas and requires relevant onsite, corporate level, and company-wide reporting. That which gets measured gets improved. The role of the CEO is to determine what is important for the C-suite team to measure. The undertaking is intended to rapidly shape and mold the leadership engagement process that was created to help pioneering employers answer:

1. How are we doing relative to benchmark employers?

2. How can we improve to a point to bend the trend on curtailing employee healthcare costs?

3. What simulation capabilities scenarios are available to find specific and optimum opportunities for interventions and that will define measures of success?

To focus on value creation in the C-Suite and yield hard returns on employee and family population health programs and "bend the healthcare cost curve," CEOs must lead by steering cross-functional work teams toward relentlessly fostering a value-centric culture of health, which becomes a self-perpetuating productive advantage. This is accomplished by providing leaders in the C-Suite with a multi-year strategic business process improvement system. Such a system focuses on:

1. Population health promotion;

2. High-value workforce wellbeing;

3. Engaging chronically disengaged employees;

4. Embracing meaningful use of health achievement benchmarks and metrics;

5. Creating C-Suite visibility for innovative health and wellbeing indices;

6. Supporting individual financial security aspirations;

7. Aligning meaningful incentives, and;

8. Helping people achieve their best possible health status.

This level of leadership engagement focuses on improved health, enhanced on-the-job professional experiences, optimization of cultural and human capabilities, and relentlessly upgrading leadership capabilities throughout the business enterprise. Other key objectives include engaging meaningful productive interactions and reducing per capita cost of a company's defined population, which includes employee satisfaction and total rewards initiatives that enable employees to define their own needs and expectations as distinct choices. Leadership engagement empowers people to deliver results and grow at work

Conclusion
Streetwise performance effectiveness specialists realize that population health management and organization health performance improvement technologies are joined at the hip. These cannot be an annual independent study, self-administered fire drill or open-enrollment season party to reduce health insurance benefit costs. Instead, they must incorporate a rigorous, multi-year SBPI leadership engagement process designed to sustain desired organization health improvements.

How can current organization health benchmarking systems be retooled to achieve healthy productive workforce advantage, while also reducing costs? It is not easy to change leadership cultures and embrace next-generation benchmarking systems to achieve optimal business results. The time has come, however, to execute robust OPS tracking methods and benchmarking innovations designed to achieve tangible, measurable business outputs and productivity gains to achieve business results. It will take adaptive leaders to resist business as usual schemes and raise bend-the-trend benchmarking systems to the next level.

References

1   Benchmarking: From Wikipedia, the free encyclopedia, See: http://en.wikipedia.org/wiki/Benchmarking (Accessed May 1, 2012).

2   Keller S, Price C. Organizational health: The ultimate competitive advantage, The European Business Review. See: http://www.europeanbusinessreview.com/?p=4526 (Accessed May 1, 2012)

3   Virgin HealthMiles Shares Four Breakthrough Ideas Driving the Future of Workplace Health and Productivity in 2012. Market Wire Press Release, January 4, 2012. See: http://www.marketwire.com/press-release/virgin-healthmiles-shares-four-breakthrough-ideas-driving-future-workplace-health-productivity-1603240.htm (Accessed May 1, 2012)

4   Crossing the Quality Chasm: A New Health System for the 21st Century, Institute of Medicine (IOM). Preparing the Workforce. The National Academies Press. 2001;(9),207-223 See: http://www.nap.edu/openbook.php?record_id=10027&page=207 (Accessed May 1, 2012)

5   Hospital employees are less healthy and accrue higher healthcare costs than the general workforce, according to Thomson Reuters Study. Press Release, September 12, 2011. See Truven Health Analytics: http://thomsonreuters.com/content/press_room/healthcare/hospital_employees_less_healthy (Accessed July 1, 2012)

6   Turgiss J. Prevention: The Best Medicine for Creating a Corporate Culture of Health. Self-Funding Magazine. June 1, 2012. See: http://www.selffundingmagazine.com/article/prevention-the-best-medicine-for-creating-a-corporate-culture-of-health.html (Accessed June 1, 2012)

7   Aldana SG, Anderson DR, Adams TB, Whitmer W, Merrill RM, George V, Noyce J. A review of the knowledge base on healthy worksite culture. Journal of Occupational and Environmental Medicine. 2012;54(4):414-419.

8   Ibid.

Key Ideas

- Organization health is having a workforce and management which are healthy and actively engaged in programs to reduce each employee's risk of disease and disability, supporting their work life goals, while achieving desired business results.

- Organization positioning system (OPS) tracking methods and benchmarking innovations were designed by performance effectiveness experts to transform data to actionable information for sound decision-making.

- Every corporate health promotion investment that CEOs make begins with the premise of achieving the advantage of a healthy productive workforce while avoiding costs.

- CEOs must drive organization health from the C-Suite in order to achieve the sustainability imperative. This is done by focusing on long-term organization health and improving quality of care, which will elevate outcomes and productivity—leading to a competitive advantage.

- Benchmarking is a practical and reliable way to pinpoint business problems in an organization. In essence, an OPS tool helps executives analyze, track, monitor and guide them toward desired results

- At least 50 percent of any organization's long-term success is driven by its health

- Effective application of benchmarking to achieve organization health goals focuses on two tools:

  1. The first tool is the strategic business process improvement (SBPI) framework employer health opportunity assessment (EHOA) program

  2. The second tool is the change-management framework

Questions

1. What is OPS?

   a. Ongoing Participation Statistics

   b. Organization Positioning System

   c. Organization Participation System

   d. Ongoing Participation Statistics

2. At least 70 percent of any organization's long-term success is driven by its health.

   a. True

   b. False

3. Effective benchmarking has how many tools?

   a. Two

   b. Four

   c. One

   d. Three

Case Study: Walk the Talk - Health System Employees Improve Health through "Wellness at Work"

By Renée-Marie Stephano

Introduction and Background

Baptist Health System (BHS) is a not-for-profit organization which own and manages four hospitals in Alabama. They are also in charge of 42 health centers and 9 senior living facilities. They employ 4300 people in north-central Alabama and has a medical staff of over 520 physicians. They are a self-funded program.

The Problem

Baptist was facing an 8-10 percent annual increase in healthcare costs. Alabama is the state with the second highest rate of obesity in the United States, they felt they had to do something to help their employees and stop the escalating healthcare costs. A break down the problems faced by BHS is as follows:

- 14.7 percent used tobacco

- 22.5 percent had no primary care physician

- 35.6 percent of men over 40 had not had a prostrate exam

- 8.2 percent of women over 40 had not had a mammogram

- 31.3 percent were overweight

- 33 percent of those overweight were obese

- 8.2 percent were severely obese.

- 32 percent had high or borderline high cholesterol

Analysis for these numbers was conducted through Aegis Health Group, and they determined that healthcare costs at BHS were chiefly from high utilization, high dollar claims, and chronic conditions.

The Solution

The employees were asked to perform a Personal Health Profile questionnaire. This was teamed with screenings for blood pressure, cholesterol and glucose. They had 74 percent of employees partici-pate in the survey and screenings. The idea at the heart of the program was to keep it simple, and to use resources available to them already. They used "internal resources" like Aegis Health

Group who developed their screenings and surveys, along with their finance, clinical and quality organizations. Their Employee Health and HR departments were tapped as well in actually administering the surveys.

With the data in hand they had to decide how to use it, thus came the Chronic Conditions Program. Using the data they had, and the knowledge of the doctors on their staff they developed the plan to target the chronic conditions among the workforce.

Prescription drugs were also a factor of in the new plan. If an employee agreed to see a health coach and see a primary care physician the hospitals would pay for 100 percent of the costs generic drugs and 50 percent of what the plan would pay for name brand.

Employee participation in the Wellness at Work program has increased from 74 percent in 2008 to 86 percent in 2011. The program has expanded so spouses can participate in screening. The leadership team has specific goals for the growing plan, these are to increase the overall health of the workers through the use of biometric screening and to increase productivity, decrease absenteeism, and impact presenteeism. The C-Suite has been behind the program from day one, and has actively participated in the program.

The Wellness at Work program is organized into three categories, each with its own approach to health. The first is exercise, which includes hospital-sponsored walking and exercise programs, participation in Scale Back Alabama to reduce weight, subsidized gym memberships, and onsite exercise classes. The second is tobacco cessation which includes a Free and Clear program and a non-tobacco discount on medical premiums. The third is preventive measures which includes healthier options in cafeterias and vending machines, screenings, Lunch and Learn Seminars, primary care physician promotion, and chronic condition management.

The Results

Baptist was able to track a $600,000 reduction in claims, and $1 million reduction in workers compensation claims. The numbers tracking the impact of the program are below from 2008 to 2011:

- Tobacco use dropped from 14.7 percent to 11.6 percent

- Employees without a primary care physician fell from 22.5 percent to 20 percent

- Women 40+ who hadn't had a mammogram decreased from 8.2 percent to 7.4 percent

- Men 40+ who hadn't had a prostate exam went down from 35.6 percent to 30 percent

- Those with high and borderline-high cholesterol declined 3.2 percent from 31.9 percent to 28.7 percent

- Hypertension dropped 1.4 percent

- Unfavorable BMI fell 2.2 percent

- Waist circumference shrank 1.1 percent

- Abnormal glucose screening levels declined 1.6 percent, which contributed to a 40 percent reduction in primary diabetes claims and complications as well as a $925 reduction in the average cost per episode

The chronic condition population decreased 10 percent , as did the total number of days missed. They track employee satisfaction and see that the program is always highly rated. Participants were given a $25 reduction per pay period for participation and an additional $10 off of their premiums per pay period.

Alan Bradford Chief Human Resources Officer at Baptist Health Systems has a few words of advice for programs. The first is to be aware that the program is a long term commitment. The second is to remind everyone that while there is an investment up front, the ROI will come. The final is that it is essential to gather data, analyze it, and act on it.

Case Study: Reinventing a Wellness Program at Hillshire Brands

By Renée-Marie Stephano

Introduction and background

Hillshire Brands is the face behind iconic food brands like Sara Lee, Ball Park Franks, Jimmy Dean Sausage, Hillshire Farms, and many others. They have approximately 9,500 employees located across the United States working at either meat plants, bakery plants, or at their headquarters located in Illinois.

Some of the issues Hillshire Brands was facing were high costs of chronic diseases, 25 percent of employees had no claims indicating they did not go to a primary care physican, and employee spouses were higher risk than the employees. The main health concerns were obesity, tobacco and alcohol use, high blood pressure and stress.

The Program

The recent wellness program at Hillshire was re-launched in July 2011. The new program is organized into three phases. Phase one is based on creating a personal health profile with biometric screenings and health assessments, called "know you numbers." Phase two is recommended care and personalized health programs, a health map for employees and spouses. The third and final phase is the use of online tools, a personal health record, and finally a reward bank.

The Results

The re-launched program exhibited many improvements over the prior program. Fifty-three percent of employees completed a health screening or health assessment; up from below 5 percent in 2010. Thirty-five percent of the employees who took an assessment actively participated in a program to become healthier. In their weight loss competition the participants lost an average of one pound a week, and the winning team lost an average of 25 pounds each. This all happened within the first year of the revamped program.

One of their most powerful tools was the use of wellness champions. Each location had a minimum of five champions, and none were turned away. Their purpose is to promote the program from the grassroots. The champions could not be from human resources, so they were the peers of many of the workers. Another innovation was the change in incentives. Originally Hillshire Brands offered the standard premium discounts, but with the re-launch they shifted to the use of gift cards instead. They did keep the amounts the same, but found that employees valued the immediate reward more than the premium discount.

CHAPTER 9
Healthcare Reform and Wellness

Consumer Engaged Health Plans and Healthcare Reform: Building the Case for an Integrated Approach to Plan Design, Employee Contributions and Targeted Wellness Interventions
By Joe Torella

For many years a basic employee benefits strategy prevailed. It was balanced upon a stool, awkwardly supported by two simple strategies – Plan Design and Contribution Modeling; but this long-held approach of reducing benefits and increasing the employee's share of the cost did nothing more than shift that cost. We had not fully developed an integrated approach that focused on consumer engagement. As an industry, we attempted in the late 80's/90's to embrace HMOs and individual ownership of prevention; but we hadn't built plan designs, aligned contributions or provided the type of transparency which was critically necessary for improving the health status of the employer's population. We had posited that early detection and copays to drive a 'well', rather than 'sick' model was preferable – and it was.

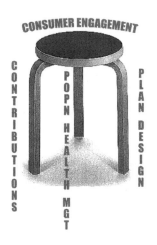

But in most markets, HMOs saw rise to more friendly POS and un-gated plans and this fragmented path was followed until the early 2000s, when we began to see Consumer 'Driven' (or 'Directed') Health Plans. And, it was a terrific idea – to create individual corridors of risk/cost together with the transparency tools that would empower employees to access the healthcare system through a more cost conscious, quality-based approach.

High deductible plans – and funding through HSAs and HRAs began to reconnect employees' healthcare decisions through a financial model that had them more truly engaged than ever before. The need for wiser choices and selection of providers through better decision-support technology forced carriers to think differently about how to move from unit-cost, to clinically-based metrics. Brokers, consultants and employers began to work more closely in developing 'Wellness' models that were more robust than HMO designers could have ever imagined. We had moved from early forms of consumer involvement and participation that focused on spending – to a model focused on activation and engagement. We were leaving behind the nomenclature of *consumer directed* in favor of *consumer engagement.*

This chapter is written in that context; that the first generation of CDH plans were built around a change in plan design and contributions . . . that we were fundamentally doing what we had always done, use only two legs of the stool – plan design and funding to manage cost. But, that we were quickly progressing by attacking the demand side of the equation and reversing the employee role from passive bystander to active participant.

It is the next generation plan design and funding – together with targeted interventions – that will drive the logical evolution of Consumer Engaged Health Plans (CEHPs) and true integration of the three legs of the stool: plan design, contribution/funding and population health management. Advisors must collapse these tools into a single strategic framework that moves the needle on cost in the short term and bends the trend needle toward 'zero' in the longer term. The following pages outline a formula for achieving these goals. Additionally, this chapter will provide statistically compelling case evidence that affirms the value of this approach and validates an employer's ability to achieve the same, in a planned way.

The Back Story

Five years ago, ABC COMPANY's group health plan faced double digit trend and had not yet made a major commitment to consumer-based approaches for managing their employee benefits program. Today they are managing to zero trend, and looking to drive even higher levels of participation in their consumer-based plans and engagement initiatives. Their employees are activated and there is a proven track record of moving employees from an incentive-based design through value-based design to the current outcomes-based model.

It's working because there is a strong collaboration between advisor, HR, Finance and Senior Management (THE TEAM) together with their employees. The client has embraced the importance of using a well-planned time-table for developing an approach that works for them (and a formula that other employers can adopt).

Evolving the Model from Consumer 'Directed' to Consumer 'Engaged' Healthcare

ABC COMPANY's first transition step centered on building a fundamental platform of transparency with consumer directed plan designs serving as a launch point for more aggressive plan management. That design provided the structure needed for employee involvement in the healthcare decision-making process. THE TEAM was facing the typical challenges – skepticism about a departure from the status quo, employee questions and confusion, and a real sense that high deductibles (even when paired with an HSA or an HRA) reflected a retreat to low cost, low quality plans. Initial opposition was expected and overcoming employee perception that they're sacrificing their rich plan for the cheap, 'deficient' plan, was necessary. Employers can capitalize on this when they embrace CEHP as the 'healthy' option.

Nevertheless, given ABC's group health plan costs at the time, and with no visible involvement by employees in their own healthcare expenditures, it was clear they needed to move to a consumer-based model. From the beginning, THE TEAM focused on an HSA option with HSA-favored contributions and employer funding. The objective was to shift communications and drive the value of choosing the high deductible plan options together with a flexible funding mechanism (that would lay the groundwork for developing an incentive-based platform) to drive healthier participant behavior.

THE TEAM, specifically HR/Communications, took the new plan design strategies and completely re-branded the employee experience. Employees were starting to engage in conversations about the health plan – and about their health – but not just because they were in a high deductible plan . . . because we very quickly tied the completion of Health Risk Profiles (HRP) to the funding of their plan options. Completing the HRP reduced their required contributions to the medical plan. Employees were actively talking about their health, and supported by a number of HR programs; they were engaging in a very different way than ever before. ABC saw the stunning transition inspired by adoption of the new concept – and it was because THE TEAM had branded the new CEHP model. ABC knew something very powerful was happening.

ABC COMPANY found that the CEHP concept changed the employee's willingness to better understand and commit – to activate. But the funding changes, tied to a 'healthy plan' option would be critical in moving to employee (or healthcare consumer) engagement. Using the high deductible approach was critical because it provided two areas where incentives can be created – as part of what employees pay for benefits; and employer funding of the HSA.

If asked today, THE TEAM would collectively advocate that first generation HSA implementation, requires a favorable contribution structure and employer 'seed' money in the account. This eases employees through the transition and helps eliminate barriers noted earlier. Additionally, it provides a safety net through the risk corridor and creates employee familiarity with employer-funding as an important component of plan design. So early on, there is simply an incentive-based model. Through progressive stages, this contribution should evolve into an employee incentive for meeting health and wellness requirements. Wellness programs are often challenged to produce clear ROI, and for ABC COMPANY, and many others, this results-based, financially-driven approach provides an ROI mechanism.

All at once, or Staged for Effectiveness through the strategic planning process?

So, what do we mean when we suggest that employees become 'engaged'? First, and as noted above, employees must make better choices when they're involved in purchasing healthcare . . . and a fully implemented CEHP provides plan members with the data and information to facilitate enhanced decision-making. But engagement goes well beyond decision-making. Engagement means employees take a greater interest in staying healthy, or becoming healthy. ABC COMPANY found that the ideal play is in developing a well-articulated series of 'activation' stages must be executed through a workforce that clearly understands what they are being asked to do and why – and that the financial incentives are increasingly tied to health as the program evolves. Some employers have tried to 'force' a wellness program on its workforce in a very short time, and other unfocused programs are mired in ambiguous messaging and struggling to move the wellness needle even after several years. Neither extreme will achieve the optimal result, but assessing cultural and business readiness and establishing a plan will minimize such wide swings.

The first phase needs to drive employee activation around key employer goals – short term in nature, such as health awareness. Mid-term, employers must focus on activating employees and creating a higher level of participation. And, longer term, the goal is improvement in the health status of the employee population. All programs, incentives, and plan design options, over time, should drive toward this progressive objective – and simultaneously reinforcing goal achievement with financial reward/penalty.

In this way, THE TEAM works closely together on the timing of critical initiatives in advance of their implementation. Setting goals allows us to develop a precise roadmap; a 3-5 year strategic benefits plan. This approach means that we can use data to identify opportunities for change, a timeframe for execution, and a plan for addressing the issues effectively. The approach I recommend defines four critical stages of activation that can be compressed or expanded, but cannot be avoided.

Introduction of ABC COMPANY Group Health Plan (GHP) Incentives

ABC had built their employee communication effort around health and wellness – well before implementation of the HSA Program. With the Awareness stage set, ABC was free in their initial roll-out of their HSA program to include completion of a Health Risk Profile (HRP) as a requisite for reducing the employee contributions in year two.

Figure 2.

In the subsequent benefit period, the stakes were raised as ABC agreed they need to apply more objective measures to the generally subjective format of the HRP. Complementing the self-reporting nature of the HRP tool, ABC felt that employee engagement in wellness would be improved when biometric screenings positioned employees to start looking at the meaning of their self-reported data and commitment to a healthy lifestyle.

In the second year, the HRP process was modified to ensure that objective measures were added as part of the employee's health management toolbox. A reduction in employee contributions that would occur in year three, would be based on successful completion of the HRP – together with clinical information from biometric screenings. More importantly, the communications messaging focused as much on the value of the data as it did on the positive financial impact it had on employee plan cost. Employees were encouraged to change the physician-patient dynamic by having their medical information in-hand when they visited their physician, not following the visit.

ABC COMPANY had begun the transition from incentive-based to value-based design; and with HSA plan participation moving significantly into double digits – even when adjusted for plan design and age – they were beginning to enjoy medical trend deceleration compared to the carrier's book of business they were benchmarking against.

Taking Control of the Future . . .

Wellness, when executed effectively, is a disciplined commitment to steady, measureable improvement in targeted population health status – and, it is a graduated, well thought-out strategy that moves from incentive-based design, to value-based design to compliance/outcome-based design. These stages (as noted in Figure 3), while compressible, are not avoidable – taking Figure 2 to a new level.

Essentially, the evolution of program incentives should be geared toward the client's appetite for 'carrot' v. 'stick' with an emphasis around increasing engagement levels (or 'activation'). This is where an understanding of organizational culture becomes critical because the more deeply-rooted the behavior, the more connected the employee needs to be to the costs they bear before behavior that can be meaningfully modified. The organization must be 'comfortable' adopting a strategy that applies the necessary pressure to activate the employee.

Stages of Activation and Incentive Modeling

Incentive-based → Value-based → Compliance/Outcomes-based

Awareness → Participation → Engagement → Accountability

Year 1 ↔ Year 2 ↔ Year 3 ↔ Year 4

Crafting a 3-5 Year Strategy is critical in building a program of employee activation

Figure 3.

A good start point for developing financial incentives is the 20 percent differential currently allowed by the Department of Labor that differentially favors employees who adhere to wellness initiatives predicated on achieving health outcomes v. those that do not. And under the Patient Protection and Affordable Care Act (PPACA), that differential increases to 30 percent (and as much as 50 percent) in 2014. Building a 3-5 year strategy ensures that at the appropriate time, employers will be positioned to take advantage of those provisions.

For HR leadership, this approach yields a true employee benefit – rewarding an increasing employee commitment to health. For the CFO, this approach more directly connects employees financially for the impact of their risk/cost to the program. The 20 percent is an important component because of its duality; both as a mechanism for helping fund wellness initiatives and as an employee incentive to 'consider' the information they receive from health risk profiles and biometric screenings. Incentives must be large enough for the employees' activation levels to materially impact the cost of their benefits – and that cost to drive activation.

Tackling Metabolic Syndrome
The next stage, moving to a compliance/outcome-based model, means that an employer is ready (together with employees) to tackle Metabolic Syndrome (MetS), which is a group of risk factors, that when occurring together, increase the likelihood for coronary artery disease, stroke, and type 2 diabetes (among others). At this point, we aggressively consider the 3-legged stool (Figure 1) in the integration of plan design, funding and targeted initiatives. It isn't enough that an employee receives his or her 'wellness' data/score; rather, it is critical that the employee gets activated based on their individual information with respect to the clinical risks he or she faces.

Incentives in this stage must be re-engineered to target the most impactful clinical risks, and drive individuals to improve upon their personal health. For example, biometric scores must be within a predetermined range, the HRP must be within normal range and/or other targets must be achieved. Those who score in the 'acceptable' range(s) are entitled to receive the incentives; those that do not, pay more or they must satisfy other types of interventions (e.g. smoke cessation, coaching, etc.).

This approach yields tremendous value for both the HR team and the CFO. From an HR perspective, this approach is not overly critical of those with health issues. Rather, they are presented with information that should allow them to live healthier because they get their metrics in the healthy range or must become activated to improve their results. This is an important distinction – the goal is not to hold employees accountable for being healthy, only for following a healthy course of action if their metrics reveal areas of concern. For the CFO, employees who pay more are only paying a fairer share of the costs to which their unhealthy behavior is contributing – contrarily, health improvement drives control over claims cost.

Longer term, the goal as more employees become engaged, is to measure the effectiveness of the employer's Disease/Case Management (DM/CM) interventions and to determine if missing elements in the continuum of care can be identified and remedied (closing gaps in care). Employers, for whom this statement resonates, have gotten to the accountability stage and need to consider whether the current solutions are working or whether more draconian interventions are needed.

Until now, we've focused on individuals getting and acting on information. This more advanced stage means interventions are available to those with clinical conditions who are unwilling, or unable, to follow the clinical protocols called for in routine treatment of their disease. This group of individuals is aware of, but not engaging in outreach efforts to improve their care. This group is typically at significant medical risk and drives higher claims costs.

This stage reminds us of how critical the 3-5 strategic planning process is. When applied properly, the employer focuses on the key deliverables over successive years. The team, working together, identifies MetS and pre-disease indicators, as well as more advanced disease requiring greater interventions. Built into the plan are the metrics by which health and wellness will be measured and MetS first identified, and then controlled. Wellness, when targeted in this manner can yield powerful results in improving the employer's risk profile, reducing cost in the short term and bending the trend curve in the longer term.

This effective process defines the means by which an employer can drive to a population health strategy. Taking the most important observations from Figure 3, employers need to move their employees through the four key stages: Awareness, Participation, Engagement and Accountability. Each TEAM must define these stages in a context that works for them.

Creating the Necessary Culture of Change

HR leaders will gain confidence that a strategic plan as outlined is a strong base from which to operate. The HR leadership team must develop an infrastructure for synthesizing health information and ensuring that communication, with all staff, is crystal clear. Then, implementing this type of program and remaining dedicated to it, while difficult, is not an insurmountable challenge. And, the definition of collaboration must be extended to the advisor who will help in managing the process of modifying employee behavior enough to improve the health status of the employee population.

An interesting factor is that throughout the life cycle of such a program, the focus on awareness must be continuous. Even as an employer moves though several stages of intervention, keeping employees fully informed is critical. New employees must be on-boarded with this in mind, and an organization that grows by acquisition, must embed this into their transition plan. A passion for building team spirit will help drive change in a positive way.

This all hinges on the HR team's ability to foster senior management confidence that financial, as well as, human assets, are being managed. Investments made must yield the expected results – namely incremental improvements and a positive return through an improving risk profile and lower claim cost. It cannot be driven through withholding of clinical attention to disease; otherwise more serious concerns would emerge thereby producing exactly the opposite desired long-term effect.

Taking the Cultural Imperative of Change to the Next Stage

In the third and fourth years of their program, ABC moved to an outcome-based model. Recognizing a high level of MetS in their population (using roll-up data principally from wellness screenings), they re-structured incentive criteria for contribution reductions based on scores tied to HRP and metabolic scores that fell into acceptable ranges.

For ABC, progress was observable and that the investments made in disease management, biometric screening and Health Risk Appraisal completions, generated a positive Return on Investment (ROI). Depending on how it's measured, ABC achieved greater than a 4:1 ROI. Soft dollar savings for projected clinical risk avoidance, contribute more dramatically. Senior management needed to see the data that showed cost savings were real due to population health risk improvement – and results were confirmed. Specifically, the CEHP participants saw 22.2 percent fewer risks, and 36.4 percent lower cost impact, in year four than in year two.

- Specfic qualifications required that individuals had to meet three of five of the following criteria:

- HRA completion – score must be above the national average for age and gender

- BMI<=30

- Glucose =<99

- Triglycerides =<149

- Total Cholesterol Ratio = <4.97

- An employee unable to meet the 3/5 requirement could satisfy an alternative qualification by completing risk-related coaching.

- And, in the current/coming year, because ABC has seen a high percentage of its claims utilization from spouses, and because smoking has been a particularly challenging risk factor:

- An incentive for no/low levels of Creatinine in the blood was added (having done both extensive education on the dangers of smoking and having required non-smokers to certify same);

- ABC will move from a contribution in the HSA for spousal completion of the HRP to a consistent employee/spouse requirement, to meet four of the five criteria noted above (with those requirements tightening).

Currently, adherence to the program is in the 80 percent range underscored by approximately 80 percent participation in the HSA – the full 20 percent differential is being utilized and the increase to

30 percent or more will be applied in 2014. All of these elements will be included in the 3-5 year model to ensure it evolves strategically over the next several years.

Will ABC continue to evolve this strategy? Given that they have continuously improved the quality of their healthcare delivery model – they have improved their risk profile, the health status of their employee population, and their financial position – and they are riding this approach to 'zero-trend'. YES, they are committed to continuing to evolve this approach!

Has ABC bent the trend curve?

Without getting into specific data, as you can see in Figure 4, ABC has been able to reshape its trend curve. It's taken a huge amount of collaboration among the team and a close working relationship with the carrier and a number of other vendors that continue to play a role in the overall success of the program. When adjusted for plan design, ABC's trend, compared to the book of business (even with a higher average age by three years), is riding close to zero – substantially better than the benchmarked comparative data (Figure 4). Beating the trend line would have been substantial, but to beat it by this much and so close to 'zero' has resonated well with senior management.

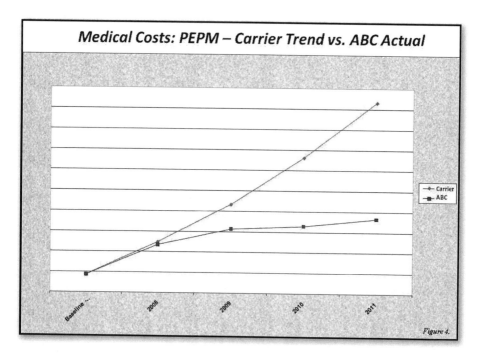

Figure 4.

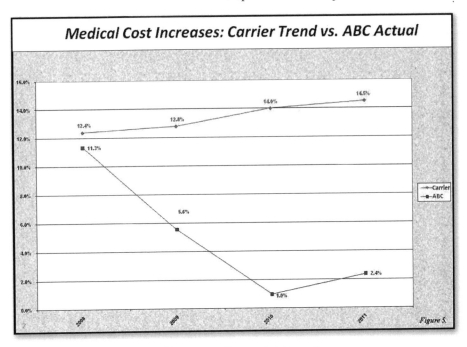

Medical Cost Increases: Carrier Trend vs. ABC Actual

Figure 5.

Translating 'Zero-trend' Into a Financial Result

Beating the trend line for the book of business was an enviable goal when ABC began this process, but translating the economic value of zero-trend was even more crucial. For the ABC COMPANY GHP, Figure 5 points to the significant amount by which their trend is better than the benchmarked book of business. More to the point, ABC has driven their trend to virtually '0'; and it would actually dip below '0' if spousal 'high' claimants were removed from the data. The delta over the four years charted, is a savings of approximately $15M.

And, while we would not seek to adjust the trend on the basis of spousal differential, the point needs to be made that most attention in group health plans, is paid to the employee with targeted wellness interventions stopping short of the spouse. This figure highlights both the success of the program as engineered, but also points to the need for broadening that effort to the spouses – the next evolution of ABC's 3-5 year dashboard, includes this change. As such, it intensifies, not negates, the work to date.

There is clearly more work to do, but the stage is set for what must come next and what ABC can expect in terms of ROI. Longer term, the focus will be on integrating the dental program in order to derive value from the connection between oral and physical health. And further integration of the wellness strategy with Disability (DI) and Workers' Comp (WC) will be pursued on a parallel basis – clearly as the health of the population improves, corollary improvements in DI and WC can be expected and ROI optimized.

Strengthening Incentives if survived through Federal Healthcare Reform

Meanwhile, as the ABC Wellness Program continues to build momentum, Healthcare Reform law evolves in Washington, with 'good wellness news' written into the statutory language. In part, these cost management tools will be necessary to help offset expanded coverage as well as an expectation that a growing number of participants will be supported by the employer-based system – bottom line, there is a strong emphasis in PPACA on employer-based wellness.

The Impact of Change

Especially for large employers, who are directly impacted by claims costs for coverage expansions, 'Health and Wellness' management is a critical tool advisors need to help employers manage cost more aggressively. Those expansions, including required health coverage eligibility for adult dependents to 26, elimination of most benefit caps, increased administrative and compliance burden, etc. are already driving costs up – and that will only accelerate.

Accordingly, employers stand at a precipice in bending the trend curve in their favor to offset expected cost escalation due to PPACA; as well as the burden they will bear if Cadillac Tax thresholds are breached in 2018. Employers must act now and take advantage of the tools outlined above to improve employee accountability in managing their health and being more accountable in their healthcare decision making. Employers will benefit from cost management opportunities while improving population health – the focus that must be on controlling claims!

The pie chart in Figure 6 makes the point – we need to focus on the 86 percent component of the cost, which is represented by claims. The larger the employer, the greater the direct benefit to the bottom line cost structure. And, given that most experts agree that 50 percent to 70 percent of claims costs are driven by controllable behaviors, it underscores the importance of keeping employees focused on staying healthy, incentivizing them to make smart healthcare purchasing decisions and managing disease aggressively and effectively. The underpinnings of healthcare reform reinforce ABC's approach and the success of its strategic benefits planning process.

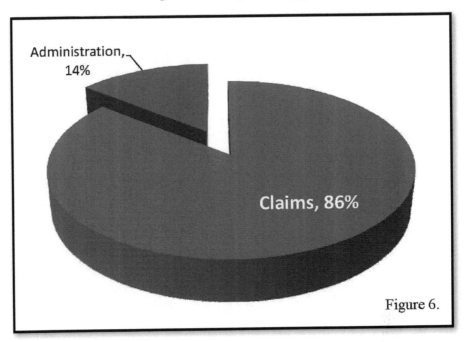

Figure 6.

Healthcare Reform – Wellness Elements

Taking an even closer look at reform, the June 2012 Supreme Court Decision upheld the provisions already in place, while still in front of us lay the impacts of the 2012 election. It is likely that even if the election results change the tenor of the political positioning, several key wellness elements of the law will survive. Such elements center on initiatives that align incentives with healthier behaviors and promote more focused wellness and disease management protocols.

- Plans will likely continue covering preventive care, mental health, and dental and vision for children;

- Chain restaurants and vending machines that sell food will be required to disclose nutritional information (already in effect in many states and municipalities);

- A new National Prevention, Health Promotion, and Public Health Council will be formed to develop a national health improvement strategy;

- The federal reimbursement program (reinsurance for early

retirees) is an employment-based plan that stipulates an employer's plan must implement programs and procedures to generate cost savings with respect to employees with chronic or high-cost conditions;

- Claim costs and wellness investments may be combined into a single category for reporting on claims and claims improvement – thus providing regulatory validation for wellness initiatives having direct impact on reductions to claim expense;

- The Comparative Research Fee ($1 per covered life for plan/policy years ending in 2013; $2 in 2014) will fund the Patient-Centered Outcomes Research Trust Fund (PCORTF). This funding will assist patients, clinicians and purchasers in making informed health decisions. The goal is using evidence-based decision making/treatment to assess protocols, and improve health outcomes, clinical effectiveness, and appropriateness of medical treatment. This provision signals a more aggressive consideration of clinical data in more effectively managing health and wellness, thereby positively impacting cost in the short term and trend, in the longer term;

- Looking ahead, by 2014, wellness initiatives could drive to an even higher level with additional market reforms. For example, Essential Benefits will include a mix of component benefits such as wellness and preventative services, chronic disease management;

- Incentive Reinforcements:

- Small group plans will be priced with disincentives for smokers: tobacco use will drive pricing in the plan (1.5:1 ratio) and age will be similarly considered (3:1 ratio) – a message that transcends group size;

- The law indicates that plan sponsors will be able to promote wellness by shifting 30 percent of premium to unhealthy employees (Federal regulators now manage to a 20 percent differential and will have the authority to raise the prescribed percentage from 30 percent or potentially 50 percent in the future). The reward can be a reduced premium/rebate, discount, cost-sharing waiver, inapplicable surcharge, or benefit enhancement;

- Plan Reporting on Care Management Provisions: And, at the end of the day, employers will have to report on provisions that improve health outcomes through quality reporting, effective case management, care coordination, chronic disease management, and care compliance initiatives.

Taking ABC COMPANY's and Your Performance to the NEXT LEVEL
To bring our discussion full circle, I've touched on ABC's program and the implications for plan sponsors in developing a program of their own. The bottom line is that any program must be developed in the context of the organization's culture and through a well-executed strategic benefits plan; with that process considering short and long objectives as well as an associated benefit plan and incentive design issues and the impacts of healthcare reform.

Through this chapter we've tracked ABC COMPANY's progress from incentive-based to value-based to compliance/outcome-based designs and from awareness through accountability. And, we took note of a changing emphasis to reach the more challenging population – spouses and smokers. Given the health and cost implications of these two sub-populations, ABC will increasingly focus incentives on accountable behavior – because they have the data, they know where to look, and they can point to proof of value. I further expect they'll take a closer look at dental health as well as the impacts health and wellness have on DI and WC as noted earlier – and rely on the team to focus efforts on managing Total Absence and Productivity.

But I don't expect ABC or other employers to stop there, but rather adapt to the changing delivery system. As the system moves toward paying for improved clinical outcomes rather than unit cost, Accountable Care Organizations (ACOs), will be held to higher standards in the delivery of improved clinical outcomes – and reimbursed accordingly. The best prepared employers will evolve their programs now, to extract the highest and best value from ACOs later. We can't cover this topic at length in this chapter, but employers that are already doing some heavy lifting, driving to an outcome-based result, will be better positioned to align their outcome objectives with those favored by ACOs.

Organizations that optimize their investments by improving the health status of the population, managing to higher quality outcomes and improving their cost structure/trend position will help. And even if not perfectly aligned, achieving those goals will put them in the category of high performing organization that so many shoot for and all-too-often fall short of.

Planning effectively, driving a strategic model and never losing sight of these objectives, positions employers to take advantage of very effective tools.

CHAPTER 10
Interventions and Best Practices

Zero Trends: Health as a Serious Economic Strategy
Dee W. Edington, Ph.D.

Introduction

This chapter is a condensed version of the *Zero Trends: Health as a Serious Economic Strategy** book. *Zero Trends* was organized into three primary sections: The Mission, The Business Case and The Solution. Companies that embrace these transformational concepts will be rewarded financially by zero cost trends, increased effectiveness in the workplace, increased health status of the workforce and its designation as a great place to work.

Poor health is a serious threat to individuals, businesses and our economy, and cannot be tolerated; we need to act now. Therefore, it requires a serious individual, business and economic strategy to reverse past and current ways of thinking and use of resources. The comments and suggestions in this chapter (taken from the *Zero Trends* book) may be irritating or challenging to some readers.

The suggestions in *Zero Trends*, and in this chapter, are presented as a challenge to all to find a new level of thinking to address the threats imposed by poor and worsening health. The intention is to raise the bar for success and thereby challenge those companies willing to make the transformation necessary to become champion companies.

The Mission: Regaining Vitality for Corporate America and for Americans. As Albert Einstein would have suggested, it is time for a new level of thinking about health management to bring about a sustainable and thriving workplace and workforce. The first section in *Zero Trends*, and in this Chapter, previews the essential elements of a new health management system for Americans and concludes with the key concepts that set the book apart. The objective is to introduce readers to the path for developing a strategy to obtain a sustainable and thriving workplace and workforce by focusing on the environment and culture of the workplace, the health status of the workforce, and the message: "Let's create winners, one small step at a time; and the first step is don't get worse."

The Business Case: Health Management as a Serious Business Strategy. This section highlights the work of the University of Michigan Health Management Research Center in developing the business case for integrating an effective health management component into the traditional employer health benefit model. The section critically examines the current medical and wellness strategies of "waiting for sickness or high health risk and then fixing the defects" which is embraced by most companies. *Zero Trends* proposed a new population-based model that positions sustainable and thriving workplaces and workforces first. The data demonstrates the potential of corporate and individual wellness and sickness strategies to be effective in controlling costs and improving overall health status of the workplace and of the individual worker.

The Solution: Integrating Health Status into the Company Culture. The solution builds upon the company's five fundamental pillars and utilizes evidence-based strategies designed to integrate health status into the culture of the workplace and workforce. The objective is to facilitate high-level health status for the workplace and all employees, therefore economically benefiting both individuals and their companies. This section does not aim to provide a tool kit of resources, but to share the process. Each pillar is outlined into four research-based levels of organizational engagement which the reader can use in selecting their appropriate investment strategy and desire level of outcome results.

Section I

The Mission: Regaining Vitality in Corporate America and in Americans.
The purpose of writing *Zero Trends* was to change the conversation around health. For too long America and the rest of the world allowed the medical profession to capture the meaning of health and define it as the absence or modification of diagnosed disease. Unfortunately individuals in the populations and companies accepted that definition. As a consequence, countries and companies acquiesced and just paid whatever the associated medical professions charged. To transform the conversation, one needs to redefine health from seeing health as not only the absence of disease but to a more inclusive concept of health as vitality, energy and positive thoughts. We always want to think about caring for those in need, or the sick; but we must also think about helping the healthy people stay healthy. In the past many decades we have focused too much on the cost of healthcare and we now need to broaden our focus also to include the

total value of a healthy person. Health is more than just the health of an individual but also the health of the population and more than just getting individual participation in healthy behaviors but also in engaging populations in total positive engagement. Finally we must enhance our focus from individual behavioral change to population health within a culture where healthy well-being is held in high esteem.

In 2008-2009 when *Zero Trends* was being written, low cost wages were being chased around the world and that was the gold standard for achieving high profitability of companies. The projection made in *Zero Trends* was that going forward the new competitive advantage for companies and countries was going to be healthy and highly productive people and systems.

The concept of self-leadership and self-efficacy is critically important to develop in each workplace and workforce. If America or any country is to regain or maintain a healthy, thriving and sustainable workplace and workforce each person needs to allowed to develop as a self-leader with the confidence that they can reach a new and higher levels of health. Most of the journey towards developing winners will be to achieve one small win at a time and the first win will be to not get worse. After self-leaders do not get worse for a period of time they can move to a higher level, one small step at a time.

At the time of writing *Zero Trends* it was apparent that a national and worldwide positive healthy well-being movement was about to happen and now the movement has continued and it will soon become irreversible.

Section II

The Business Case: Health Management as a Serious Business Strategy.
The business case as presented in *Zero Trends* is a summary of over thirty years (1977-2008) of experience and over 200 publications from the UM-HMRC. The observational methods consisted of a variety of cross-sectional and longitudinal studies using workplace and workforce populations. Personal health risk factors were chosen as the criterion for health status with respect to the early Framingham and other longitudinal studies which identified certain health behaviors or risks as precursors to future occurrence of disease.

The systematic research strategy during those years was to first establish the risk-cost relationship. This had to be established because the previous proven relationships were between risks and disease. In 2012 this seems trivial but in 1977-1982 it was necessary to establish that risk-cost relationship. The next step was to investigate the impact of change in risks on change in costs and finally to demonstrate the time course of the change in risks and costs.

Risk-Cost Relationship. The initial set of observations was to examine the impact of using medical definitions of high risk for each of 15 individual risk factors. The data demonstrated that for each of the risk factors the high risk individuals (for that risk) were more expensive on average than the low risk individuals. In certain populations alcohol consumption did not follow the general cost trend.

For the purpose of statistical analyses and as an index of general health status of the population, it was discovered that a grouping of the behaviors and risks make more sense. Later it was discovered why the combinations made sense: risks typically do not travel together but they travel in various combinations. The most simplistic stratification was found to be low-risk at 0-2 single risk factors; medium-risk at 3-4 risks; and, high-risk status at 5 or more individual risks. These three groupings showed remarkable and consistent relationships with costs, including medical, pharmacy, worker's comp., absent days, short term disability and lost time at work and in each of the industry sectors.

Excess Risks related to Excess Costs. Many providers of health promotion or wellness programs use the excess costs calculations as the basis of showing a financial impact from their intervention programs. The excess cost calculation assumes that the cost of the low risk individuals (0-2 risks) is the ultimate achievable base cost for the population. The cost of the medium risk minus the cost of the low risk individuals is the extra costs due to the extra risks for that medium risk population. The same calculation is appropriate for the high risk and the non-participants. The next step in the calculation is to multiply the excess costs in each category by the total number of people in the respective category, which when summed is the total excess costs for the total population. The total cost in the population is the number of people in each category times the total cost for the category.

The final step is to calculate the percent excess cost which is obtained by dividing the excess costs by the total costs. The percent excess costs is then the maximum potential savings if everyone in the organization reduces their risk to two or fewer and that the costs followed the risk reduction. Most likely the maximum potential savings will not be achieved but some portion (perhaps 20 percent to 25 percent) is likely to be realized.

Change in Risks lead to Change in Costs. The set of observations in this journey explored the relationship between change in risks or risk status to the change in costs or cost statue. The data demonstrated that these change scores followed the expected direction with medical and pharmacy costs. When the other outcome measures were used the direction of the change was not as consistent.

These observations were the most critical is demonstrating that when risks changed, costs changed in the same direction. This finding was the first step in recognizing the critical importance of helping the low risk individual stay low risk because as was demonstrated later the natural flow of a population (or the do nothing strategy) is to high risk.

Natural Flow of Risks and Costs in a Population. Without knowing the natural flow (or the do nothing strategy) of a population it is nearly impossible to know the results of any attempt to calculate the impact of any program or initiative. Thus, knowing the natural flow of health risks and health care costs in a population is critical since any intervention or program needs to beat the natural flow or value of the program should be question.

In a cross-sectional study the age ranges of the population is categorized and the number of risks for each categorization is determined. As the age categories increase the number of risks increase up to a certain point where the risks level off and then decrease into the older categories. The cross-sectional studies are interesting but their weakness is that the data do not indicate what happened to the people as they aged. When this is examined by longitudinal methods age continues to increase over time but the total number of risks is the sum of those that increase risks and those that decrease the number of risks. The major learning in this series of observations was that the number of low risk individuals, typically the objective of a health program, can be impacted in one of three ways: increase the number of people who stay low risk over time; increase the number who decrease risk to the low risk level; or decrease the number of people who increase their risks to a higher level of medium or high risk.

The importance of this work was to redefine the outcome measure of medical or wellness intervention programs. The bottom line is not the number of risks reduced but the number reduced minus the number increased. Net risk reduction is the key metric related to change in risk status.

Section III

The Solution: Integrating Health Status into the Company Culture
There is a major disconnect between the expected results of behavioral change programs (interventions) and the past and current evaluation of the performance of these programs. What is seriously missing is an operational framework that results in a systematic approach. The five-pillar system in *Zero Trends* was designed to meet the observed flaws in the simplistic behavioral change tactics typical of most workplace health promotion programs. This systematic approach can be broken into the following five pillars:

- Senior Leadership: create a health related vision for the organization that is connected to overall company strategy

- Operational Leadership: typically this is implemented by human resources to create a supportive environment and culture which supports all employees to do the right thing

- Self-Leadership: encourage all employees to develop as self-leaders so they have the self-efficacy and are empowered to make decisions for themselves and their families

- Recognize and reward positive actions

- Quality Assurance: measure and share all strategies and outcomes and use the outcomes to improve and evolve the strategies in the journey to a Champion Company

The focus of the systematic framework is to incorporate the vision of a healthy and high performing workplace into the environment and culture of the company. Most Companies already have incorporated

Safety and Quality into the culture. These two successes provide a roadmap to do the same for health.

The ultimate objective is to facilitate high-level positive health status and high performance for the workplace and for all employees which benefit the individuals, their families, their co-workers and the company. This strategy has the potential to engage the total workplace and population to enable all employees to capture the total value of health and create and support health as a place in the environment and culture.

Create a vision for the Company to implement a Value Based Health System.

Senior Leaders and all managers, including union leaders, have to recognize that healthcare costs are a threat to the company (and unions) and are core survival issues in these times of intense competition (locally and globally) and financial pressures. In contrast they need to recognize the healthy wellbeing is a positive force to create a sustainable and thriving workplace and workforce. If they do not recognize these two fundamental drivers of and do not create environments and cultures where they can grow healthy wellbeing in the workplace and workforce someone else will and the company will lose employees, competitive advantage and their overall way of life.

Senior leaders others must provide a vision for the company and for the employees where everyone shows up for work, regardless of their work location, on time and with high energy and resilience; they are high performers during the work period; and, when they finish their work period, they leave with high energy and resilience. They will then apply that same energy and high performance to their family life and to their community.

The process of communicating the vision means that the leaders will have to be committed to the concept of health as a competitive advantage in order to provide the appropriate resources across the full spectrum of the health management continuum; be role models of the concept; continuously communicate the message and vision; and, have the courage to continue along the journey.

Create a supportive environment and culture which encourages managers and employees doing the right thing.

The vision will not be implemented without a planned and integrated strategy and seamlessly implemented at the level of the local leadership. The vision from the senior level will come alive in the environment and culture created by the company managers. The combination of vision and environment/culture will be the heart and soul of a champion company and will create the structure for a healthy and high performing workplaces and employees and great pride in the company.

The structure part of the environment includes, among others, fair wages, integrated and well-designed benefit plans, easily accessible health promoting resources, resilience training, self-leadership training, and healthy choices at each opportunity.

The culture piece of the environment starts with the senior leaders and permeates throughout the organization as positive role models, peer support, managers' support, mutual trust, norms, positive expectations, creativity and enthusiasm. In addition the culture is complete only when feedback and creative information flows from the individual member of the organization up through the ranks.

Once everyone understands the vision, realizes the intent of the environmental factors and sees and trusts the individual and organizational support, the culture reaches a point where individual and organizational energy is renewable and sustainable. Although the concept of addressing cultural issues in healthcare is not new, identification of a health initiative as a cultural phenomenon departs dramatically from the long standing practices of the new or modified benefit package. This new focus, i.e. creating a culture where health is integral, represents a major breakthrough in both measurement and benefit design.

The transformation to a vision of a champion company system requires a new set of tools to educate, communicate and engage all employees in the urgency (financially and potential pain and suffering events). An example is the next generation health assessments which include components related to determinates of health beyond health behaviors and risks, such as positive health wellbeing attributes and health and performance issues related to the workplace, community and family environments and cultures.

Leaders and managers need to extend their involvement from only doing plan design to seriously soliciting employee feedback about barriers to healthy wellbeing and then acting on that feedback. The transformation will require a move from best practices as the standard to "next" practices which incorporate a higher level vision.

Encourage all employees to become self-leaders and feel empowered to take care of themselves and their families.
Companies need employees who are self-leaders in order to be competitive going forward. This will be accomplished by recruitment, mentoring and on-the-job training. The organization will need to utilize the supportive environment and culture to provide opportunities for employees and their families to become winners, help all employees not get worse and help the low-risk and healthy employees stay low-risk and healthy.

The needed tactics will include communications to manage expectations at all levels of the organization; special orientation and training opportunities centered around the characteristics of positive healthy high performing individuals; low-risk maintenance programs; and some of the traditional risk reduction programs. Wellness programs, disease management programs and traditional acute and chronic care programs will remain core to a comprehensive health benefit program in this pillar of the *Zero Trends* system.

Recognize and reward positive actions in work teams and employees.
The emphasis on self-leadership continues throughout the year in order to reach the desired outcome of a positive healthy high performing individual working in an environment and culture that supports positive and healthy actions. This is in contrast to cash or other individual incentives that happen once or twice during the year. Constant communication and recognition keeps the momentum going and keeps participants engaged, either maintaining their health status or making improvements.

Another effective strategy could be to have positive activities in the current year lead to a qualification threshold for recognitions during the following year. Regardless of the type of motivation that is used, it is crucial that they are not viewed as entitlements. An effective incentive follows positive actions such as an investment for current of future returns. On occasion negative incentives may be necessary.

A health-oriented environment and culture reinforces the population-based strategy. Engage everyone in skill development and motivational opportunities. A highly productive member is not only healthy but one that also has competitive skills for their job and is highly motivated to be a champion within a champion company.

Measure and share all strategies and outcomes and use the outcomes to improve and evolve the strategies.
The quality assurance pillar involves data-driven decision making and is a critical component of integrating positive healthy wellbeing performance at the workplace and in the workforce into the culture of the company. The highest level objectives are those champion organizational and individual traits identified in earlier parts of the systematic pillar system.

The senior leaders should identify at least three metrics which will give them a sense of the progress of moving the employees and thus the Company towards a champion Company and moving individuals towards self-leadership. The quality assurance system needs to be capable of measuring progress towards these selected outcomes.

There are preliminary and intermediate objectives (early indicators) for the company and individual engagement in which a few outcomes might be measured (program participation rates or health risk prevalence, for example). A champion company, however, will take the major step of measuring, evaluating and making decisions based on a whole host of available data. These might include: member satisfaction, changes in the environment and culture, management and alignment of policies and procedures, employee progress on the modules and coaching, employee participation and then engagement, maintenance or reduction in health risks, family and community involvement, shift from costs to investment, beating the natural flow, bending the cost trend lines, etc.

The accomplishment of an effective and real time quality assurance system would be realized by a comprehensive data integration system. The data systems need to be connected to the appropriate data sources (data warehouse) and integrated to create data information systems from which a wide variety of metrics can be calculated and then the appropriate metrics provided upon request in order to facilitate effective and timely decision support.

Section IV

Epilogue: Moving Forward, Beyond Zero Trends.

At the time of writing *Zero Trends* it was apparent that a national and worldwide positive health awareness and healthy wellbeing movement was beginning to take shape. Now, in 2012 the movement has continued to escalate and it will soon be irreversible.

Since the writing of *Zero Trends*, I have left the University of Michigan and formed a private company, Edington Associates along with four other Associates. The purpose of the University spin-off company is to build upon 30 years of research and implement The Solutions section in the *Zero Trends* book.

The process of implementing *Zero Trends* in private and public sector organizations and populations has led me to an additional transformation of the Five Pillar Solutions system described in the book. The revised Solution utilizes the five pillars approach but superimposed upon that system are the guiding concepts of Strategic, Systematic, Systemic and Sustainable and a completely new set of new and innovative tools. The solution for the 21st Century must be created by applying strategic, systematic, systemic and sustainable healthy and economic solutions. The strategic emphasis is about providing a plan that addresses the current problems and opportunities for the company. Almost all Companies take their lead from senior managers balanced by consensus agreement throughout the organization and bottom up feedback (systematic). The process is continuous and sets the expectations and "rules" how all plan participants feel and act (systemic). The final (sustainable) part of the process comes through feedback to each level in the organization and movement in the outcome metrics.

- The Solution in the *Zero Trends* book began with a vision from the Senior Leaders connecting the value of healthy employees with company strategy. The revised strategic vision connects the value of a healthy workplace and workforce with a sustainable and thriving company strategy.

- The Solution in the *Zero Trends* book emphasized the importance of creating a supportive culture of health to allow the vision to come alive. The revised systematic environmental and cultural strategies includes closing the gaps between the vision and the current state: real and ideal, levels of managers, manager and other employees. Additional training in the why and how of healthy wellbeing strategies and leading to systemic solutions.

- The Solution in the *Zero Trends* book emphasized low-risk being the health-related outcome. In the revised solution is now clear that becoming and remaining low-risk is not enough to achieve healthy wellbeing. The revised health-related systemic outcome includes several other determinants of total health or well-being, including other person-centric behaviors and attitudes; the workplace environment and culture; the family environment and culture; the community environment and culture; and other synergistic determinates of the being a best place to work and high quality of life and well-being.

- The Solution in the *Zero Trends* book emphasizes rewards and recognition of positive actions. The revised systemic solution maintains this feature but also includes tracking progress from extrinsic-tangible to intrinsic-tangible to intrinsic-intangible recognition

- The Solution in the *Zero Trends* book emphasized measured economic and qualitative outcomes as quality assurance. The revised sustainable quality assurance process sets the measurement as a journey rather than a destination. The revised quality assurance system tracks progress along the journey based upon real time measures and indicates when the initiative is off track and how to get back on track. It provides this feedback to all stakeholders.

Changing Workplace Health Culture
By: Scott Pedersen, Ph.D., Casey Mainsbridge, Dean Cooley, Ph.D.

Addressing Prolonged Occupational Sitting Time

Prolonged occupational sitting time (POST) is a silent killer for even the healthiest of working adults. Currently, an office-based worker spends an average of 80,000 hours sitting during the course of their working life[1]. Recent data suggests that POST of four hours or more is a health risk for all desk-based employees[2-7]. Exposure to this hazard increases the risk of suffering from diseases related to increased morbidity and mortality. Moreover, a worker's increased level of fitness may only ameliorate some of the risk[8-10]. That is, even workers with high levels of physical fitness may still be at risk if they sit for more than four hours per day. Research from the Baker IDI institute[11-13] showed an association between POST and increases in waist girth, weight, body mass index and negative blood lipid profiles (i.e., blood glucose, lipoprotein lipase [LPL]), irrespective of current fitness level. Evidence[14] from bus drivers involved in sedentary employment has demonstrated that they are twice as susceptible to contracting cardiovascular disease (CVD) than bus conductors who regularly engage in standing or light activities during work. In more direct evidence related to POST[8], individuals who sat for prolonged periods were nearly three times more likely to experience CVD relative to individuals who sat for shorter amounts of time. Data[3] revealed that when individuals were immobilized during bed rest, this resulted in a 27 percent lower level of LPL, which is comparable to levels seen in routine sedentary living. Individuals who work in desk-based workplace environments have very little choice in the amount of sitting they do during the typical workday or the type of activities they perform. There is a need for POST to be addressed in the design and prescription of workplace health and wellbeing programs (WHWP) to reverse the adverse health effects associated with such sedentary behaviour.

Many WHWPs are currently predicated on a traditional "huff-and-puff" exercise attitude and represent a "one-size-fits-all" approach. These programs target the "fitness fanatic", not necessarily the individuals who could benefit the most from an appropriate WHWP. The unhealthiest adults, who have never engaged in physical activity programming, stand to receive the most benefit from WHWPs predicated on reducing the risks associated with the workplace hazard of POST. Traditional WHWPs fail to adequately address the issue of changing habits; rather they rely on happenstance. For example, pedometer-based interventions like the Global Corporate Challenge[15] are of short duration, require the employee to dedicate personal time to the initiative, offer little feedback to the worker, and thus, tend to have low uptake and adherence rates for employees not previously engaged in voluntary exercise. Consequently, when evaluated in terms of success these types of WHWPs may provide a false positive because they recruit the already-active and miss those most in need of help. Moreover, for those who have changed their behaviours from sedentary to active, once the program finishes these employees often regress to their old health habits of sedentary workplace behaviour. There is a body of literature that advocates the need to reintroduce incidental physical activity back into the workday because such a change may have greater reach than current WHWP practices. For example, more employees are likely to adhere to a WHWP that requires them to simply stand while talking on the phone rather than having to change into a swimsuit and swim laps during lunch. Chau and colleagues[16] lamented from a review of specific literature the absence of WHWPs that target a reduction in POST. Therefore, aiming to reduce POST by introducing short bursts of physical activity throughout the workday may offer an innovative approach to improving employee health. Integral to this approach is the recognition that when employees make decisions about their health, there are multiple factors that influence their decision making. These influences are encapsulated in social-ecological theories.

Behaviour Change Underpinned by Theory

Without conscious awareness many employers create a desk-based work environment neglectfully planned to promote sedentary behaviour[17]. Leather roller chairs, ergonomically fit desks, and electronic forms of intra-office communication are all examples of technology designed to keep employees seated for as long as possible in the name of work productivity. The evolution of technology in the office environment has morphed it into one of comfort, convenience and limited space. This has led employees to develop work habits that result in increased sedentariness because employers equate time spent at a desk as a sign of work productivity. Nevertheless, recent evidence suggests that the philosophy of requiring desk-based workers to perform all of their daily tasks while seated at their desks to facilitate production may be counterintuitive[18]. Findings suggest that a reduction in employee longevity due to negative workplace attributes like absenteeism and presenteeism may be attributed to long bouts of sedentary behaviour[1]. Moreover, it has been proposed that healthy employees are more productive than unhealthy workers[19]. Therefore, business leaders and officers who are concerned with the bottom line should consider improving their workplace health culture, namely through creating a workplace environment that fosters social support for becoming more active during working hours.

Researchers use social-ecological theory as an overarching framework for understanding the dynamic interrelations among diverse personal and environmental factors related to health behaviour change[20]. More specifically, in an attempt to promote workplace health behaviour, some employers have utilised environment-focused interventions (e.g., employers challenging employees to use the stairs instead of the lift as a type of workplace competition) to improve the social acceptance of physical activity in the workplace by the employees[21]. Perhaps unbeknownst to these employers, practical applications such as the one illustrated above have utilised elements of Bronfrenbrenner's[22] ecological systems theory of human development, which depicts multiple "layers" of the environment to influence behaviour change. These layers include the microsystem, mesosystem, exosystem and macrosystem. Specifically applying these layers to the typical office-based workplace environment, the microsystem may include structures with which employees have direct contact with on a daily basis, such as their desk and their office colleagues. These structures have a direct influence in shaping behavior, and in turn, may be shaped by behaviour[23]. The next layer, referred to as the mesosystem, represents the connections between the various structures within an employees' microsystem. For example, all employees within a workplace may choose to take the lift to the fifth floor instead of using the stairs because peer pressure dictates this to be the preferred means of transport. The next social-ecological layer within this theory is the exosystem, with which employees do not interact with directly, but by which the microsystem may be manipulated, as in the case of workplace policies that mandate the amount of break time call centre employees can be off the phone and away from their workstation. Finally, the macrosystem layer is composed of cultural values and norms common to all desk-based workplaces; such as early-career employees believing that they should not leave their desk in fear of the perception that they may be seen as unproductive and wasting company time. In further interpreting this theory it is important to note that these four layers are not mutually exclusive, but are intertwined in how they may contribute to workplace health behavior change.

A WHWP underpinned by social-ecological theory could incorporate elements of the physical environment and social environment, in combination with a physical activity focus, in an attempt to attract and maintain greater employee interest and adherence in the initiative[24]. Identifying all of the factors within the workplace environment that are influential in encouraging sedentariness should provide guidance in the development of WHWP strategies for transposing these barriers into physical activity affordances, and thereby reducing POST. For example, employees in a shared office space may choose to have a walking meeting where instead of meeting around a conference table, they choose to walk around the building together while discussing work-related agenda items and strategic plans for corporate growth. Interpreting all of the influences within the workplace environment, and effectively addressing them, presents an opportunity to increase the effectiveness of WHWPs.

A Case Study into Effective WHWPs: Project PAUSE

In 2010, a research team from the University of Tasmania was approached by Tasmania Police to help solve a problem identified in a large-scale survey of the health and wellbeing of public servants in Tasmania. Specifically, one result showed that Tasmania Police personnel who were assigned to desk-based work sat for long periods of time. Based on emerging research, Tasmania Police recognized that POST may present health risks for their desk-based personnel. Subsequent meetings between Tasmania Police and the research team used a solution-focused approach that incorporated principles of cultural flexibility (an intervention that solves a specific problem within a specific environment) prevention rather than rehabilitation (fix the problem before it occurs) and small changes to a large group (a solution for all workers rather than specific groups within the population). Meetings between Tasmania Police and the research team reached a consensus that the health risks associated with POST could be minimized if desk-based workers became engaged in regular short bursts of physical activity. The rationale was that if desk-based workers were regularly performing physical activity through their work hours, their POST would be regularly interrupted. Subsequently, there would be an amelioration of the health risks associated with POST. Tasmania Police and the research team recognize The Corporate Health & Wellness Association's (CHWA) annual event e that an e-health approach presented the best solution because it was low in cost and delivery, and had the potential to reach across a large number of police stations throughout the state. Guided by the socio-ecological theory, the research team designed and implemented an internet-based WHWP called Project PAUSE (Physical Activity Using Short-burst Exercise). The researchers recognized that the health decisions for this intervention had multiple inputs. In reflecting this, changes were made at an organizational policy level whereby senior Tasmania Police management provided public and organizational support for the intervention by allowing personnel to participate in the intervention (time off from work duties to attend induction sessions), providing financial (allocation of money to develop the intervention, provision of equipment, and making free health assessments available to participants) and workplace (allowing employees to be away from their desks to participate in short bursts of physical activity regularly throughout the day) policy support. At an individual level, participants were provided with educational sessions highlighting the adverse health effects associated with POST; health screenings, including blood analysis; and most importantly, an innovative time-based prompting system delivered through a software application on employees' desktop computer, called Exertime.

The Intervention: Exertime

In comparison to the more typical WHWPs common in today's corporate organisations, Project PAUSE's objective was to change the sedentary nature of desk-based work by engineering physical activity back into employees' daily work habits. This strategy was orchestrated by using a desktop application called Exertime, an e-health solution that primarily reduces the amount of POST associated with desk-based work by replacing a health risk habit (sedentary behaviour) with a health-promoting habit (regular short bursts of physical activity). This unique e-health approach was designed to show desk-based employees how simple small changes to work habits, such as periodically executing small amounts of physical activity during work time, could result in positive changes to their health and wellbeing. To attract workers who do not normally engage in leisurely exercise, this e-health project utilised a regular "low-intensity, short duration" approach rather than the traditional once a day "huff-and-puff" exercise attitude.

Exertime encompassed a variety of technological innovations designed to improve desk-based employee health by allowing the employees to decide for themselves the most beneficial strategies for reducing their own workplace sedentariness. For example, Exertime initiated automatically at timed intervals throughout the workday; it contained a wide range of video demonstrations of an employee performing short-burst physical activities within an office space; and it provided employees with a recording function so they could track their daily progress in terms of daily energy expenditure, non-sitting time and frequency of activity choice. Each of these personalized features helped to motivate employees to adhere to the WHWP, allowing them to reap the health benefits of physical activity during working hours.

Exertime targeted employee health by utilising a passive-prompting system to help employees break the unconscious habit of POST. This was predicated on findings that demonstrated passive, automated prompts remove employees' need to act; whereas more active prompts, such as signs or posters, allow employees more freedom to choose to act or ignore the prompt[25]. The Exertime prompt is purposefully intrusive; if ignored, it will take over the employees' computer screen, forcing them to engage with the WHWP several times throughout the workday. Exertime forced employees to acknowledge the prompt by either immediately engaging the Exertime sequence, or by postponing the prompt for 5, 10, 30, or 45 minutes. The postpone feature was included in the design because it was understood by the researchers that there are times during the workday when it is undesirable to stop working to engage in short-burst physical activity. Nonetheless, Exertime prohibited employees from postponing the prompt for longer than one hour based on national guidelines for POST[26]. Regardless, employees must make a point of decision when prompted by the software. If the employee ignored the prompt for a period of time, Exertime took over the employee's computer screen and required him/her to get out of the chair and engage with the program before the person could continue working. This passive prompting promulgated an environmental influence on employee health in the workplace, forcing employees to reconsider how they spend their time while performing work responsibilities.

Once employees chose to engage the Exertime sequence, they were provided with a choice of more than 60 short-burst physical activities suitable for the working environment. The autonomy Exertime provided employees regarding choice, frequency and intensity of activities was an attractive element for the employees involved in Project PAUSE regardless of their prior experience in physical activity pursuits. Exertime activities included a wide variety of brief, low-impact physical activities suitable to be completed at a desk or around the office, and were designed to be fun and quick so as not to detract from daily work productivity. For example, one employee may choose to do only one desk squat when prompted, while another may walk to collect the office mail; one may select to do a stork stand while taking a phone call while another employee may choose to do five wall touches while waiting for the copy machine. All of these activities would be considered part of the program because they required employees to interrupt their sitting posture and substitute this behavior with a form of short-burst physical activity. Unlike other prompt-based health interventions, employees are not told what to do; Exertime merely provided a range of activity suggestions. In essence, this WHWP was completely self-directed, with employees free to individualize their own daily workouts while utilizing the office space environment as their own personal gymnasium. Enabling employees to perform their daily exercise in the office during work hours illustrated that the employers placed an emphasis on employee health and wellbeing. A health-promoting work environment has a culture that encourages all employees, regardless of fitness levels, to engage in movement-based activity while at work. In Project PAUSE, Exertime was the foundational component of a healthy work environment. Although each Exertime activity was initiated by the individual in response to a desktop prompt, this WHWP had a profound effect on the workplace health culture by having employees share their activities and progress with other co-workers.

The employees involved in Project PAUSE, not to mention several co-workers who were not directly involved in the trial, reported nearly a 100 percent adherence rate to the WHWP; that is, they responded to every prompt by at least standing. A contributing factor to this motivational maintenance was the real-time feedback feature of Exertime. For example, caloric expenditure was provided to employees at the end of each Exertime sequence in the form of a progressive bar graph. This bar graph contained a pre-set adjustable goal for how many calories employees should burn throughout the day. Many participants relayed that this feature was the key factor in making them adhere to the program, although not all participants were motivated by weight loss to maintain healthy behaviours at work. Many employees did not wish to burn calories, they just wanted to get out of their chair to break POST. For these employees, Exertime allowed them to view the amount of non-sitting time they accumulated over the workday by responding to the prompts. Although these feedback options, which could be viewed on a daily, weekly, or monthly basis, were only provided to the employees on a personal level to maintain confidentiality, this information became a source of social status for the employees to share with each other regarding their goal accomplishment. This change in the immediate workplace culture helped to reinforce a culture change throughout the rest of the workplace environment. For example, employees not involved in the study began to ask when they would be receiving Exertime on their computers.

In summation, there are two take-home messages for health professionals, occupational health and safety managers and employers. First, the use of an e-health solution increases the flexibility of health interventions; in this case, Exertime addressed workplace health issues. Consequently, a well-designed e-health solution increased the reach of an intervention and offered the opportunity to do so at lower costs than other interventions. Secondly, health interventions designed to change the number of interdependent but intertwined factors that influence health decisions offered substantial benefits over those that do not.

More specifically, it appeared that employees preferred to engage in regular, short bursts of physical activity that were suitable for the work environment. Employees involved in regular short bursts of physical activity recorded reductions in POST, had improvements in blood pressure, blood lipid profiles, self-reported quality of life and work productivity. Interview data revealed a spill-over effect where employees reported being more cognizant about the amount of sitting they did at work and at home and changed their behaviour accordingly. Moreover, we believe a key to the success of Exertime was that employees held in high regard the social capital that Exertime provided for enhancing their workplace health culture. Although many employees experienced an initial hesitation to perform the Exertime activities in front of others, in a relatively short amount of time they developed a sense of group belonging in becoming a healthier workplace, which led to a stronger overall adherence to the WHWP.

References

1. Thorp A, Dunstan DW, Clark B, Gardiner P, Healy G, Keegel T, Owen N, Winkler E. Stand up Australia: Sedentary behaviour in workers 2009. Medibank Private Limited. Queensland, Australia.

2. Dunn AL, Marcus BH, Kampert JB, Garcia ME, Kohl HW, Blair S. Comparison of lifestyle and structured interventions to increase physical activity and cardiorespiratory fitness: A randomised trial. JAMA 1999;281:327-334.

3. Hamilton MT, Areiqat E, Hamilton DG, Bey L. Plasma triglyceride metabolismin humans and rats during aging and physical actvity. International Journal of Sport Nutrition and Exercise Metabolism 2001;11:S97-S104.

4. Hamilton MT, Hamilton DG, Zderic TW. Role of low energy expenditure and sitting in obesity, metabolic syndrome, type 2 diabetes, and cardiovascular disease. Diabetes 2007;56(11):2655-67.

5. Hong Y, Rice T, Gagnon J, et al. Familiality of triglyceride and LPL response to exercise training: the HERITAGE Study. Medicine and Science in Sport and Exercise 2000;32(8):1438-1444.

6. Rankien T, Church TS, Rice T, Bouchard C, Blair S. Cardiorespiratory Fitness, BMI, and Risk of Hypertension: The HYPGENE Study. Medicine and Science in Sport and Exercise 2007;39(10):1687-1692.

7. Rankinen T, Church T, Rice T, et al. Effect of Endothelin 1 Genotype on Blood Pressure Is Dependent on Physical Activity or Fitness Levels. Hypertension 2007;50(6):1120-1125.

8. Weller I, Corey P. The impact of excluding non-leisure energy expenditure on the relation between physical activity and mortality in women. Epidemiology 1998;9:632-635.

9. Powell KE, Blair SN. The public health burdens of sedentary living habits: Theoretical but realistic estimates. Medicine and Science in Sport and Exercise 1994;26:851-856.

10. Jakicic JM, Wing AL, Butler BA, Robertson RJ. Prescribing exercise in multiple short bouts versus one continuous bout: effects of adherence, cardio-respiratory fitness and weight loss in overweight women. International Journal of Obesity 1995;19:893-901.

11. Dunstan DW, Salmon J, Healy GN, et al. Association of television viewing with fasting and 2-hr post-challenge plasma glucose levels in adults without diagnosed diabetes. Diabetes Care 2007;30:516-522.

12. Dunstan DW, Salmon J, Owen N, et al. Physical activity and television viewing in relation to risk of undiagnosed abnormal glucose metabolism in adults. Diabetes Care 2004;27:2603-2609.

13. Dunstan DW, Salmon J, Owen N, et al. Associations of TV viewing and physical activity with metabolic syndrome in Australian adults. Diabetologia 2005;48:2254-2261.

14. Morris JN, Healy GN, Raffle PA, Roberts CG, Parks JW. Coronary heart-disease and physical activity of work. Lancet 1953;265:1053-1057.

15. Global Corporate Challenge 2012. Retrieved from http://www.gettheworldmoving.com/about-us

16. Chau JY, van der Plog HP, van Uffelen JGZ, al. e. Are workplace interventions to reduce sitting effective? A systematic review. Preventative Medicine 2010;51(5):352-356.

17. Owen N, Leslie E, Salmon J, Fotheringham MJ. Environmental determinants of physical activity nd sedentary behaviour. Exercise and Sport Science Review 2000;36(4):153-158.

18. Brown W. A systematic review of the evidence exploring the association between sedentary behaviour in the workplace and health outcomes, and the strategies which encourage a change in sedentary behaviour in the workplace 2009. Health Promotion Branch, Population Health Queensland, Australia.

19. Medibank Private. The health of Australia's workforce 2005. Australia.

20. Schneider M, Stokols D. Multilevel theroies of behaviour change: A social ecological framework. In Shumaker SA, Ockene JK, Riekert KA. The handbook of behaviour change 2009. New York. Springer.

21. Quintiliani L, Sattelmiar J, Sorensen G. The workplace as a setting for interventions to improve diet and promote physical activity. Background paper prepared for the WHO/WEF Joint Event on Preventing Noncommunicable Diseases in the Workplace 2007. World Health Organisation.

22. Bronfrenbrenner U. Ecological systems theory. In Vasta R. Six theories of child development: Revised formulations and current issues 1992. London, Jessica Kingsley.

23. Sallis JF, Owen N. Ecological models. In Glanz K, Lewis F, Rimer BK. (eds.), Health Behaviour and Health Education: Theory, Research, and Practice (2nd ed.) 1997. San Francisco: Jossey-Bass.

24. Bennie JA, Timperio AF, Crawford DA, Dunstan DW, Salmon, JL. Associations between social ecological factors and self-reported short physical activity breaks during work hours among desk-based employees. Preventive Medicine 2011;53:44-47.

25. Roberts MC. (1978), Public health and health psychology: Two cats of Kilkenny? Professional Psychology: Research and Practice 1978;18(2):145-149.

26. Worksafe Australia. Guidance note for the prevention of occupational overuse Syndrome in keyboard employment. National Occupational Health and Safety Commission 1996. Canberra, Australia. National Government Publishing Service.

Key Ideas

- Prolonged occupational sitting time (POST).

- Recent data suggests that POST of four hours or more is a health risk for all desk-based employees. Exposure to this hazard increases the risk of suffering from diseases related to increased morbidity and mortality. Moreover, a worker's increased level of fitness may only ameliorate some of the risk. That is, even workers with high levels of physical fitness may still be at risk if they sit for more than four hours per day.

- Aiming to reduce POST by introducing short bursts of physical activity throughout the workday may offer an innovative approach to improving employee health.

- Leather roller chairs, ergonomically fit desks, and electronic forms of intra-office communication are all examples of technology designed to keep employees seated for as long as possible in the name of work productivity.

- Recent evidence suggests that the philosophy of requiring desk-based workers to perform all of their daily tasks while seated at their desks to facilitate production may be counterintuitive.

Questions

1. What is POST

   a. Prolonged Occupational Sitting Time

   b. Prolonged Occupational Standing Time

   c. Positive Occupational Stress Threshold

   d. Prolonged Occupational Stress Threshold

2. True or False: The best way to reduce POST is by allowing employees at least an hour of time away from their desk for prolonged workouts.

   a. True

   b. False

3. True or False: Workers with high fitness levels may be at risk if they sit more than 4 hours per day.

   a. True

   b. False

Combating the Job Stress Epidemic with Wellness
By: Kaye Kennedy

The Great Recession has changed the outlook of both workers and employers. Companies have had to adjust their business models and make tough decisions to survive and remain profitable. Downsizing, layoffs, cutbacks and consolidations have led to workers feeling an inordinate amount of stress. Subsequently, loyalty and trust are at an all-time low for many employees. Hence, the employee-employer relationship has been profoundly altered.

Background
Stress and work are synonymous. The inherent qualities of work will always cause some level of physical, mental and/or emotional tension on workers. Deadlines, budgets, presentations, sales quotas and such remain critical elements to job performance. However, the demands of the modern-day work environment are broadening. The landscape of the workplace remains dynamic and continually poses new types of stressors that require fresh solutions. The 2008 economic downturn added an acute level of stress that arguably had not been seen since the Great Depression. As economists wrangled over whether to call it an economic depression or recession, American workers were already feeling the undeniable effects of what President Obama would eventually call the Great Recession.

The recession left many jobless, as 8.8 million jobs were lost during the height of the downturn. Roughly, 8.4 million workers were forced into "involuntary" part-time employment. The Bureau of Labor Statistics reported that 2.8 million people were only "marginally attached" to the labor force. A million or so of these could be described as "discouraged" people who had abandoned all hopes of re-entering the workforce. Many college graduates were denied entry into the workforce as they were forced to compete with older, more experienced workers willing to work for less pay. Workers able to maintain their jobs faced new hurdles. Namely, a shrinking workforce, increased responsibility, a consolidation of roles, pay cuts, a reduction in benefits and looming uncertainty about the future of their jobs. A 2011 survey by the American Psychological Association found that in the U.S. 36 percent of employees reported experiencing chronic work stress, 31 percent were dissatisfied with their jobs and 32 percent planned to seek employment elsewhere.

Northern California-based Mervyn's was one of the first in the retail industry to fold under the pressure of a weak economy. In 2008, the 59-year-old department store chain closed its doors, rendering about 18,000 employees jobless. A former senior manager who put in 20 years with the organization said that many of her former co-workers are "still pounding the pavement looking for work." She described the morale of displaced workers at the time as bitter. The former Mervyn's employee stated that "losing a job is one of the most stressful things one can experience. It makes you question your self-worth and self-confidence but it also makes you become mentally tough. Sending out numerous resumes and not getting any feedback is disappointing. If you are contacted by a prospective employer it is very encouraging, whether it leads to a job offer or not."

Employers are not oblivious to the feelings of workers. Many not only sense the tension and disengagement, but they are seeing it as well. According to a 2009 Hewitt Associates LLC survey, 47 percent of employers think that employee trust has declined as a result of the way their company has managed its cost reductions. Even though companies may have real business reasons for not expanding their workforce, the existing employee base is stretched. Current employees are being asked to do more work and in some cases they are doing the job of two or three people. Companies are seeing this take a toll on the morale and motivation of workers. CareerBuilder Inc. reported that nearly a quarter of employers rated their organization's employee morale as low in 2009.

Key Problems

Job stress is a real issue. The World Health Organization has classified work-related stress as "a major challenge to workers' health and the health of their organizations." Job burnout, the result of chronic stress, is a growing problem. While stress is the precursor for burnout, the two have distinct differences. Stress is about having too much to deal with at work or at home, but there is still a sense of being able to get beyond it. The Mayo Clinic defines burnout as a particular type of job stress that manifests itself in a state of physical, emotional or mental exhaustion combined with doubts about one's competence and the value of one's work. Researchers from the University of Zaragosa (Spain) found that workers dealing with burnout typically attempt to adapt or protect themselves from it. Once they have reached the point of emotional exhaustion and lack of energy, workers believe that they are no longer able to participate on an emotional level. In an effort to deal with the onset of negative attitudes and feelings towards persons for whom work is done, depersonalization ensues.

Organizational psychologists describe three types of burnout: frenetic, under-challenged and worn-out. Frenetic burnout often occurs when workers become overzealous, ambitious or forced by circumstances to overload themselves with work to the point of "workaholism". There tends to be a correlation between the number of hours worked and the occurrence of frenetic burnout. The under-challenged worker is one who is not engaged and is often bored; a degree of cynicism often accompanies the under-challenged worker. Finally, the worn-out worker usually feels he has no opportunities for growth, or does not receive adequate recognition for his contributions. Employees who have held the same position for several years are more likely to show signs of being worn out. Researchers believe that burnout is on the rise for many reasons. Some reasons include the need to continually learn and adapt to new technology, less opportunities to engage in meaningful, face-to-face interaction with other workers, having to settle for jobs they are over-qualified for and having to take on more responsibility as a result of organizational changes, restructuring and such.

Job stress and burnout are salient, pervasive problems in the workplace that often manifest themselves in multiple ways. Some of the symptoms include fatigue, insomnia, negative spillover into personal relationships, headaches, high blood pressure, more frequent periods of sickness, depression, anxiety and alcohol or substance abuse. Classic, more performance-related symptoms that an employee may display range from poor memory, poor time management, and more sick calls to a negative attitude. Behavioral changes often occur, wherein employees are putting in more or less hours than normal. Employees are individuals, so the actual manifestations of stress and/or burnout will vary. In the early stages, they may not notice their own attitude shift or behavioral change. Some may become more withdrawn or resort to humor as a coping mechanism. Employees are often reluctant to ask for help and will attempt to mask any problems. In extreme cases, they will act out. Many remember the story of the JetBlue flight attendant who exited via the plane's emergency exit chute when no longer able to deal with the demands of his job.

The impact on employers is reduced productivity and potential medical claims. Hence, employers have a vested interest in helping workers better deal with stress in the workplace and preventing job burnout. The American Psychological Association found that 51 percent of employees said they were less productive at work as a result of stress. While the research is not clear on exactly how much work stress costs US businesses, most experts agree that the price tag has reached billions of dollars. Furthermore, companies need only to take a closer look at things like medical claim data, average amount of sick day's taken and turnover rates to understand the scope of the problem in their organization.

Alternatives

Employers can and should take steps to prevent, identify and address the stress problem. It would be ideal if companies could staff according to need. This would distribute workloads more equitably and likely alleviate the stress that plenty of workers feel having to do the work of multiple people. This, however, is not feasible for many companies trying to remain viable in a fragile post-recession economy. Some companies are starting to increase their workforce; however, there are far more companies that are still feeling the pinch and are unable to resume hiring.

Many organizations are looking to wellness programming to help prevent and address health issues in their employee base. Education is an easy first step for a wellness program and is often effective when done right. It can also be a good preventive measure. However, merely disseminating information can often fall short. If employees are overwhelmed, cynical or disengaged, there is a significant chance that the information will not reach its target audience. Furthermore, stress and burnout are serious problems with far-reaching effects. To truly address the problem, a multipronged approach that extends beyond education is necessary.

Many companies rely on management to recognize the signs of extreme job stress and burnout in its workers. Ideally, they would be the eyes and ears of the company, trained to catch such problems. This works in a relatively healthy work environment, but in a company ravished by layoffs and severe cutbacks, managers may be just as stressed as those they are trying to manage.

Finally, most human resources professionals want to create a healthier workforce because they understand that healthy employees are more productive. However, implementing a wellness program can be a daunting task. It is time-consuming and there is a cost associated with creating a comprehensive program. A 16-year account executive with a large brokerage firm on the west coast explained, "Most companies want to implement a formal wellness program with quarterly focuses, but most start with education. I find that companies that want to jump in with a full-blown wellness program find that it is difficult and too time-consuming and they end up doing nothing at all."

Proposed Solutions

The rising cost of healthcare, the obesity epidemic and employee engagement are key factors fueling the trend to wellness in the workplace. An HR professional with a California-based pharmaceutical company said, "Our Company just launched a formal wellness program in January. Our initial focus will be getting employees to participate and we are also building ROIs and metrics into the program." A 2008 survey conducted by Guardian Life Insurance Company of America found that 85 percent of employees who participated in a wellness program in the past three years agreed that the programs are effective in promoting good health. Dr. Thembi Conner-Garcia, Assistant Professor of Medicine at the University Of Illinois College Of Medicine at Peoria, IL, explained that "Employees suffering from work-related stress and burnout are more susceptible to problems with depression, anxiety, fatigue, insomnia and even substance abuse. When these employees seek help from their family physician for these symptoms, it can be quite challenging. It is very helpful when employers can take steps to prevent and alleviate stress for workers." So, while companies will contend with barriers to entry as they embark upon starting a wellness program, the benefits are well worth the effort.

Whether there is a wellness program in place or not, one of the most important components to effectively combat the job stress epidemic is quality management. The management team overseeing the day-to-day operations can be the first line of defense when it comes to managing job stress. Train and equip managers to recognize the signs of extreme job stress and burnout. They need to become astute at identifying and managing their own stress before they can help their teams. Well-trained managers will recognize things like reduced productivity amongst a normally highly productive employee or unusual rates of absenteeism. They should have the communication skills necessary to talk to and advise employees dealing with stress-related issues. Good managers are skilled at helping workers to manage workloads, energizing their teams and conducting helpful evaluations that recognize great employees and assist struggling employees.

Those seeking to use wellness programming to effectively prevent, identify and address job stress and burnout often start with education. The key to a successful education campaign is using savvy marketing tools to dispense targeted and concise information in regular intervals. Most successful companies are experts at marketing their brand, product or service. That same care and expertise should be used when marketing a wellness program to employees. After all, when it comes to offering a wellness program, they are the target customers. Companies should meet employees where they are – online. An increasing number of companies are using the web and social media platforms to convey wellness messages and solicit participation and feedback. A 2009 study done by Pew Research revealed that 59 percent of individuals who use the Internet for medical reference have consulted blog comments, hospital reviews, doctor reviews and health-related podcasts to obtain the information that they were looking for. The use of social media at work automatically sends up red flags for most. The truth is no other medium is as far-reaching and instantaneous as social media. If used properly, it can help companies keep their wellness message in front of employees even when they are not at work. Social media makes it convenient and fun for employees to stay engaged. Also, it can provide a quick and easy way to for employees to give feedback. Moreover, it is absolutely free.

Educating workers on workplace stress and burnout should include key information such as: managing stressors, evaluating options, adjusting one's attitude and seeking support. Workers should be made aware of any programs that the company offers, such as employee assistance programs and community resources that could aid them in dealing with the issue. The education efforts can be enhanced by encouraging stress- relieving activities throughout the work day. A thoughtful wellness program can include activities like Boardroom Yoga, where employees can engage in simple yoga stretches to decompress and relax during the noon hour. Walking meetings are effective ways to stir creativity, break up the monotony of the day and invigorate the body in an outdoor setting, while still getting work done. Lincoln Industries added a wellness component to its performance review. The employee creates a specific wellness goal that can be as simple as having dinner every night with the family but it makes wellness and work-life balance a priority. More forward-thinking companies like Google have sleeping rooms where employees can take brief naps and return to work refreshed.

Employers really seeking to address the stress problem should also strive to create a company culture that is compassionate and conducive to everyone's wellbeing. One employee who has spent 12 years with one of the oldest investment firms in the US stated, "Our founder's philosophy is to hire the best people, treat them well, give them a good working environment and they'll reward you with good work and service." While this firm does not have a formal wellness program in place, they recognize their employees with monthly company luncheons, birthday cards signed by the management team, bonuses when the firm does well and free health insurance. Each organization must determine what is most consistent with their brand image and what matters most to their employees. Armed with that understanding, they can begin to formulate wellness programming that makes sense for their brand.

Finally, companies can create a compassionate work environment by promoting positive communication. Doing so helps to build resilience, energy and vitality while improving working relationships. In such an environment, workers struggling to deal with stress and burnout are more prone to reach out and get help. Positive communication should also include recognition for work done well. Most workers know that big bonuses and huge pay raises are not likely in the current climate, but verbal recognition and public recognition should not be forsaken.

Recommendations

As mentioned, making wellness a priority in the workplace is critical to solving the job stress epidemic. Well-executed educational campaigns, highly skilled managers and innovative wellness activities can do much to combat job stress. Even more important is company culture. Companies that not only say they value their employees, but show it as well, tend to have the healthiest and most productive workforces. There are many who feel the recession is easing, the worst is over and the employment outlook is slowly improving. This is a good time for companies to reassess their practices to make sure they are doing all they can to retain and attract great employees.

References

The Bureau of Labor Statistics. (2012) The January 2012 Employment Situation.

American Psychological Association. (2009) Stress in America 2009.

Hewitt Associates LLC. (2009). Cost reduction and engagement survey.

CareerBuilder Inc. (2009c) Nearly a quarter of employers rate their organization's employee morale as low, finds new CareerBuilder survey.

World Health Organization (2007) Stress at the Workplace.

Department of Psychiatry. University of Zaragoza. Zaragoza. (2010) A and broader definition of burnout: Validation of the "Burnout clinical subtype questionnaire (BCSQ-36)."

MayoClinic.com (2010) Job burnout: Spotting it – and taking action.

Guardian Life Insurance Company of America. (2008) Benefits and behavior: Spotlight on medical groups.

Pew Research Center. Pew Internet and American Life Project (2011) The Social Life of Health Information, 2011.

Key Ideas:

Organizational psychologists describe three types of burnout: frenetic, under-challenged and worn-out.

- Some of the symptoms include fatigue, insomnia, negative spillover into personal relationships, headaches, high blood pressure, more frequent periods of sickness, depression, anxiety and alcohol or substance abuse.

- Classic, more performance-related symptoms that an employee may display range from poor memory, poor time management, and more sick calls to a negative attitude. Behavioral changes often occur, wherein employees are putting in more or less hours than normal.

- Some may become more withdrawn or resort to humor as a coping mechanism. Employees are often reluctant to ask for help and will attempt to mask any problems. In extreme cases, they will act out

- Educating workers on workplace stress and burnout should include key information such as: managing stressors, evaluating options, adjusting one's attitude and seeking support

Questions:

1. Which of the following are symptoms of employee burn out?

   a. Fatigue

   b. Insomonia

   c. Poor Time Management

   d. All of the above

2. Employees are not reluctant to ask for help

   a. True

   b. False

Diabetes Disease Management—Everyone Benefits!
By Laurie Van Wyckhouse

Wellness platforms can directly save companies money while also receiving noteworthy outcomes by including diabetes disease management training in their arsenal of benefits. One hundred seventy-six million Americans receive health coverage through their jobs, and 14 million of these Americans have diabetes ("Value-Based Benefit." n.d.). People with diabetes, on average, have medical expenditures that are more than double those of their non-diabetic counterparts ("National Diabetes Fact Sheet." 2011). Diabetes places tremendous stress on United States employers in the form of expensive health insurance contracts, absenteeism and reduced productivity. In fact, Aurora Healthcare has identified diabetes as the third most costly physical health condition for employers ("Diabetes and employers". n.d.). Worse, within the next 38 years, the incidence of diabetes is expected to rise from 8 percent of staff to 33 percent of staff, severely exacerbating the impact on employers ("*Diabetes Successes and Opportunities*". 2011). By partnering with Diabetes Self-Management Training (DSMT) programs, wellness plans can offer employers a $4.34:$1 return on investment, significantly improve employee health and experience striking outcomes (Boren, 2009).

Diabetes Is a Complicated Disease
Diabetes is a complicated disease and diabetes training is, by necessity, multifaceted. Contributing factors to this disease are numerous and variable, as are the progressive and devastating body-wide effects. Moreover, treatment regimens differ significantly in approach and efficacy. The primary culprit, uncontrolled glucose, fluctuates every minute of every day based on a host of factors. Added to these complexities, hypoglycemia and hyperglycemia can be life-threatening scenarios, the risk of which many people with diabetes live with day to day. Clearly, one-size-fits-all training strategies cannot effectively meet the objectives of diabetes treatment (namely, providing minute-by-minute glucose control and inhibiting disease progression). Equally apparent is the fact that the person who lives with the disease is the one who must be trained to care for the disease under the changeable conditions of life.

The American Association of Diabetes Educators (AADE) tells us as few as one percent and as many as 50 percent of people with diabetes receive education for their disease ("Diabetes Education Fact Sheet." 2010). Unfortunately, this statistic bundles together those who receive comprehensive self-management training with people whose training is superficial (e.g. visiting a dietitian or attending a seminar). Combine this with the fact that diabetes and blood vessel diseases mutually reinforce each other, and it should come as no surprise that diabetes affects such a comparatively small percent of the workforce but is responsible for such a high proportion of its healthcare costs! Nationally, individual health competency for diabetes treatment is poor. The medical industry is addressing this problem by encouraging the patient-centered medical home model at the primary care level, but transition is slow and entirely dependent upon reimbursement and government endorsements. Leading the way out of this morass is the corporate wellness industry. For wellness plans to demonstrate improved outcomes and save tremendous healthcare dollars for employers, it must be presumed that employees have not yet received foundational self-management training for diabetes control.

Knowing that comparatively few people with diabetes actually receives foundational training for this complex disease, how suitable are current wellness interventions for meeting the needs of this population? Providing group seminars, literature, weight loss coaching and preventive online programs can be effective strategies to help prevent diabetes and support those who have already received thorough training; however, they are grossly inadequate and can even have detrimental outcomes for people with fully-onset diseases who have not yet learned how to care for their disease. Consider the example of a coach encouraging weight loss for an insulin-dependent diabetic whose concept of weight loss implies meal abstinence. Then consider the resulting life-threatening hypoglycemic emergency this could bring on. Fragmented, non-individualized training can create confusion for learners. Worse, few coaches are credentialed to understand the complexities of diabetes treatment, contributing to learner confusion. In fact, wellness coaches are in the same untenable position as physicians when it comes to driving real change for patients who do not know how to manage their disease in the first place. Unlike medical practitioners, health coaches are without the organizational support necessary to be safeguarded from litigation. Fortunately, the National Business Coalition on Health (NBCH) and a small number of highly motivated wellness organizations are beginning to provide clear disease management guidelines and offer organizational support.

Diabetes Self-Management Training

Diabetes Self-Management Training (DSMT), as outlined by the AADE and the American Diabetes Association (ADA), is considered to be the national 'gold standard' for diabetes training by medical organizations around the country. In fact, the Standards of Medical Care for Patients with Diabetes declare that self-management education is a critical component of comprehensive care for people with diabetes, such that "diabetes care without adequate self-management education can be regarded as substandard and unethical," ("*Standards of Medical Care.*" 1998). The NBCH, in its diabetes guidelines published for the corporate wellness industry, endorses a comparable training model. Furthermore, since just eight percent of workplace health plans currently do not have diabetes programs written into their contracts, the NBCH urges companies to focus their efforts on adding diabetes disease management to their health plan contracts ("*NBCH Action Brief.*" 2012). DSMT meets that need.

In the DSMT model, the onus for diabetes management rests on the person who has the disease. This person can single-handedly precipitate change and is aware of all potential causal factors affecting glucose levels. The team that is educated and credentialed to assist the person with diabetes is the physician (of whom the endocrinologist is the diabetes specialist), certified diabetes educator and registered dietitian. To prevent learner confusion and litigation, diabetes counseling should come from these credentialed sources in a HIPAA-secure manner. Comprehensive diabetes training provides the foundation upon which current wellness strategies can then effectively motivate employees toward healthful change.

New evidence-based information is rapidly altering treatments for diabetes; therefore, medical standards of care document the need for DSMT every five years. People with prediabetes should also receive DSMT, as it prevents full-onset of disease by an impressive 58 percent ("*Report of the Task Force.*" 1999). DSMT programs provide patients with the foundational learning necessary to:

- Prevent and control obesity, high cholesterol, elevated glucose and high blood pressure

- Prevent and control glucose-related organ damage such as blindness, nerve damage, blood vessel damage leading to amputation, heart disease and renal failure

- Establish sound overall nutrition and lifestyle behaviors

- Differentiate proven diabetes information from false reports

Learners receive training in the following measurable self-care behavior topics ("AADE7™ Self-Care Behaviors." n.d.):

- Healthy eating

- Being active

- Monitoring glucose

- Taking medications

- Problem solving

- Reducing risks

- Healthy coping

DSMT program requirements extend beyond training to include behavioral goal-setting, customized clinician assessment and remediation, ongoing support, and the collection of individual and aggregate outcomes. This translates to comprehensive self-management training, offering people with diabetes their best opportunity for disease control. In fact, DSMT far exceeds the reach of medication-focused disease management programs now receiving media attention for saving companies money, which only further supports its considerable potential ("Diabetes Disease Management." 2009).

If wellness strategies are to effectively save companies money, both prediabetes and full-onset diabetes must be treated and DSMT must be included in employee benefit plans. A recent survey by Boren found that DSMT provides a direct return on investment of $4.34 for every $1.00 spent (Boren, 2009). With the advent of web-enabled learning, which is individualized and interactive, we can expect even better returns. There are additional advantages to partnering with DSMT programs. Utilizing standardized medical treatment programs such as DSMT can help to protect wellness companies from lawsuits. Also, since DSMT programs are required to collect and aggregate outcomes, these statistics can be shared with wellness companies to prove program efficacy and gain business contracts. Corporate wellness can best address the diabetes gap in its programming and save companies money by partnering with DSMT providers.

Guidelines for Choosing a Diabetes Disease Management Provider

How does one go about choosing a diabetes disease management program with which to partner? Look for the DSMT or Diabetes Self-Management Education (DSME) nomenclature. Such programs utilize the requirements published by the AADE or ADA, often becoming accredited by these organizations. These programs are frequently offered at hospitals, endocrinologist offices and government health departments, and can now be found online as well. While all DSMT programs follow the same basic AADE or ADA guidelines, there is a significant variation in practice between them. With this in mind, seek to partner with patient-centered programs for the most dramatically improved outcomes.

Local Onsite Programs

Local DSMT programs employ the classroom-style learning model. Learners are usually given a small amount of structured time with their personal clinician, followed by 9-10 hours of group lecture. Medicare recognizes this traditional paradigm by allowing for its reimbursement as a medical program.

The weakness of onsite training lies in its *clinician / instructor-centered* teaching approach. Many learners find class schedules to be inconvenient, lecture-style teaching unsuccessful for developing practical skills and group training to be devoid of personalization (*Peyrot, 2010*). In view of these and other potential barriers, when choosing an onsite program with which to partner, ask the following pointed questions:

- Is class time set aside for skill development? If so, how much time?

- Are patients given a comprehensive manual to use as a reference after the class is over? (Distribution of an ad hoc collection of free pamphlets published by pharmaceutical companies does not comprise a manual!)

- Are class schedules convenient for employee participation in that they do not require the employee to leave work or be away from home repeatedly to complete their training?

- Are learners free to return to class as needed for further instruction, and for how long is additional training accessible?

- How accessible are the clinicians to providing one-on-one counseling as needed beyond the initial structured time built into the program?

The reach of your company will help you to quickly determine whether or not to partner with onsite programs. There are a limited number of large companies that provide DSMT nationwide, while most programs are solo operations. National wellness companies may find that working with multiple providers will add unnecessary complication, confusion and misdirection; whereas local employers may enjoy developing business relationships with other local companies.

Web-enabled Programs
The future of disease management and DSMT lies in web-enabled programming with electronic clinician interface. The medical industry, led by Medicare, has been slow to integrate the new cost-effective models, while the wellness industry, which is lighter on its feet and inexorably more progressive, has welcomed e-learning with open arms. Emerging data are convincing. Chandler Macleod, a recruiting firm that surveyed 1,200 companies, found that employees prefer to learn online ("E-learning good way." 2005). In support of this, Training Magazine reported a 50-70 percent savings when corporations replace instructor-led training with self-paced electronic study (About Us, 2000). The reason for this is that web-enabled training tailors learning to the individual far more than is possible in the classroom setting, simply by offering more "learning by doing." SRI International, while working for the U.S. Department of Education, concluded that the effectiveness of e-training exceeds that of classroom training (*"Evaluation of Evidence-Based Practices."* 2009, p. 41, para. 3). Best yet, online DSMT meets the disease management standards outlined by the NBCH while also being compatible with value-based purchasing strategies. During a time when chronic disease is escalating at an exponential rate and healthcare costs are spinning out of control, web-enabled disease management training offers a high-quality, cost-effective solution that is easily scalable for large populations.

What of the learner experience with online training? Web-enabled DSMT is abundantly more patient-centered than that of its classroom counterpart. Using self-directed study with structured flexibility, training is individualized and interactive, thereby solving the learning barriers found in onsite programs and ensuring improved outcomes. Learners log in at their convenience and easily move between topics, satisfying knowledge gaps as they arise and focusing on the negative behaviors they are most willing to amend. Practical skills are developed through tailored remediation. Properly credentialed clinicians and/or health coaches intervene when learner activity is seen to have ceased or when help is requested, thereby curbing the cost of genuine medical training and reserving clinician time for legitimate treatment and counseling. (The web-enabled "medical" model, when it is finalized, will likely demand more clinician interface than that which is necessary for the employer-paid wellness programs.) The volume of information covered in DSMT is enormous; therefore web-enabled programs allow learners access to material for months rather than hours. Since members apply the information as they learn it, new knowledge is progressively solidified into new habits. Enthusiastically lauded during the most recent AADE annual conference, electronic DSMT achieves numerous benefits for both learners and payers alike.

While there are many fractured educational offerings online for diabetes, genuinely comprehensive web-enabled DSMT programs are not easy to find. The online paradigm for DSMT has yet to be approved for reimbursement; thus, few companies have ventured into this arena. With this in mind, it is not necessary to seek out an ADA or AADE accredited DSMT program. Rather, a legitimate online provider must be able to demonstrate full compliance with the ADA or AADE educational standards (Funnell, 2007). This will effectively separate the authentic medical providers from the imposters, making your list of prospects much more manageable. Then ask the following pointed questions and confirm the answers by program inspection:

- Is practical skill development a significant part of the program?

- Are customizable weight change meal plans provided?

- What is the membership duration?

- Is electronic support group included in membership?

- Do learners receive a downloadable manual?

- Do clinicians and/or coaches interface with learners? If so, what prompts them to do so and what are their credentials?

- From what URL is training provided; the website of the DSMT provider, wellness company or employer?

Summary

Diabetes is a costly and complicated disease that is not amenable to improvements using preventive and supportive wellness strategies, even when those strategies are specifically targeted at the disease. The diabetes gap in wellness programming can best be filled by offering the medical 'gold standard' for diabetes education; DSMT. By partnering with a DSMT provider, companies can expect significantly improved health outcomes and savings. Web-enabled DSMT, in particular, fills the diabetes gap in wellness programming with extraordinary ease and affordability, further lowering employer costs and also improving the quality of training.

References

AADE7™ Self-Care Behaviors. (n.d.) Retrieved April 3, 2012 from https://www.diabeteseducator.org/ProfessionalResources/AADE7/index.html

About Us. Web Advantage referencing Training Magazine. (2000). Retrieved April 3, 2012 from http://webadvantageinc.com/about/about.htm

American Diabetes Association Position statement: Standards of medical care for patients with diabetes mellitus. (1998). *Diabetes Care* 21 (Suppl 1):S23-31.

American Diabetes Association: Report of the task force on the delivery of diabetes self-management education and medical nutrition therapy. (1999). *Diabetes Spectrum* 12:44-47.

Boren S.A., Fitner K.A., Panhalkar P.S., Specker J. (2009). Costs and Benefits Associated with Diabetes Education: A Review of the Literature. *The Diabetes Educator* 31 (1): 72-96.

Diabetes and employers. (n.d.). Retrieved April 3, 2012 from http://www.aurorahealthcare.org/aboutus/caremanagement/diabetes/diabetes-employers.asp

Diabetes Disease Management Pilot Program Yields Big Cost Savings. (2009, April 13). Retrieved from http://www.workforce.com/article/20090413/NEWS01/304139996

Diabetes Education Fact Sheet. (2010). Retrieved April 3, 2012 from http://www.diabeteseducator.org/export/sites/aade/_resources/pdf/research/Diabetes_Education_Fact_Sheet_09-10.pdf

Diabetes Successes and Opportunities for Population-Based Prevention and Control at a Glance 2011. (2011). Retrieved from http://www.cdc.gov/chronicdisease/resources/publications/AAG/ddt.htm

E-learning good way to keep employees keen. (2005, May 2). Retrieved April 3, 2012 from http://www.nzherald.co.nz/employment/news/article.cfm?c_id=11&objectid=10123231

Evaluation of Evidence-Based Practices in Online Learning, a Meta-Analysis and Review of Online Learning Studies. (2010, September). *U.S. Department of Education.* p. 41, para. 3. Retrieved from http://www2.ed.gov/rschstat/eval/tech/evidence-based-practices/finalreport.pdf

Funnell, M.M., Brown, T.L., Childs, B.P., Haas, L.B., Hosey, G.M., Jensen, B...Weiss, M.A. (2007). National Standards for Diabetes Self-Management Education. doi: 10.1177/0145721707305880

National Diabetes Fact Sheet. (2011). Retrieved from http://www.cdc.gov/diabetes/pubs/estimates11.htm.

NBCH Action Brief. 2012,February. Retrieved from http://www.nbch.org/nbch/files/ccLibraryFiles/Filename/000000002106/NBCH_AB_Diabetes.pdf

Peyrot M. (2010, September 1). *AADE DSMET Access Grant Project, 2007 End of Year Report.* Retrieved from http://www.

diabeteseducator.org/export/sites/aade/_resources/pdf/AADE_DSMET_Access_Grant_Project--07_EOY_Report_M._Peyrotx_PhD.pdf

Value Based Benefit Design Introduction. (n.d.). Retrieved April 3, 2012 from http://www.nbch.org/Value-Based-Benefit-Design-Introduction

Key Ideas

- Worse, within the next 38 years, the incidence of diabetes is expected to rise from 8 percent of staff to 33 percent of staff, severely exacerbating the impact on employers

- The primary culprit, uncontrolled glucose, fluctuates every minute of every day based on a host of factors

- The Standards of Medical Care for Patients with Diabetes declare that self-management education is a critical component of comprehensive care for people with diabetes, such that "diabetes care without adequate self-management education can be regarded as substandard and unethical,"

- Diabetes Self-Management Training (DSMT)

- Seek to partner with patient-centered programs for the most dramatically improved outcomes.

Questions

1. What is the primary concern with diabetes?
   a. The patient is overweight
   b. Uncontrolled glucose
   c. Undiagnosed
   d. None of the above

2. What is DSMT?
   a. Diabetes Self-Management Training
   b. Diabetes Self-Medicating Treatments
   c. Diabetes Self-Medicating Training
   d. Diabetes Self-Management Treatment

3. Web-based and classroom DSMT are equally effective
   a. True
   b. False

Components of a Healthy Office
By Kathy Gruver

We spend at least one-third of our lives at work. There are ways to create a healthier environment in order to spark creativity, productivity and better health. With repetitive stress injuries on the rise and obesity a national epidemic, here are some things that can help you maintain your health while you work.

Avoid Injuries In my 20 years of therapeutic massage and natural health experience, I've treated injuries ranging from torn rotator cuffs to whiplash and sciatica. What I see increasingly on my table are the repetitive stress injuries like carpal tunnel. I'm noticing that my desk job clients are coming in more beat up than my extreme athletes. What is causing this increase, and what can be done about it? One of the most important things you can do is stretch. Not just bend over and touch your toes, or do yoga on the weekends; I mean really specific stretches for your shoulders, neck, low back, hips and legs.

Why Bother Stretching?
"It's so boring," some bemoan. Well, according to the National Institute of Occupational Safety and Health, repetitive stress injuries are now the single largest cause of occupational health problems in the U.S., with 25 percent of workers in occupations that can cause RSIs. It's in your best interest to stretch and keep yourself healthy.

Carpal tunnel and tendonitis can be avoided with proper posture, stretching, breaks, nutrition and station setup. We can't just blame ergonomics for these problems, though. Forty years ago, secretaries didn't have the latest contoured chair or a consultant measuring how far their typewriter was from their eyes. They varied their activities and, even if their day was composed of just typing, they had to wind the tape, roll the paper, make corrections, etc. Now, with the word processor, we can type for hours, never having to change positions or move at all. We have convenienced ourselves into a state of injury. And the smaller the gadgets get, the harder it is on our arms and eyes. Blackberrys and PDAs are contributing to finger and wrist issues. Obviously we need to use them, but counter that activity by stretching and putting them down occasionally.

We can't hold technology solely responsible for these problems, either; employees have to be conscious about their bodies and their health. Many staffers work too long in one position without stopping. By law, breaks are provided, but I know so many who don't take them. In many cases there are imposed deadlines, too little staff and too much work. We have to find the balance between productivity and our own wellbeing. It's also common to find people eating poor-quality food at their desks or never stopping to walk around or go to the bathroom, let alone stretch and exercise. It benefits everyone in the long run to take time to stretch, eat a nutritious meal or snack and walk around in the sun for just five minutes.

Even though technology is faster than ever, we still need to wait for things to load, print, fax or copy. Use that as a cue to stretch or do some calisthenics. Suggest that your office keep theraband in the office, which looks like a giant rubber band and is a gym itself. Perhaps stretches could be posted in the lunchroom or by the copy machine. Maybe some light weights could live in the closet. Or you could have an "exercise of the day" and encourage participation. It's easy to forget to do these things during a stressful day, but it is key to our health to fit in fitness.

And once the workday is over, it's important to stay active. Working on the computer all day and then going home to play computer games is a big problem. Management can't control what staff does outside the office, but logic dictates this isn't the best choice. Try to find hobbies that use different parts of your body than you are overusing at work. Data entry people who go home and knit, garden and do beading are just asking for hand issues. And often times it becomes a Workers Comp problem. It's time for us all to take responsibility for ourselves and our wellness. Stretch, eat right and exercise.

Diet at the Office

Let's talk about eating. My first suggestion to ensure a healthy office diet is to make sure what you've eaten *away* from the office will sustain you. Try to make time for a hearty breakfast before you get in your car to zoom off for the day. Many people skip this essential meal, but it is important for energy, thought processes and weight management. I suggest a morning meal that has a combination of protein, fats and carbohydrates. This gives you the best variety of nutrients, and long- and short-term energy supplies. A breakfast of eggs, cereal, toast, fruit, a meat, etc. is a great start to the morning; grabbing a carbo-loaded donut or bagel is not.

I don't have to tell you how important it is to drink pure water throughout the day. Most offices have a water cooler or bottled water available. Some also provide coffee, tea, juice and soda. I'm not opposed to coffee or tea; however, relying on caffeine to get you through the day may backfire when the afternoon crash occurs. Caffeine late in the day can cause evening wakefulness and anxiety; so don't depend on artificial stimulants. And if you are adding artificial sweetener to your coffee or tea, it might be causing health issues (more about that later).

Juice is a great beverage, but make sure it's not just colored, sweetened water with some juice flavor added. Unfortunately, pure juice is rather expensive and most of what you get in the store has very little fruit in it. Read the labels.

And, just so you know, I'm not a fan of soda. Diet or regular, soda has no nutritional value and its consumption can lead to poor health and weight gain. High fructose corn syrup has not only been linked to obesity, but may also be contributing to diabetes and hyperactivity. Soda is high in phosphorus, which leeches calcium and other minerals from our bodies. And artificial sweetener contained in the diet variety is a dangerous chemical. Numerous illnesses have been associated with these compounds including headaches and migraines, anxiety attacks, MS and seizures; it has also been shown to decrease leptin (the hormone that tells us we are full) production in the brain. If you are a sodaholic, please consider switching to a healthier habit. And if you need to sweeten your coffee or tea, try a natural product like honey, sugar, xylitol or stevia (my favorite).

There are always one or two staffers who practically live in the kitchen. They're always there, grabbing a handful of this or another piece of that. If this is you, why are you in there? Heading to the kitchen is a great distraction from our work, which can be both good and bad. I do encourage taking breaks, but munching through them is not the healthiest choice. If you find yourself wandering to the food area, ask yourself if you are really hungry or just bored, anxious, stressed, angry or looking for a diversion. Many people struggling with their weight realize that they eat to satisfy some other aspect of their lives that is currently unfulfilled. Emotional eating can lead to weight and health issues. If you aren't hungry, explore why you might be in the kitchen and what issues might need to be addressed. Keeping a food diary is a great way to chart when and what you are eating; sometimes the evidence will shock you. And studies show that people who keep a food diary lose more weight than those who don't.

If you are hungry and need a snack, select fruit, nuts or popcorn as opposed to processed foods, cookies or chips. Many conventional snack foods like Doritos contain MSG, an excitotoxin that causes a negative reaction in sensitive people. Headache, heart palpitations, digestive issues, nausea and numerous other reactions might be associated with MSG consumption (a list of about 40 can be found at http://www.truthinlabeling.org/adversereactions.html). Unfortunately MSG is often hidden in the ingredients as something else, like "spices" or "natural flavors." If you are sensitive to MSG, make sure you avoid those hidden sources. For a list of pseudonyms for MSG, see the website: http://www.msgmyth.com/hidename.htm

As I mentioned before, it's very important to take breaks throughout the day; lunchtime is no exception. There are days when there is a deadline or something just can't wait, but making a habit of working through lunch and eating at your desk is an unhealthy practice. Our digestive system works best in a relaxed environment, so shoving food in your mouth as you're coding documents and stressing about a deadline is going to lead to stomach and bowel issues. If you're rushing through lunch, you're also not chewing enough, which is harder on your stomach. Take some time, relax for a few minutes, chew and enjoy your food. And, make sure what you're eating is real food and not a processed "Franken food." It is much more convenient to choose a pre-packaged microwavable meal, but the nutrition is often not present. And many of these foods contain Trans Fats, MSG, high fructose corn syrup, additives, preservatives or ingredients that have been genetically modified. We are not only getting subpar nutrition from these foods, but the added components may be making us sick, fat and tired. Pack your lunch from your home or eat at a healthier restaurant in town.

Building Up Energy

As mentioned above, making sure you get proper nutrition is key to your energy levels. Since most of the food we eat is either processed, irradiated, minerally depleted, genetically modified, sprayed with a chemical, or is artificial, I recommend taking a high-quality vitamin and mineral supplement. The B vitamins are essential for good energy; increasing B6 and B12 is my first suggestion for weary clients. Don't take them too late in the day, though, or they may interrupt your sleep.

Getting a wide variety of minerals is also essential. Everyone stresses the importance of calcium, but there are so many more minerals we need, such as iron, magnesium, molybdenum, copper, zinc, etc. Taking a good multi-mineral supplement can help. Also, remember that we need protein for energy. Amino acids, which are the building blocks of protein, can be taken in supplement form. I especially recommend this for vegetarians or non-red meat eaters.

When we hit that afternoon slump, most people reach for the soda or candy bar. We use glucose as an energy source, so we often crave something sweet. Make sure that what you're getting contains real sugar and not high fructose corn syrup or some artificial sweetener. These trick our bodies into thinking we're getting sugar, but it's really an unusable substance. Don't overdo it on the sugar, though, or you'll crash later and feel worse. Often, what we really need is fresh air or water. Do some deep breathing, get outside and have a big glass of water. That will probably perk you up as much as the afternoon cup o' joe. Make sure you're not dependent on caffeine, ginseng or energy drinks. In moderation these are not all bad, but remember low energy is not a caffeine deficiency. Try the other options first.

I know the last thing you want to do when you're already tired is exercise, but a review of 12 large-scale studies on the connection between exercise and fatigue found a direct link between a reduced level of fatigue for people who were physically active compared to those who were inactive. Other research shows that even among people with chronic illness like cancer or heart disease, exercise can ward off feelings of fatigue and help people feel more energized. This doesn't mean you have to run five miles; even 15-20 minutes of walking or light exercise -- something you can easily squeeze into your busy workday -- can make a difference. Head to the bathroom on the floor above or below you, or walk around the building once or twice before you return to your desk. Even that little bit of extra exercise will perk you up.

Since our bodies are 80 percent water, keep yourself hydrated. If you wait until you feel the sensation of thirst, it's too late; you're already dehydrated. Drinking water throughout the day helps with blood flow and the removal of toxins. Remember, caffeine is a diuretic that causes increased output of urine, so caffeinated drinks don't count. Pure water is the best! We can also boost energy by deep breathing. Oxygen carries energy to our cells, which will give us a natural perk. Try four slow deep breaths (use your abdomen not just your chest) and get a natural high.

Get enough sleep. It stands to reason that if you're not sleeping well, you're going to have low energy the next day. It's a myth that we need eight hours of sleep. We need as much as we need. Some people are fine on six hours, others need 9 or 10. Go to bed when you're tired if at all possible. Don't force yourself to stay awake at night, especially by artificial means. And during the day, if you're really tired and can take a nap, take one. But make it short. Don't sleep too much or you'll have trouble sleeping that night.

Attitude makes a difference. If we are constantly telling ourselves that we're tired and have no energy, we're just programming the body to behave that way. Change your mind to change your body. Try affirmations like: "I am well-rested and energized," "I am filled with vigor," and, "My energy is boundless." You'll have better results with positive thinking.

If you're finding that your energy is consistently low, make sure there's not an underlying condition like anemia, hypothyroid, adrenal insufficiency, infection, Fibromyalgia, low blood sugar, depression or cancer. Blood tests can help rule out a medical problem. Also check any prescriptions or over-the-counter medications you're taking to see if fatigue might be a side effect.

Stocking Your Office

Most offices keep a medicine chest in the office. In addition to pain reducers and cold medicines, keep some multivitamins and minerals on hand. I also recommend some immune boosters like Wellness Formula or Airborne. If you provide your employees with what is needed to keep them illness-free, you'll have healthier and more motivated employees.

Many companies offer a gym membership or have one on the premises. If you can't go that route, at least provide a few hand weights, a yoga ball or exercise bands. These are small additions that will help your staff fit in fitness during their busy day. And since we all have to leave our desks at some point, keep some charts of stretches and easy exercises in the break room or kitchen. When people head for a snack or to the bathroom it's the perfect time to take a break to stretch and move their body. You can also post the stretch of the week near the copy or fax machine and encourage people to stretch while they're waiting.

Throughout the day, have scheduled breaks when everyone in the office stops and stretches or exercises. If you have everyone participating, even for a few minutes a day, you'll have a built-in buddy system. If you want to take that concept further, sponsor an office Olympics or "biggest loser" contest. Get everyone involved and supporting each other. Start a point system for exercise or weight loss. Put a big chart on the wall and give everyone stars for their achievements, like we had in grade school.

Let the sun shine in. Try to get as much natural light in your office as you can. This can be difficult in a space with many cubicles and moveable walls. If you own the building, Solar tubes and skylights might be an option. You can also replace your florescent lights with full spectrum light bulbs. These seem to cause less eye strain and prevent people from getting SAD (Seasonal Effective Disorder) during the winter months.

Bring nature inside. Plants can not only brighten a room but also provide oxygen and clean the air. Here are a few that are especially known for their oxygenation power:

- Reed palm
- Dwarf date palm
- Boston fern
- English Ivy
- Peace Lily
- Australian sword fern
- Rubber plant
- Weeping fig

I see many offices with artificial plants; I recommend getting live plants instead. There are services that will bring plants and flowers into your office and maintain them for you. One of the downsides of artificial plants is they tend to collect dust and other particles which might irritate allergen sensitive people. Turn to real nature if you can.

And, speaking of sensitive people, we are seeing more and more folks developing multiple chemical sensitivities. The office is an environment ripe with these compounds. Toner fluid, copy machine chemicals, out-gassing from carpet and assembled furniture, even the smell from markers, whiteout and pens can put someone over the edge of reactions. So much of that is out of our control, but you can try to make the best choices when looking at office chairs, carpet and paint.

Chair-wise, provide your staff with what they need to be healthy at their desks. Listen to their concerns about chair height, computer placement and office setup. And make sure the chairs are good quality and fit the employees. I had a client who had to wait 6 months to get her chair approved because "only the management was allowed to have chairs with arms." I was appalled and disappointed that she ended up injured because of such a ridiculous and outdated policy.

So, in conclusion, by eating right, stretching, taking breaks and having an office stocked with good food, fresh water and some key supplements, you are guaranteeing a healthier office.

Key Ideas

- It's important that you listen to your body's cues and stop when we need to (every 50 minutes or so).

- I suggest a morning meal that has a combination of protein, fats and carbohydrates

- It's a myth that we need eight hours of sleep. We need as much as we need.

- Chair-wise, provide your staff with what they need to be healthy at their desks

- Plants can not only brighten a room but also provide oxygen and clean the air

Questions

1. Everyone needs eight hours of sleep a day.

   a. True

   b. False

2. Live plants can help clean the air, and brighten a room.

   a. True

   b. False

3. What is missing from the suggested breakfast components: protein, fats, and _____?

   a. Grains

   b. Sugars

   c. Carbohydrates

   d. Caffeine

Diabetes Management: Corporate Programs Can Make a Difference

By Maureen Young

If you don't have diabetes, you may assume that managing the disease is a simple matter of staying away from sugar, testing your blood sugar and giving yourself an insulin injection. It's not that easy. Putting aside the fears that many people have regarding needles and the finger pricks required for managing this disease, it is much more complicated than simple testing, injections and medications. Diabetes is an individual battle that people fight every day. It differs for everyone regarding what works, what they can eat and which particular outside factors affect them. Corporations can have an impact on their employees' ability to manage their disease, which will ultimately impact their bottom line.

The Rising Incidence and Cost of Diabetes

Diabetes continues to be a problem for millions of Americans, and is costing billions of dollars to manage and treat. According to the American Diabetes Association[1], over one-third of all Americans will develop type 2 diabetes by the year 2050 unless radical changes are made in our lifestyle and eating habits. Over 57 million people have prediabetes or metabolic syndrome with a very high risk of developing diabetes, and over 24 million children and adults already live with type-1 diabetes. The difficulty lies not only in managing your blood sugar to prevent serious life-threatening side effects, but also in keeping your health insurance to cover you if any serious complications arise. If you have diabetes and you aren't paying attention to your glucose levels every day, you could be setting yourself up for severe problems.

In 2007 the total cost of Diabetes in the United States was $218 billion. Of this number $44 billion goes toward undiagnosed diabetes, pre-diabetes and gestational diabetes. Diabetes contributed to 231,404 deaths during 2007, and the number continues to grow as more Americans develop type 2 diabetes.

Of the remaining $174 billion spent on diabetes each year, $116 billion goes toward excess medical expenditures attributed to diabetes and $58 billion in reduced national productivity. People with diagnosed diabetes have medical expenditures that average 2.3 times higher than the expenditures of those without diabetes. Almost $1 in every $10 can be attributed to diabetes. The indirect costs include absenteeism, reduced productivity and lost productive capacity due to early mortality[2].

People with diabetes between the ages of 18-64 average 8.3 lost work days per year as compared to 1.7 days per year for those without diabetes. The medical expenditures are significantly higher for diabetics at $10,071 per person and only $2,669 per person for non-diabetics[3]. Any headway that corporations are able to make in guiding people who live with diabetes toward better management of their disease would offer a considerable cost-savings to the corporation and to the American public.

Diabetes Complications Are Serious
There are so many factors that can affect glucose levels, and many of them are difficult to control. If the pancreas is working just fine, the body handles daily, small changes without any active intervention. Job or personal stress, lack of sleep, skipping a workout, a little too much salt, and obviously, too much sugar can interfere with balanced blood sugar. What if an employee's job is stressful causing a poor night's sleep, or they catch a cold or the flu? Even minor illnesses can cause glucose levels to rise. For diabetics, staying in touch with their doctor during these times is critical when blood sugar levels are difficult to manage. Doctors may recommend additional insulin injections or reduce the amount if the patient is taking oral insulin.

Diabetes is an underlying cause in many health conditions, including heart disease and stroke, blindness, high blood pressure and kidney disease. Maintaining a healthy, stable blood sugar level over time can reduce the risk of serious complications. Watching for stressful situations, which no one can avoid completely, and then making changes to account for fluctuations in glucose levels can mean the difference between saving a person's sight or limbs and continuing to be a productive employee.

Diabetes is the leading cause of new cases of blindness among adults ages 20 to 74 and the leading cause of kidney failure. Forty-four percent of new cases of kidney failure were attributed to diabetes in 2008. In combination with heart disease and stroke and non-traumatic amputations, the downside of ignoring large fluctuations in glucose levels can be disastrous. Every person is different, and this holds true for those trying to manage diabetes. Something that causes a major glucose shift in one person may be barely noticeable in another. In addition, beyond each person's individual reactions, over time those may shift within an individual that require constant adjustments to what may have been stable diabetes maintenance. Providing guidance and help for diabetics dealing with shifts in glucose levels and new symptoms is critical to a diabetic's long-term health and productivity.

What Can Businesses Do To Help Diabetic Employees?
The CDC has partnered with the National Institutes of Health to improve the treatment and outcomes for people with diabetes, to promote early diagnosis, and ultimately, to prevent diabetes. Together these organizations developed the National Diabetes Education Program (NDEP). Their document, *Making a Difference: the Business Community Takes on Diabetes*[4], offers some guidelines to employers:

- Develop a supportive work environment so that employees with diabetes feel comfortable adopting and performing the behaviors that promote good diabetes control

- Provide encouragement and opportunities for all employees to adopt healthier lifestyles that reduce risks for chronic disease.

- Coordinate all corporate diabetes control efforts within the organization to make them more efficient as well as accountable. (The NDEP publication shows successful examples.

- Demand the highest quality medical care for people who are dealing with diabetes.

If corporations decide to embark on a program specifically tailored to diabetes management, one of the obstacles they will face is employee resistance for many reasons. Employees may worry about privacy and not want others to know that they are diabetic. They may not be ready to accept that they are ill and need to seek treatment. Whatever the cause of employee apathy, there are ways to increase employee awareness and participation in a new diabetes management program. Without employee buy-in, the program will falter and fail wasting dollars that could have been saved when employees control their diabetes, reduce absenteeism and lost productivity and reduce complications due to diabetes. The website diabetesatwork.org provides tool kits and reference materials designed to help employers start a diabetes management program within their organization.

Promote Employee Awareness

Employees first need to become aware of the prevalence of diabetes and prediabetes in their community and in their workplace. Highlighting behaviors that contribute to the development of diabetes type 2 and how avoidance of those behaviors can reduce the chances of developing diabetes can alert employees to how easily their own behavior can increase their risks.

Specifically, some steps to increase employee awareness[5] include:

- Including the local medical community in your efforts, so that they see the program as an aid to compliance and not competition.

- Work with other businesses in the community who may be interested in sponsoring specific events or promotions for the program.

- Invite an educator specializing in diabetes in for a company hosted brown bag lunch to discuss warning signs and symptoms of diabetes type 2 with focus on the importance of balanced nutrition and exercise.

- Post NDEP flyers and posters and include the NDEP newsletter in the internal corporate newsletter.

Promote Employee Participation

Once employees are aware of the program the proper employees need to be encouraged to participate in the program[5] to really see cost savings from decreases in absenteeism and medical complications. Make sure that employees know that you value their privacy, information will not be shared with other employees and will not increase their health insurance premium.

Develop an incentive program for participation. Financial incentives such as bonuses are effective, but other forms of financial incentives can be effective as well. Provide financial coverage for testing supplies and in-house testing or health fairs to encourage frequent testing to control glucose levels.

Use in-house activities such as lectures or brown bag lunches and take advantage of national campaigns such as Diabetes Awareness Month, which is November. Use targeted mailings sent to prospective participants.

It's Not a Sprint, It's a Marathon

Most of us deal with little surprises or changes every day and just plow ahead. For diabetics the small changes in blood sugar caused by these little "inconveniences" could raise blood sugar consistently, leading to serious long term complications and increased healthcare costs. Insurance companies see people who do not manage their blood sugar well as high risk, increasing the cost of health insurance or raising the chances of losing it.

It will take time to see the financial benefits of a corporate diabetes management program, but with sincere effort and commitment, it can reap large rewards, like those recognized by GM with their LifeSteps Initiative[6]. GM saw a $2.70 to $1 ROI, the reduction or elimination of 185,000 health risk factors and an increase in low risk participants from 55 percent to 63.1 percent. Diabetes is not a disease to be taken lightly. It requires serious attention, every day, and can't be ignored. Help your employees manage their disease better so they are in control of their diabetes and keep them happy, healthy and productive!

References

1   http://www.diabetes.org/diabetes-basics/diabetes-statistics/

2   The Lewin Group, "The Economic Costs of Diabetes in the U.S. in 2007," *Diabetes Care*, **March 2008**, vol, 31 no. 3, **595-615**

3   American Diabetes Association, Economic consequences of diabetes mellitus in the United States in 1997. *Diabetes Care*, 1998; 21:296-309.

4   Centers for Disease Control and Prevention. Making a Difference: the Business Community Takes on Diabetes. Atlanta, Georgia: U.S. Department of Health and Human Services, Public Health Service, Centers for Disease Control and Prevention, National Center for Chronic Disease Prevention and Health Promotion, 1999. NDEP Pub #33.

5   http://www.diabetesatwork.org/NextSteps/AwarenessAndParticipation.cfm

6   Tim McDonald, PA, Michigan Department of Community Health, *Workplace Wellness Chronicles*, August 2005. Online at http://www.michigan.gov/documents/MDCH-Chronicles-GM-0805_134908_7.pdf.

Key Ideas

- Over 57 million people have prediabetes or metabolic syndrome with a very high risk of developing diabetes, and over 24 million children and adults already live with type-1 diabetes.

- one-third of all Americans will develop type 2 diabetes by the year 2050 unless radical changes are made in our lifestyle and eating habits

- Diabetes is the leading cause of new cases of blindness among adults ages 20 to 74 and the leading cause of kidney failure.

- Diabetes Awareness Month is November.

Questions

1. Diabetes is the leading cause of new blindness.

    a. True

    b. False

2. When is diabetes awareness month?

    a. March

    b. June

    c. September

    d. November

Musculoskeletal Health: A Critical Determinant of Productivity and an Important Element in Overall Wellness

By Tiziano Marovino and Julie Sabo

Introduction:

There has been such a great emphasis placed on the emerging epidemics, including heart disease, cancers, COPD, diabetes and obesity; that in some cases, musculoskeletal disorders (MSDs) have been left out of the dialogue. It is important to note that there is an interconnectedness between MSDs and today's epidemics; namely, when musculoskeletal injury is present, it often prevents the person from working and being active, especially with spine and lower extremity cases. For this very reason, there is no separating the importance of MSDs in the overall health profile of a person. When we break down physically, we often stop optimal physiologic functioning as well. People who have advanced coronary heart disease (CHD) often have poor MSK health, including being overweight, diabetic and, in many cases, smokers [1].

There is considerable research showing that unhealthy behaviors come in clusters; they typically do not exist in isolation [2]. Persons can continue to work and function with varying levels of underlying disease such as CHD, diabetes, obesity and chronic obstructive pulmonary disease (COPD); in contrast, if you have a full thickness rotator cuff tear, it will mean significantly restricted work capacity or possibly no work capability at all depending on the nature of your job. Human function is predicated on certain musculoskeletal (MSK) attributes, including mobility, strength, stability, flexibility, muscle endurance and power. When there are deficiencies or limitations in our MSK system, work abilities are compromised and overall health declines because without movement, there is steady de-conditioning. With increasing de-conditioning there is greater risk for heart disease, diabetes, cancers and obesity. In some cases, underlying MSK disease has greater implications to work specifically, and requires higher treatment priority, than mild to moderate systemic disease, at least in the short term. A case in point is hypertension, a known risk factor for stroke and heart/kidney disease. Hypertension is in many cases both insidious and idiopathic, with persons not necessarily exhibiting overt symptoms. From an employer cost efficiency standpoint, resources to improve the health of employees should be allocated according to the injury/disability profile of their particular population. Gaining an understanding into where the high-risk exposures are located within a workplace is paramount in building a worksite wellness plan that yields a high return on investment. Employers are encouraged to increase their understanding and awareness into where the problem areas are within their work environments by examining medical records, OSHA logs, workers' comp. claims data and/or other data sources that might implicate certain work practices or stations/lines as being vulnerable to higher risk of injury and critical to target for intervention.

Epidemiology of MSK Disorders

The total cost of treating MSK injuries in 2004 was estimated to be nearly $127.4 billion, with approximately 20 percent of this total cost being apportioned to hospitalization related to the injury. The proportion of musculoskeletal worker injuries continues to account for more than half of all non-fatal injury cases involving days away from work.[3] The share of this cost attributed to prescription drugs used in treating MSK injuries was approximately 17 percent in 2004. Eleven percent of people ages 65 and older reported they were currently experiencing limitations in their ability to perform activities of daily living (ADLs), stemming from MSK injuries such as fractures or joint injuries [4]. In 2005 approximately 72.1 million work days were lost due to work injury. The combined direct and indirect costs of injury identification, surgical and/or medical treatment, rehabilitative and vocational costs and worker re-integration into the workplace costs are enormous, not to mention any lost time and worker replacement costs. In 2010, the US Bureau of Labor Statistics reported that the incidence rate of non-fatal workplace injuries and illnesses for the non-manufacturing sector was 3.6 cases per 100 equivalent full-time workers, an overall decline from years past. The manufacturing sector incidence rate is continuing to rise, however, and was estimated at 4.4 cases per every 100 full-time workers. All other sectors, including construction, healthcare, private industry and the public sector showed either unchanged or declining incidence rates [5]. It would seem prudent then that interventions aimed at reducing the burden imposed by MSK injury should focus on the manufacturing sector of industry. It's important to also note that recordable level injury is not the sole cost driver in the injury equation. Simply having untreated early-onset musculoskeletal pain can account for a significant reduction in productivity; this, in turn, can ratchet up the total eventual cost of repairing a vulnerable MSK system. It is estimated that lost productive time from common pain conditions among active workers costs approximately $61.2 billion dollars per year. The majority (>75 percent) of this estimate represents reduced performance while at work (presenteeism), and not work absence (absenteeism) [6].

Avoiding Claims at All Costs: What is the Cost?
Some would argue that the current workers' compensation system is heavily slanted toward claimants (i.e. biased against employers). Whatever your viewpoint is on this topic, I think we would all agree that it is in the best interest of employers (and society in general) to avoid these Workers comp. claims whenever possible. How can this best be done and how much would it cost? To answer these questions, we must first determine which factors are associated with MSK injury claims. In an ideal world, we would be able to predict who is at high risk for injury using some type of testing protocol or human function equation. Presumably, this protocol would somehow be linked to the essential demands of a particular job, which should logically be consistent with the specific job description. If injury prediction testing triggers a "déjà vu" sensation, it's probably because you remember how we tried this in the 1980s and called it "pre-employment spinal screening." It was done in the form of radiography (x-rays) of the lumbar spine prior to the hiring event. At the time, popular wisdom suggested that spinal x-ray findings could be predictive of future injury; that is, certain radiographic findings (scoliosis, spurring, disc height changes, foraminal narrowing, malalignment, etc.) predisposed prospective workers to future back injury.

Significant time and a few lawsuits later, the entire notion of pre-employment radiographic screening was dismissed and would now, in today's world, be considered a baseless and discriminatory practice with little evidence to support it. But was the problem really the notion of pre-employment screening, or that we used and relied on the wrong method (x-rays)? I suppose the point is moot, since the idea of actual pre-employment testing has been bypassed for the more politically correct version of post-offer testing. In the latter scenario, the applicant is hired conditionally, based on a successful testing session (musculoskeletal screen). If the applicant fails, the offer is rescinded. This method complies with both ADAA and EEOC regulations as long as the testing methodology is valid and complies with agency criteria. The review of these criteria including how to administer valid testing is beyond the scope of this paper. However, the idea that we can identify potential problems or risk factors prior to either employment, and/or for selection of best job type once employment is confirmed (job fit) is very real. We now perform post hire testing (contingent hire) when evaluating the fit between a prospective worker and a certain job. Employers who perform this type of prospective worker screening must adhere to standards of testing set forth by agencies and legislation such as EEOC and Department of Justice (ADA) as mentioned previously. What this means to employers from an MSK standpoint is that since the total available working population (pre and post hires) is going to be a subset of our entire work eligible population, the very epidemics that besiege our society should manifest, in roughly similar proportions, in our workplaces. Using a very broad classification system, we should then find that any employee falls into one of three possible categories from a population health standpoint. A worker can be classified as healthy, positive for risk factors, or have overt clinical disease. There is no other status. Some might argue the veracity of the "healthy" status, remarking that if you think you're healthy, it's because you just haven't been tested enough. If we agree that MSK predisposition to injury would be an important piece of information to know, then the true MSK status of a new hire becomes important. Can the applicant safely perform the essential tasks of the job in question without breakdown? Is there a legal and ethical method of testing new job applicants for their suitability to a job? Is this method consistent and in compliance with agencies (EEOC) and laws (ADAAA) regulating fair hiring/testing practices. What we do know (or strongly suspect) is that worker compensation (WC) insurance companies are probably paying for injuries that didn't necessarily occur at work; injuries that are more likely a culmination of personal, recreational and work activities (life ADLs); and most certainly, regardless of etiology, injuries that might have been prevented. How do you really know (if it's even possible to know) whether the workplace was the primary causative environment of a repetitive strain disorder (RSD)? The question is rhetorical, since we already know the answer to this; there is no reliable, consistent, standardized or accurate method for determining causation for many RSD conditions in the WC system today-arguably the most vexing component to work injury management. At times, we can't even agree on the presence of the condition and will rely mainly on subjective patient reports and clinical testing to guide interventions. The implications of this statement have clear manifestations for employers in terms of cost containment and overall claims management. How do you manage something that you can't really verify? There are no lab tests or reliable biomarkers of disease for many MSK problems, especially in the early stages. It is not prudent or cost effective to send all workers complaining of tendon pain for an MRI; even if it was, MRI requires signal generation that simply doesn't exist for many MSK disorders. The conclusion is that employers are exposed in many different ways to employee injury scenarios; and continuing to wait and treat these injuries as they occur and/or worsen is simply not good risk management within our rising healthcare cost environment. What are the alternatives, if any, for many of these problems?

Prevention Philosophy

Given the complexity of treating the problem, an actionable plan is not as complicated as one would expect, comparatively speaking. Our medical system has been designed to be a reactive one that responds to injury and disease after a diagnosis is made. This tertiary care model of health services delivery is cumbersome, expensive and rewards provider over utilization instead of provider performance. It is a system whose time has elapsed, an anachronism if you will. Up until now we have had sick care, not healthcare. And now, the system itself is sick and in dire need of transformation. Cost savings can be achieved only through promoting and implementing a system of true healthcare that is proactive and provides incentives for being well, with a focus on prevention and lifestyle/behavioral change. In the workplace, employers don't have to wait for legislative changes that typically advance into practical reform with glacial swiftness. Employers can implement prevention strategies that help identify MSK problems before they become MSK disease (early detection programs). Some proven cost reduction strategies will be discussed and evaluated for feasibility. Before specific intervention strategies are described, it is important to note that companies who implement prevention programs without a real commitment or dedication to the concept of prevention will either limit their successes or fail outright. In every organization there needs to be leaders or champions of the "movement." Company leader buy-in is critical to the long-term success of prevention strategies. As a company leader your mantra has to be: "If you don't really believe, you will fail to achieve." The injury prevention equation is actually really simple and costs a fraction of the back-end costs paid to identify and treat overt MSK disease. If we can mitigate injury costs by reducing the prevalence and/or the severity of injury cases, we reduce the number of licensed services (including prescription medication, invasive procedures, hospitalizations, surgeries, rehabilitation, vocational and durable medical equipment) required to treat those cases.

Achieving MSK Health in the Workplace

A two-pronged approach is recommended to start any wellness initiatives directed at reducing MSK and/or overall morbidity in general. Initially there is data collection and analysis. Whether it is a review of company health records, injury claims, health insurance data or a vendor-specific health risk appraisal (HRA), employers need to know about their workforce's aggregate risk; specifically, what are the problems and the extent of these problems? During this information-gathering phase there should also be a concurrent health awareness/promotion campaign at each worksite, with particular attention being paid to consistency in messaging. The message should be similar regardless of who is doing the talking. In this first phase of a wellness program directed at MSK health, the employer-chosen vendor gathers all available information and synthesizes, analyzes and creates summary reports of the problems of interest; either by types of disease or injury, risk levels or exposure types. The data can be arranged in a number of ways, depending on the questions being asked. With data in hand, we now have a better idea of where our work population is in terms of health status. In terms of MSK health, we can begin to get a better idea of who might be susceptible to certain types of problems based on retrospective data. Generally, companies have a good idea as to where the problem areas are in a workplace (e.g., certain lines in the assembly plant). These are the areas that have a higher-than-normal rate of worker complaints and subsequent lost time or restricted duty (DART rates). For these areas, it becomes important to include the ergonomic experts to be part of the problem-solving process, since an engineering control will often be necessary. Video tape analysis of the biomechanics of the job is a more comprehensive approach to work site analysis in those more subtle situations where the problems are not apparent. This can be a very useful exercise, since the data can be taken back to an office and re-played for better and more precise evaluation. The important point is that information gathering is step one in this process and there are several ways to get the information. Information is then provided to the employer in the form of aggregate, or group data useful in identifying problematic areas and trends of interest. Information is always de-identified when provided to employers; however, individual data must be made available to wellness vendors who are charged with providing on- site services to allow for one-on-one targeted interventions such as smoking cessation.

Beyond the Data: Some Key Interventions
It is not possible to avoid all MSK injury burden in the workplace, but it is possible to mitigate the overall injury risk by implementation of important cost-effective initiatives. It is critical to recognize the link between MSK health and overall health of the person. They cannot be separated, and as such, a multifaceted set of options needs to be available for workers to engage in. How does a company choose which interventions are going to be the most meaningful for its workforce? What are your most pervasive problems? The data might identify your population as being mostly "at risk" and not overtly diseased at this point in time, in which case, risk factor modification strategies would be an obvious choice. These would undoubtedly involve exercise programming and, nutrition and diet counseling. Some companies have onsite facilities, but most do not. Companies can begin relatively inexpensive programs (e.g., a walking program at lunch) and perhaps even splurge by providing pedometers to employees so they can monitor their activity on a daily basis. Some companies create competitions among departments to see who can rack up the most mileage in a month and reward participants at the end. The value of incentives cannot be overstated; in many cases, they're necessary to get workers to even consider wellness interventions. Those who have overt diabetes, cardiovascular disease, COPD and obesity can be even more at risk from a MSK standpoint due to the complicated interactions between the body's various systems, as well as reduced activity that is brought about by the emergence of these diseases. An afflicted person's ability to exercise and/or perform a strength training regimen might be more limited and require more intense coaching from healthcare professionals, but the interventions still apply to these populations as well. Health promotion and participation applies equally to the entire spectrum of health status, from young and healthy to older with morbidity.

The key interventions that apply universally to all three categories of health status include smoking cessation, weight management, stress management, regular exercise, proper lifting mechanics, maintaining good posture, proper sleep, proper hydration and rational medication compliance. Let's discuss further some of these key interventions that are easy to implement and have a high ROI.

Smoking Cessation: The link between smoking and MSK health was suspected and verified many years ago through epidemiology studies. A purported causal link is postulated that smoking has a detrimental effect on the vascular system, robbing tissue of oxygen and contributing to atherosclerotic build-up and narrowing of the arteries (vasoconstriction). Smoking can also cause emphysema, a disease that robs the lungs of the necessary elasticity required for proper breathing mechanics. There is evidence to support the link between smoking and lower back pain, probably mediated through tissue hypoxia resulting from the already-poor circulation in the lumbar spine region, which appears to worsen with age. Smoking reduces the oxygen availability even more, adding to the already-poor circulatory status in the area [7]. Work has been defined as the ability to perform and repeat certain essential tasks comprising a job. By definition this implies the inherent ability to endure repeated movements with or without an external MSK load, in both cases requiring aerobic and muscular endurance capabilities. In the absence of oxygen, the MSK system cannot utilize the aerobic energy pathway required to perform continuous activities. Type 1 or red muscle fibers (oxidative fibers) eventually waste, consequently leading to stiff joints with impaired function stemming from poor muscle activation. Smoking cessation promotes better physical function through improved tissue oxygenation and subsequently increased cellular metabolism, while at the same time reducing the risk of cancers [8].

Weight Management: The estimates all vary depending on the source, but suffice it to say that a significant percentage of our total population is officially classified as obese when using BMI as the measurement tool. It's important to note that the BMI has significant limitations, including overestimating persons who are shorter in stature relative to weight, since this measure cannot discriminate between fat versus lean mass [9]. When we add the proportion of the population that is classified as overweight and combine it with those people classified as obese, we have close to 65 percent of our population falling outside the recommended healthy weight ranges, putting them at risk for a myriad of systemic diseases. This translates into higher general disease risk, which is associated with escalating healthcare costs, including the possibility of catastrophic events to the worker population. It is these catastrophic events that represent a large portion of total healthcare expenditures and need to be avoided. Controlling weight is a complicated problem and requires a commitment to lifestyle changes, including regular exercise and active food management strategies. Employers should promote and provide avenues for weight management options, including incentives to facilitate positive behavioral changes. Higher-than-normal body weight can excessively tax the MSK system and predispose a worker to injury and/or early degenerative joint changes, adding to the already-present risk of injury simply from exposure to high or repetitive loads at the workplace. Excess weight has implications for posture and body mechanics that work against productivity, not to mention the emotional/social and psychological stresses that weight gain can bring on. High blood pressure and high cholesterol are blood parameters that need controlling, since both have been linked to lower back pain and smoking. They also increase susceptibility to other serious and life-threatening conditions such as heart disease and stroke.

Stress Management: The relationship between stress and weight gain has been well established over the years, specifically the role of cortisol in the biochemical cascade that leads to increases in fat storage [10]. Apart from the strong relationship between this hormone and weight gain, stress has generally been recognized as detrimental to our physiology, causing a depletion of catecholamines and leading to overstimulation of the CNS. The general upsetting of homeostasis has been linked in chronic cases to cancers and heart/renal diseases [11]. Stress is also detrimental to cognitive acuity and performance in general. Although mild CNS stimulation is associated with an improvement in mental functions and physical performance, too much stress becomes negative and is associated with decaying functions in both simple and complex tasks.

Regular Exercise: The MSK system operates under the "if you don't use it, you lose it" principle; thus, activity cannot be overstated. Employers who provide options for their employees to engage in regular exercise are counteracting the de-conditioning process inherent in aging and work. We are a nation of overweight, underactive, overstressed and poorly fed people who are overwhelmingly fed a steady diet of mass marketing misinformation, so we continue to believe the illusion of being in control. Employers are in a position to begin to reverse the health degradation downspin that is steadily sucking the life from American workers and the productivity levels from American industry. Employers must take the lead and invest more on primary prevention. Employers who implement regular exercise as part of their wellness service line will be providing the best medicine available for their employees now and will reap the downstream rewards later. The key to ROI is to act sooner rather than later. In MSK health, nothing is more effective than prevention. Simple strategies to prevent MSK disease now are a better option than treatment for a problem later on. Early detection is good, but preventing injury is still the best option. Muscles need controlled multi-planar movements with and without resistance to build strength and endurance.

Posture/Body Mechanics/Lifting: All of these areas are important and are known to be causative agents at worst, and/or facilitators of MSK pain at best. When there is a chronic presence of any, or all of these factors, the probability of MSK morbidity is heightened. Any and all of these MSK status determinants can be managed by cost-effective intervention. Simple, targeted and low-cost remedial strategies can be implemented to reverse the pathological processes that bad posture, faulty body mechanics and unsafe lifting practices can induce. Workers can be educated on safe and efficient lifting actions, including proper biomechanics. Education regarding how to properly strengthen weaker muscle groups to reestablish improved trunk postures, effective stretching, appropriate bracing/supportive strategies and the application of heat/cold and analgesic balms can all be part of worker education. Information/advice needs positive reinforcement on more than one occasion to be sustainable and prevent positive behavior from being extinguished.

Prevention vs. Intervention:
The interventions listed above can all be implemented as part of an injury prevention program and/or as interventions in cases where risk factors or disease are present. Clearly, the highest dividend or ROI for a company is made when a preventive approach is undertaken. The next best program is an early intervention program that seeks to halt the progression of an existing or potential problem as it manifests. Workers should be encouraged to report tissue irrita-

tion early and not wait until symptoms worsen. Reporting should be a positive endeavor, not one filled with anxiety and angst for fear of retribution. Furthermore, potential joint and muscle aches can be recognized and managed using a simple triage system that recognizes the beginning of an irritation with potential to worsen and become a recordable event, if ignored. Some industrial clients have opted for very simple MSK screens to be part of their wellness programs. Employees who experienced the start of joint pain would be sent to a work coach trained in triage and MSK assessments, with subsequent recommendations made on how to manage the condition primarily at home. Advice on strength/stretch exercises, icing protocols and use of appropriate over-the-counter NSAIDS would be at the core of this education. The use of home-based TENS application and/or ointments and other home remedies could be discussed so that The Problem does not progress into a recordable medical event. The application of onsite imaging has become very popular, especially in industries having high rates of orthopedic injuries. MSK screening can save companies thousands of dollars in unnecessary MRIs and diagnostic injections and can be repeated over time, allowing medical staff to verify status of irritated tissues. The use of onsite trained health coaches who can provide this type of MSK surveillance in an ongoing manner has demonstrated benefits to employers. Early recognition of MSK disorders is widely accepted as being a fundamental truism in the dialogue of cost-containment efforts. Many of the services listed can be contracted out to appropriate vendors and do not require companies to have elaborate onsite resources.

Conclusion:

The burden of MSK injury costs on employers cannot be understated and needs to be addressed by a comprehensive wellness and disease management program. It is difficult to understand the rationale for focusing only on cardiac risk in the presence of a workforce with concurrent MSK limitations. In fact, we see MSK injury manifestations well before we see any measurable biomarker elevation for CAD in those without congenital coronary heart disease. Shoulder rotator cuff tears or idiopathic lumbar spine pain occur with the advent of physical work and consequently appear earlier in the lives of workers as compared to modifiable coronary heart disease, which typically appears later in life. Although we are not making a case for not treating early-stage coronary artery/heart disease, we believe that to focus solely on CAD and its sequelae will not necessarily lead to higher work productivity when the rate-limiting factor is underlying MSK disease. We believe that it is prudent and more cost effective to concurrently address all body systems using specific exercise progressions to maximize a person's work efficiency and total health. An exercise program can and should try to mitigate the risk of both cardiac and musculoskeletal disease simultaneously, especially since MSK problems directly and adversely affect worker productivity; at the same time, these problems are highly modifiable and, ultimately, very treatable.

References

1. Adamson J, Hunt K, Ebrahim S. "Association between measures of morbidity and locomotor disability: diagnosis alone is not enough." 2003. *Soc Sci Med.* Oct;57(8): 1355-60.

2. da Costa BR, Viera ER. "Risk factors for work related musculoskeletal disorders: A systematic review of recent longitudinal studies." 2010. *Am J Ind Med.* Mar;53(3):285-323.

3. Dailey B. "Musculoskeletal injury prevention." 2006. *J Emer Med Ser.* April; 1-11.

4. Leigh P, Markowitz S, Fahs M et al. "Costs of occupational injuries and illnesses." University of Michigan Press, 2000.

5. Bureau of Labor Statistics. Workplace injuries and illnesses. www.bls.gov/news.release/osh.nr0.htm

6. Stewart W, Ricci J, Chee E et al. "Lost productive time and cost due to common pain conditions in the US workforce." 2003. *JAMA.* 290(18):2443-2454.

7. Shiri R, Karppinen S, Leino-Arjas P, et al. "The association between smoking and low back pain: a meta analysis." 2010. *Am J Med.* Jan; 123(1). E7-35.

8. Jyrrkio S, Bostrom P, Minn H. "Smoking and cancer-what are the benefits of cessation?" 2012. *Duodecim.* 128(10):1081-1087.

9. Norgan NG. "Population differences in body composition in relation to the body mass index." 1994. *Eur J Clin Nutr.* Nov; 48 suppl 3:S10-25.

10. Rosmond R, Dallman MF, Bjorntop P. "Stress related cortisol secretion in men: relationship with abdominal obesity and endocrine, metabolic and hemodynamic abnormalities." 1998. *J Clin Endocrinol Metab.* Jun; 83(6): 1853-1859.

11. Reiche EM, Nunes SO, Morimoto HK. "Stress, depression, the immune system, and cancer." 2004. *Lanc Oncol.* 5(10): 617-625.

Key Ideas

- Musculoskeletal disorders (MSDs)

- Gaining an understanding into where the high-risk exposures are located within a workplace is paramount in building a worksite wellness plan that yields a high return on investment

- The total cost of treating MSK injuries in 2004 was estimated to be nearly $127.4 billion, with approximately 20 percent of this total cost being apportioned to hospitalization related to the injury.

- Companies who implement prevention programs without a real commitment or dedication to the concept of prevention will either limit their successes or fail outright.

- A two-pronged approach is recommended to start any wellness initiatives directed at reducing MSK

- Initially there is data collection and analysis.

- The key interventions that apply universally to all three categories of health status include smoking cessation, weight management, stress management, regular exercise, proper lifting mechanics, maintaining good posture, proper sleep, proper hydration and rational medication compliance

Questions

1. Twenty percent of total cost of treating MSK injuries in 2004 was for what?

   a. Paying for a chiropractor

   b. Medications

   c. Physical Therapy

   d. Hospitalization

2. Having untreated early-onset musculoskeletal pain can account for a significant reduction in productivity.

   a. True

   b. False

3. What is missing from the key interventions: smoking cessation, weight management, exercise, proper lifting mechanics, maintaining good posture, _____, proper hydration, and rational medication compliance.

   a. Ergonomic offices

   b. Proper nutrition

   c. Proper sleep

   d. None of the above

Walking Program Best Practices
By: Jonathan Edelheit and Renée-Marie Stephano

Walking Programs are an excellent method to start-up any wellness initiative. A large benefit of such a program is that it easy to start and most people are able to participateThey can also be as cheap or as expensive as you want them to be. It can be as simple as just bringing a pair of sneakers and a change of clothes, to a full competition involving online portals and wireless pedometers which track the participant's steps.

Walking programs are very simple for offices. Many employees like to take a break where they get to stretch their legs. It becomes easy then to set up a small walking route around the office, so people can even take a few minutes to do a quick lap during a break. Even the unassuming act of strolling around the office can have a big boost to fighting a sedentary lifestyle and increasing productivity.

If a walking program that walks around the neighborhood or that tracks steps taken using a pedometer is desired, there are some basic tips every walker should know. Prior to walking, make sure to be well hydrated, even though it is not as strenuous as jogging or running, walking can still cause someone to break a sweat. Keep focused on your posture while you walk; stand tall with shoulders back and eyes straight ahead. Another important thing to keep in mind is to stretch before and after walking, and start off with a gentle stride as a warm-up, and end with cool-down. These tips improve the efficiency of the walking program and will reduce injury.

For a solo pedometer program, the above steps are useful, but there are additional things to known before dedicating to a walking program. Start off gradually; do not begin to walk long distances until your body has had time to adjust to the activity. Start with a short amount of time walking at a leisurely pace. After a week of this slowly begin to increase either time, distance or pace; but do increase all of these at once, only introduce them one at a time. Eventually you will become a dedicated walker.

These were some basic examples of walking programs, from simple laps around the office to dedicated programs which tracks steps and reward results. This information is not as helpful without instruction on how to walk for exercise safely. If an employee injures themselves walking in the program it defeats the purpose of the plan entirely, these programs are intended to reduce medical claims and personal injury not encourage it.

Weight Program Best Practices
By: Jonathan Edelheit and Renée-Marie Stephano

Obesity is a major issue in America, and with the rates of obesity are expected to continue to grow it becomes important to help these individuals try to become healthy, and to sustain healthy behaviors. Besides health costs, an employee who is in better health is a more productive one, so the benefits of helping become two-fold. There are many ways wellness programs can help employees who are struggling with their weight, which will be detailed below.

A common practice which has proven effective is by making the weight loss initiative a game. The popular television show *The Biggest Loser* is an example of how to do this. The game is simple; form a team or compete individually and the team or individual who loses the most weight wins. Many programs will offer a prize of some sort for winning; it could be anything from a cash prize or gift card, a trophy, or just recognition in a wellness bulletin about the person's accomplishment.

A second effective method is to hold Weight Watchers meetings at the office, and/or to pay for the employee's membership fees. Many will feel awkward about going to a Weight Watchers meeting but let these people know that the program has been around since 1963 and has helped countless people lose weight. Weight Watchers has meetings that can take place in the office, and regularly does so not only in the United States, but across the world.

Some companies offer their employees coaching to improve their health. In the case of weight loss, it can be done with dieticians, nutritionists, and fitness trainer who can help set up an exercise regime. Many of these companies make it easier for their employees to use these services by bringing in one of these coaches into the office so people can meet face-to-face, through phone interviews and hotlines, and through web portals and web chats. By making these coaches more accessible, more people will be likely to utilize them in their weight loss goals.

Finally, an often over-looked aspect is to offer healthy food in the workplace. If you want your employees to lose weight, it is not fair to them to have a vending machine full of soda, candy bars and potato chips. If your company has a cafeteria onsite, make sure it is offering healthy alternatives to meals and to make sure that these taste good, if the healthy alternative tastes bad no one will use it. Instead of leaving out bowls of candy, leave bowls of fresh fruit. It is small changes like this that can have a big impact.

There are several small, yet powerful, words of advise for weight programs. First, encourage employees to set realistic goals for themselves. We all would love to lose twenty pounds in a few weeks, but the reality is that this will not happen. By setting realistic goals, the employee will not be discouraged when an unreasonable goal is not met and give up entirely. The next relates to the first one, as the leader of the wellness program do not expect instant results programs like these take time. Just because the ROI does not come immediately does not mean it will never come ever, it will take some time but the returns will come.

Fitness Program Best Practices
By: Jonathan Edelheit and Renée-Marie Stephano

As Thales, the pre-Socratic philosopher famously said, *"Mens sana in corpore sano."* This roughly translates to "a sound mind in a healthy body." This is the logic behind fitness programs. These are ultimately for encouraging healthy behaviors to improve productivity and to reduce health expenses. There are many ways to go about this, as will be detailed below.

One of the first aspects a fitness program needs is a gym. Some companies have a gym onsite. Although this can be expensive, exercise equipment can be costly to buy and to maintain, it is very effective. It allows the employee easy access to a gym facility at no expense to them. The ease of use of the gym is important, because if an employee has to go across town to do thirty minutes of cardio after work it is unlikely they will do it. If the employee is given time off of work, even better because this shows the employee that their employer cares about them and wants to see them healthy.

An alternative to onsite facilities is for the employer to subsidize or reimburse gym memberships for its employees. This can be much less expensive, especially when the employer negotiates a deal with a nearby gym, to get lower rates for their employees. This is a viable option even for smaller companies.

If these things are not in the works for a company, or the company cannot or does not want to cover gym memberships or establish an onsite center there are still options available. A simple way is to encourage employees to take the stairs, there are many ways to do this, play music in the stairwell or move the water coolers in there. Hire a fitness instructor to come in and teach a class about exercise to your employees, or have employees set up one on one interviews with the instructor to get better guidance. At meetings, bring in healthy foods instead of the regular unhealthy foods.

There is one word of advice for people creating a company fitness program. You cannot treat a program like this as one size fits all solution. What works for one company will not work for another. If you spend a lot of money for a wellness center, and it is impossible or impractical for employees to use it then it just becomes a massive waste of funds.

Health Fair Best Practices
By: Jonathan Edelheit and Renée-Marie Stephano

Many companies are seeing the good that hosting a health fair at work can have for a wellness program. A health fair, at its core, is an educational event where various health vendors, health experts gather to teach about certain health initiatives. Biometric screening and other health screening can take place at this time also. As can health demonstrations. Although these events may seems like a confusing mess, and irrelevant to a wellness initiative, this is not the case as will be outlined below.

The first step to forming a health fair is to form a team that can help organize and draw attention to the event. This is an important first step, if there are no people attending or no exhibits then it becomes a waste of time. When forming a committee, use people you can trust who will get the job done; whether it is getting exhibits and demonstrations, or creating a buzz among the employees.

Remember to keep your organization's culture in mind during this planning step. Design and advertise a health fair which is relevant to your company's needs. If your company already has an effective communication strategy to get in contact with employees, continue to use these methods. Use multiple channels to advertise, put up fliers and table tents in the break room, send out emails, have your committee spread the message by word of mouth. Make sure the message you are sending out is consistent across all mediums, a jumbled message will only cause problems and confusion.

Now that the event is off on a strong foot, what will actually happen at the health fair needs to be discussed. There are three principle varities of activities at health fairs; educational, screenings, and demonstrations. The educational events can and should be interactive. Some typical events for an educational display are; back care, child safety, stress information, dental and oral health, ergonomics, office safety, and child safety. Screening events are meant to inform the participant about their own personal health concerns and how to stop or prevent it. Some screenings that are typical of a health fair are; blood pressure, BMI, glucose, hearing, bone density and HRAs. The demonstrations are meant to be fun and spread awareness and the proper way to perform activities. Sample demonstrations include CPR, yoga, first aid, proper techniques for lifting, and healthy cooking classes.

These are just some simple examples of practices for a health fair. In reality, the activities of a health fair are limited only by your imagination. The intention of a health fair is to create a fun and educational environment for people to learn how to live healthier lives. With this in mind go out and begin the process of educating employees, start with a committee of dedicated people and then begin to put the pieces together from there. The suggested events for the health fair are jumping off points, remember to keep the needs of your company in line with the events of the fair and plan accordingly.

Case Study: Best Practices at Work
By Renée-Marie Stephano

Introduction and Background
Zurich Financial Services Group is an insurance-based financial services provider founded in 1872 in Zurich, Switzerland. They have approximately 60,000 employees in 70 countries. Their program was designed to change personal health behavior, lifestyle decision making and disease reduction. The Program launched in 2008.

The Program
In order to start the program, Zurich had their employees complete health risk assessments of which 74 percent completed the online HRA and 56 percent showed some for health risk. Most of this risk was related to body weight. This assessment paved the way for their program and set the stage for how they would proceed. One of the first things they did was follow already established best practices like securing support from leadership, and creating a program tailored to the workplace culture. Another important aspect was to establish multiple communication channels with employees so they could know the benefits of the program.

In order to gather more date to further tailor the program to Zurich's specific needs, they employed online health risk assessments, onsite biometric screening, analysis of medical insurance claims, and employee self-identification and employee referrals. To help the employees Zurich brought in wellness coaches to aid in exercise, tobacco cessation, weight management, nutrition and heart counseling. Employees are even able to take advantage of some of these tools through an online web portal.

Another aspect of the program is a six week walking challenge with a pedometer. This was the most visible program, with executive level support. Over two challenge events, one held each year, employees recorded more than 2 billion steps.

The Results
At least 64 percent of the employees at Zurich participated in the wellness program in one form or another. 13 percent participated in one-on-one with a health coach, and 33 percent with the online coaching. 50 percent participated in the biometric screening.

One of the proudest accomplishments is an ROI of 3.8:1. A noticeable decrease in healthcare costs is also evident. Zurich has also noticed a decrease in disability spending and worker compensation claims. This is all coupled with an increase in Productivity.

CHAPTER 11
Social Media and Corporate Wellness

Embracing the Revolution: Using Social Networking to Power Your Employee Wellness Program

By Rajiv Kumar

For a myriad of reasons, it's now crystal clear that social networking has gone into the mainstream. The 35 and over age group is the fastest growing demographic online and Facebook now has 350 million users, not to mention the explosion of the widely popular business and social networking micro-blogging site Twitter. Amidst this growth, there's increasing evidence that social networking is making its way into companies across the country to augment many human resources functions. For one, more than 45 percent of employers are now using social networking tools to research job candidates according to a CareerBuilder survey.

Benefits and wellness professionals are also harnessing the power of connectivity to drive participation, long-term engagement and successful outcomes in employee wellness programs. This growing trend comes at a time when many are turning to financial incentives to drive employee engagement in these programs. In fact, the average annual incentive for wellness programs rose to $329 per employee in 2009, according to a joint survey by the National Association of Manufacturers and Health 2 Resources. Employers focusing on the power of social incentives over financial incentives, however, are finding that they are empowering their employees to effectively communicate and share information in a manner that makes wellness more fun and engaging.

Maximizing Participation

Social networking tools enable colleagues to directly invite and challenge each other to participate in a wellness intervention, such as a weight loss challenge, walking group or health fair. This peer-to-peer dynamic creates a grassroots, viral approach to recruitment, and it's proving to be a more effective mechanism to drive involvement. While the support of senior leadership is important to the success of any company's wellness initiative, employees are much more likely to participate in a wellness program when personally invited by a trusted colleague than they are by simply walking past a poster designed by the human resources department. At one distribution company, eighty-four percent of employees who participated in a competitive, team-based wellness program reported that it was the very first time they had signed up to take advantage of the company's numerous offerings.

Boosting Retention

It is difficult for wellness managers to think of new ideas to keep a wellness program fresh, relevant and suitable to everyone, since employee interests and goals are different and constantly changing. Employers can "crowd-source" their annual wellness calendar by giving employees access to social media tools that enable them to create their own groups based on any interests (healthy recipe-sharing club, softball team, lunch-time walking group, etc.). Employees can also use these tools to share information such as recipes, upcoming events, educational articles and motivational messages with one another. This customized, employee-driven content increases the relevancy and appeal of a corporate wellness program. Participating alongside colleagues also provides employees with motivation, peer support and accountability, all of which are crucial to driving long-term engagement. As a result, some employers are seeing long-term engagement rates as high as eighty percent.

Achieving Behavior Change

The latest research from Dr. Nicholas A. Christakis, MD, PhD, MPH, an internist and social scientist with Harvard Medical School who conducts research on social factors that affect health, shows that the people around us have a tremendous impact on our health. When people lose weight, quit smoking or increase their exercise, the people in their trusted social network, such as colleagues, are more likely to do so as well. For example, if someone quits smoking, his or her co-workers are thirty-four percent more likely to quit as well. This is because the people we interact with on a regular basis influence our perception of social norms. By uniting employees and encouraging them to make healthy commitments together, employers can harness this network effect to spread healthy behaviors at the workplace and increase the likelihood that their employees will succeed. When employees begin to make a shared commitment to being healthy, they begin to throw away traditions like "muffin Mondays" and "bagel Fridays" and start to bring fruit to the office, take the stairs instead of the elevator, and park at the far end of the parking lot in order to accumulate more physical activity.

Saving Money

Given the current economic climate, paying employees to improve their health can be a cost-prohibitive proposition for many employers. There is also research showing that the compensation effect wears off quickly, people expect increasing amounts of money for changing their behavior, and that once the incentive is taken away participants often revert back to old habits. The good news for employers is that social incentives are free – and far more powerful at creating long-term, sustainable behavior change. Creating a supportive environment of peers working together demonstrates that everyone has a stake in the health of the workforce and helps tap into the intrinsic motivation that we all have to be healthy. Support from colleagues is the most effective way to encourage healthy habits.

A recent Watson Wyatt Worldwide study concluded that companies with robust wellness programs achieve greater financial success. But a robust wellness program requires high participation, long-term engagement, and clinically-significant outcomes. As social networking continues to spread, employers must evaluate how they can harness the power of these tools to improve the health of their employees and their bottom line. Many companies have already embraced the concept of social networking in wellness to achieve these goals. Your company cannot afford to wait to join them.

Key Ideas

- Social networking tools enable colleagues to directly invite and challenge each other to participate in a wellness intervention, such as a weight loss challenge, walking group or health fair. This peer-to-peer dynamic creates a grassroots, viral approach to recruitment, and it's proving to be a more effective mechanism to drive involvement.

- Employers can "crowd-source" their annual wellness calendar by giving employees access to social media tools that enable them to create their own groups based on any interests (healthy recipe-sharing club, softball team, lunch-time walking group, etc.

Questions

1. Social Networking does not help create a grassroots approach, but instead creates a large center for involvement.

   a. True

   b. False

2. What is meant «crowd sourcing»?

   a. Using a crowd to gather enthusiasm for a program

   b. Making people exercise in large groups

   c. Allowing a group to create their own wellness groups

   d. Dividing a large project among a large group of people.

Health Gaming: Make the Hard Work of Getting Healthier Fun and Engaging
By Tom Abshire

More and more organizations are using game mechanics to engage employees and drive behavior change in areas across the organization. The analyst firm Gartner predicts that, by 2014, about 70 percent of Global 2000 organizations will have at least one gamified application. And for good reason. Game mechanics help break down large tasks into small, achievable, short-term goals and reward achievement. They convert passive users into active "players" – that is, they drive employee engagement and participation. They have a subtle power to turn actions into habits. Plus, they can create a unifying experience around an unfamiliar and often changing array of tasks.

But what do game mechanics have to do with health? As it turns out, plenty.

Game mechanics are a proven, effective strategy for higher employee participation and completion in technology-based Wellness 2.0 programs. These games-based strategies not only drive engagement in programs, they provide the bridge to the all-important offline healthy behaviors and can reinforce behaviors across programs. Game mechanics motivate employees to make the healthy choices that help organizations improve workforce health and gain control over skyrocketing healthcare costs.

Gamifying Health: A Means to an End
Before your organization sets out to incorporate game mechanics into your employee health strategy, it's important to first do some thinking. Keep in mind that "gamifying health" isn't the end goal, but merely one strategy for creating a healthier workforce. Game mechanics help your employees easily learn how they can participate in your programs, what they need to do to make healthy behavior changes, and better understand their progress against goals.

And just like in real life, not all games are created equally. Good games are well designed. They're interesting and engaging. They're built with the needs and desires of their audiences in mind. They provide the triggers that reinforce the behaviors you seek to drive. And, if properly designed, they offer opportunities to leverage social connections with peers to enhance the game and your outcomes.

Game On: Quick Tips to Consider

- So, how do you apply game mechanics to your employee wellness initiatives that will successfully turn your employees from passive users into active players? Consider these quick tips:

- Keep it simple, easy, and achievable.

- Points, levels and rewards help drive engagement and ongoing employee participation and healthy behaviors. Having a common set of game mechanics across programs makes it easier to understand what to do, and easier to cross promote programs and have a higher impact.

- Employ regular challenges and competition.

- Ongoing competition and healthy challenges provide opportunities to keep employees motivated towards good health. They also offer important points in time for employees to connect socially with their peers and cheer one another on the path to good health.

- Make it easy to track and monitor progress.

- Traditional Wellness 1.0 programs were manual-based and put the burden on employees to track their progress, and for HR to monitor overall success of the initiative. But today's new wellness technologies, coupled with effective game mechanics, turn tracking and monitoring into an easy and validated online process.

- Make it social.

- Provide ways for employees to connect socially to share scores, talk about leaderboards, exchange tips and tricks, and generally brag about their success.

- Get C-level buy in.

- The most successful employee health initiatives enjoy strong, visible support from the top. If you're struggling to get senior executives in the game, conduct your own challenge (among departments, locations, etc.) and share data about participation (average activity levels prior to challenge, during challenge, after challenge). These numbers may be enough to make believers of even the most skeptical management team.

- Capture data to know your game's working well.

- Organizations need strong reporting capabilities to understand the impact of the employee health effort. With reporting tools, companies can use the data from their health games and nimbly adjust/adapt the game to changing needs to drive ongoing results.

Successful Health Gaming in Action
Let's look at a couple of examples of successful health gaming in action. At Ochsner Health System, a large Louisiana-based health-care system with seven hospitals and 35 clinics, more than 85 percent of the company's 10,000 benefits eligible employees are playing an employee health game. Of those employees participating, more than 50 percent earned enough points to achieve Level 3 in the game, and received a substantial health insurance premium discount for 2010. Ochsner's internal studies are showing actual cost savings from this approach. In 2010, Ochsner held the growth in its cost of healthcare to nearly one-third the national average.

Another example is Columbus, Indiana-based Cummins Inc., a corporation of complementary business units that design, manufacture, distribute and service engines and related technologies. Cummins began incorporating a game component into its wellness program in 2011. This summer, Cummins held its first company-wide competition, called the Champions' Challenge. All employees participating in its employee wellness program were invited to join the challenge and earn activity points. For every 500 activity points accrued, one entry into a random prize drawing was earned. So far, Cummins reports the challenges and gaming aspects have received a very positive response, with a large number of people engaged in at least one challenge since they enrolled (roughly 73 percent of the company's eligible U.S. population is enrolled in its wellness program).

Social and Mobile Technologies: Supporting the Success of Health Gaming

Two other technologies that can drive greater success of your health gaming strategy are social networking and mobile.

Social relationships and culture play a tremendous role in our health. Science shows an individual is 171 percent more likely to become obese if their friends are obese. As mentioned earlier, health gaming and social media are a complementary pairing. The power of peer-to-peer motivation and support can motivate employees to engage in the employee health effort – and stay in the game for the long term.

Mobile apps are also important because they provide employees with greater freedom to participate whenever and wherever they happen to be. Apps today can help to track physical activity or nutrition, and employees can even engage each other using handheld devices. The freedom to record and monitor biometric and activity progress, get support from peers, and get real-time updates on game standings provides instant motivation.

Workplace Wellness: Let the Games Begin!

Game mechanics are proving to be one of the most winning strategies companies can tap to boost employee health and productivity. Game mechanics offer a short-term reinforcement cycle and are a great way to keep employee health momentum going over the long term. But when thinking about adding game mechanics to your employee health initiatives, keep simplicity in mind so your employees can easily understand what they need to do to succeed on the path to good health. People become easily frustrated with conflicting, complex rules, so boil health gaming down to short steps and reinforcement cycles. By achieving small tasks, employees can achieve a level of confidence that keeps them moving into higher levels of the game.

Remember, too, that getting employees to play the game isn't the end goal. Rather it's one strategy that helps you create a workplace culture of health and drive sustained offline behavior shifts.

Employee engagement and/or retention is a challenge for employers today. If you want to attract and keep the best talent, it helps if your employees are having fun and are engaged. And games can help immensely in achieving both of those goals.

So when it comes to workplace wellness, "let the games begin!"

Key Ideas

- Game mechanics help break down large tasks into small, achievable, short-term goals and reward achievement. They convert passive users into active "players" – that is, they drive employee engagement and participation.

- Game mechanics motivate employees to make the healthy choices that help organizations improve workforce health and gain control over skyrocketing healthcare costs.

- "Gamifying health" isn't the end goal, but merely one strategy for creating a healthier workforce.

- When thinking about adding game mechanics to your employee health initiatives, keep simplicity in mind so your employees can easily understand what they need to do to succeed on the path to good health.

Questions

1. Gamifying health is the end goal.

    a. True

    b. False

2. Simplicity should be a part of any game mechanic

    a. True

    b. False

3. How do games drive employee involvement?

    a. They provide an easy to understand environment

    b. They allow people to work together

    c. They make participants into players, driving engagement

    d. They reward positive behavior

Chronic Disease Management, Smartphones and Corporate Wellness

By Pamela Swingley

In a perfect world, none of us would have to take any medications. Our meals would consist mostly of fruits, vegetables and grains. We would exercise daily, sleep eight hours a night, meditate and avoid stress.

A few employees do consistently practice healthy behaviors. These employees are the ones that usually take full advantage of corporate wellness programs. But, the majority of employees would rather take a pill than change their lifestyle; even if it means managing a chronic disease for the rest of their lives.

Americans are taking more medications than ever before. In fact, 81 percent of adults in the U.S. take at least one medication during a given week, and 27 percent take at least five medications. However, while we may be taking more medications, we frequently fail to take them as prescribed.

Taking medications correctly is a challenge for people of all ages, with all types of conditions. It may be Greg in accounting with high blood pressure, or Nancy, that has diabetes, or Eileen who is nearing retirement. Or it may be an employee's family member who struggles to manage their medication. The fact is, many of us simply forget to take our pills, stop taking them because we feel better, forget to reorder, or can't afford them.

The cost of poor compliance is astronomical. Estimates of the total annual healthcare costs in the U.S. resulting from patient noncompliance vary from $177 billion to $300 billion. Unfortunately many of these costs are passed on to employers who must manage escalating health insurance premiums.

Smartphones Hold the Secret to Healthier Employees

Medication compliance is not a new issue. Nor is it one that is easily solved. One of the challenges in improving compliance has been a lack of solutions that address the complexity of chronic disease management. To be effective, solutions must fit seamlessly with the patient's lifestyle.

Enter the smartphone. Since the introduction of the Apple iPhone in June, 2007, smartphone adoption rates have exploded. These phones are quickly changing the way we manage relationships, pay our bills, get the latest news, and manage our health.

The smartphone is the perfect device to provide daily support between medical appointments. The most logical point to start is with medication reminders. Studies show that electronic reminders reduce healthcare costs. In the 2003, in a Division of Medical Services report by the State of Missouri, it found the average monthly Medicaid Costs for Diabetic patients with reminders was $949 compared to $1,233 without reminders.

Reminders to take the right medication, at the right time, in the right dose are just the beginning. The next generation of health management services now on the market incorporates comprehensive tools to help employees manage their health. These solutions take a holistic approach, consolidating patient information to provide feedback that supports behavior changes.

Features of these health 2.0 solutions include medication and event reminders, compliance reporting, goal and bio-metrics tracking, health charts, account sharing across a health team, as well as a personal health record and vault to store documents.

Through their smartphones, employees not only receive medication reminders, but can monitor their blood glucose levels, record their weight, report health events, receive disease-specific wellness tips, participate in exercise challenges, and have their personal health record in the palm of their hand.

Questions to Ask When Selecting a Chronic Disease Management Service

When it comes to selecting a chronic disease management service to offer employees, you want to consider flexibility, security, support, accessibility, employee friendliness and cost.

How flexible is it?

Flexibility is an essential feature because everyone has a unique medication schedule. The service should be able to support all different types of medications, like oral, patch, injection, supplements and more. It should also support medications taken at different times, changes in the time zone, and the ability to add special instructions, such as how to take it, where it's stored, and more.

Does the service take security seriously?
This is a crucial feature to evaluate when dealing with employee health information. The service should offer password protection, care communities with different administration and privilege levels controlled by the main user, tier 1 data hosting, audit trails, inactivity time-out, and HTTPS transmissions. These steps indicate a company is invested in protecting your employees' health information.

What type of support is available? No matter how simple a service, at some point everyone will have a question. Whether help is online, by phone, or by email, make sure it's easy to find an answer. If secured account sharing is available for tricky support questions, even better. Don't forget to ask about support for your HR department as well. Vendors that offer employee training, and marketing programs to encourage adoption will increase your return on investment.

What platforms does it work on? Another factor to consider is the accessibility of the service. Whether it's a text messaging service or a smartphone application, the service needs to work with the phones that the majority of your employees use. A medication reminder service offered for iPhones only has a limited market potential. The service should be available from any browser "in the cloud" to support employees at home, at work, or on the go.

What functionality is included?
While thousands of individual smartphone apps exist to remind employees to take pills, track exercise, count calories, monitor goals, motivate, educate and more, most apps are only used a few times. When it comes to making lasting changes it helps to use a service that consolidates information all in one place. This provides a holistic view of the patient's health and only requires one download, one password, and one system to learn.

Is it Employee-Centric?
Offering a wellness service to manage chronic diseases is great, but be sure it is a service that employees will voluntarily use. It should be designed from the employee's point of view to be easy to use. To

be portable so that if they change jobs, they can take their medical history with them. To keep health information confidential from employers and health plans. To enable them to opt-in, or out, of services, and to choose what information they share, and who they share it with.

How Much Does It Cost?

While some large employers have invested millions in personal health records, or wellness solutions for their employees, chronic disease management services do not have to be expensive. In fact, most of us have become accustomed to using free services that rely on advertising or sponsorship. For example, Google, Facebook, Mint, WebMD, TripAdvisor and LinkedIn. Following this model, vendors are able to offer innovative chronic disease management services at no charge to employers or employees.

Key Ideas

- 81 percent of adults in the U.S. take at least one medication during a given week, and 27 percent take at least five medications.

- Reminders to take the right medication, at the right time, in the right dose are just the beginning. The next generation of health management services now on the market incorporates comprehensive tools to help employees manage their health. These solutions take a holistic approach, consolidating patient information to provide feedback that supports behavior changes.

- Features of these health 2.0 solutions include medication and event reminders, compliance reporting, goal and bio-metrics tracking, health charts, account sharing across a health team, as well as a personal health record and vault to store documents.

Questions

1. What does the last generation of health management services do?

   a. Notify what medication to take when

   b. Sets up doctor's appointment

   c. Warns doctor when blood glucose is low

   d. Automatically reminds people when prescriptions are running low

   e. All of the above

2. What does the new generation of health management services do?

   a. Takes a holistic approach

   b. Medication reminders

   c. Biometrics tracking

   d. Personal Health records

   e. All of the above

Case Study: Wellness on Aisle Five
By Renée-Marie Stephano

Background and Introduction
Wegmans is a chain of supermarkets across the East Coast of the United States. They have been voted as one of the top 100 places to work in the U.S. many times. One of the things which make the company so great is the comprehensive wellness program. They have approximately 35,000 employees across their various locations and are headquartered in Rochester, New York.

The Program
One of the main foundations of the program, in its ninth year, is the "Eat Well, Live Well" challenge. The idea is to use competition to fuel wellness. Employees form teams within their stores, and then the stores compete against each other in a walking competition where they count the number of steps each day. Another aspect of this is they count the number of fruits and vegetables, where they compete amongst the team to see who has the highest average. The competition happens for eight weeks out of every year, where 11,000 to 12,000 employees participate. The winners receive bragging rights. Other parts of the program include providing Weight Watchers to employees. Twice a year the stores provide free screening for employees as well.

Wegmans also provides a team of dieticians to teach the employees about healthier food options. This goes from recipes to the "Half-Plate Healthy" tip. The "Half-Plate Healthy" premise is that half of a plate should be fruits and vegetables and the rest of the plate should be the rest of the food.

The overarching idea of the wellness program is to provide fun and social activities to promote wellness. They do things like sponsor a team of employees who want to run a 5k or a triathlon. They do like to work up to these strenuous events however, and they have small walking groups.

Part of their plan of the future is quite innovative. As a chain of supermarkets, they have pharmacies in their stores. They would like to partner with someone who would allow them to use their own pharmacies to supply their employees with prescriptions at a reduced cost.

The philosophy of Wegmans is "that good people working towards a common goal can accomplish anything that they set out to do." This is goal for their health and wellness initiatives. By working together they can create a healthier workforce, and happier employees.

CHAPTER 12
Multinational Wellness

Multinational and Global Wellness Programs
By: Jonathan Edelheit and Renée-Marie Stephano

What is a multinational?

A multinational corporation may seem like a complicated amalgamation of business, politics, people, and cultures; and this is mostly true. A multicultural corporation is simply defined as a company who does business in at least two countries. These companies make money by operating in multiple countries through a number of ways; through selling to two separate and diverse markets, by taking the resources in two countries and making their goods, and the ability to sell goods tariff free due to their production in the native country, and many more. A simplified way to say all of that is that multinationals make money by streamlining production and not spending money needlessly. In order to do this many multinationals are establishing wellness programs in order to keep from spending money on medical expenses, the global medical trend was 10.5 percent as of 2011 for example[90], but there are many problems these multinational faces in their implementation.

What problems do Multinational wellness programs face?

Many of the items mentioned above, the factors which make multinationals complicated, also complicate the wellness efforts of multinationals. Issues like the local government and culture, employee cooperation, availability of care and communication are the major problems. These problems are universal. Some governments have certain regulations on healthcare, or what employers can or cannot know about the health of their employees. Certain cultures may respond well to incentives while others may not. Other countries have different access to medical care, for example hospitals are easily available to people who need them in the United States, while this might not be the case in say Somalia. These issues must be kept in mind when establishing a wellness program for a multinational, or expanding an existing program to another nation.

A recent survey conducted by MetLife entitled "The MetLife Study of Global Health & Wellness"[91] reveled issues besides the cultural ones, like age and management style. The survey also outlined some of the problems above, and listed some ways to counter these. For instance, the study recommends tailoring wellness programs to the specific needs, health issues and location of a wellness program. Another which is discussed is related to the first one, and deals with the issue of medical costs in other nations. Governments who offer their citizens healthcare do not face the problem of healthcare costs like in the United States, and thus employers in these countries do not have to institute wellness programs to keep these costs down; instead they institute these programs to increase productivity and the firm's reputation[92]. These are just some of the issues facing multinational programs and will be discussed further in the chapter.

The Growth of Multinational Wellness
In the arena of business, firms and corporations will take any competitive advantage they can find to get an upper hand. Wellness programs are just another way these companies are producing this advantage. This works in many ways, it increase productivity by reducing presenteeism and absenteeism and by increasing the overall health of the workforce. These programs are becoming available in countries which offer their citizens healthcare. The purpose of this, as stated above, is not to reduce healthcare costs but improve productivity by reducing health risks like stress, obesity and heart disease.

Trends show that wellness programs will continue to grow, as many multinationals are planning on implementing these programs. A Towers Watson survey conducted in 2011 show these trends of growth. The survey shows that 32 percent of respondents have a wellness strategy, which was up 6 percent from 2010.[93] It goes on to say that within the next two years, 47 percent of the respondents plan on adopting a wellness program.[94]

This seems to be holding true for most regions except for programs in the Asia-Pacific region, who reported only 62 percent usage of wellness or health promotion programs compared to the global average of 75 percent. Like the United States, Asian nations are facing a sharp rise in the costs of healthcare; of the four top countries with rising costs three were Asian; China, Singapore, and India. Corporations headquartered in this area are turning to wellness programs to help with these costs[95].

The Future of Wellness
With the Supreme Court decision upholding the Patient Protection

and Affordable Care Act (PPACA); more employees will have health insurance in the United States, and some of the costs associated with employee health will be placed on the employer. This is leading to a trend of offering wellness programs within the United States to help bring these costs down. This is not just a trend in the United States, as seen above 47 percent of employers are planning to offer wellness programs within the next two years, it becomes apparent that wellness program implementation is becoming a global trend.

Many employers are concerned about the rising costs of healthcare not just in the United States but across the globe. In the same Tower Watson survey, 75 percent of respondents said that emphasizing their wellness programs will be a priority within the next one to two years, while 87 percent said that will be a priority within the next two to four years. So the trend is building. Of the respondents, 52 percent stated that rising healthcare costs is a purpose of their wellness programs[96].

So wellness is an objective for multinationals, and keeping rising medical costs down is a driver in the implementation. This is not to say that the entire plan is based around lowering these prices, it is only a factor in the decision. Making the direct costs and ROI a priority for the implementation is always important for the C-Suite.

Conclusions

So multinationals are beginning to embrace the idea of keeping their employees, regardless of location, healthy happy and productive. Although this can be difficult when dealing with countries that have different cultures, customs, and attitudes and laws regarding health. This can be overcome readily by tailoring the program to the needs of the location, culture and health issues of the where the program will launch; this is sound advice for any program and not just multinationals. A multinational wellness program cannot be a one-size-fits-all design, it must be specific to issues at hand or it will not be effective and just be a waste of money. Some governments may offer their citizens healthcare coverage and thus in these nations the focus will not be on keeping company health costs down but will instead be focused on the health and happiness of the employees and on increasing the productivity of the workforce.

Case Study: HP is Winning with Wellness
By Renée-Marie Stephano

Introduction and Background
HP is a very large company. With roughly 290,000 employees globally in over 170 countries, they are a prime example of a global wellness program. Headquartered in Palo Alto California, in 2011 the company's total sales were $127 billion. The workforce is divided 66 percent male and 33 percent female, a trend which carries in the US and globally; with the median age of employees is 39 globally and 46 in the US. The HP wellness program obviously has a heavy emphasis on wellness not only in the United States, but across the globe. This creates many issues, for example in the US their program is self-funded while globally it varies because some nations offer their citizens healthcare while others do not; HP pays a tax to nations who do.

The Problem
There are many health and cultural issues facing HP. They are a large, global, hi-tech company. This creates issues because of how dispersed the company is. The employees work hard, they arrive at work early and leave late. They face health issues because of the hard work schedule there is neoplasm as a result of high blood sugar, circulatory problems as a result of stress, and musculoskeletal problems as a result of weight. These figures are for the US participants because of legal concerns getting the information from other countries.

Their health trend prior to implementation was around the national average of roughly 10 percent which is good considering the age of the workforce but after implementation was 3 percent. Their annual healthcare increase since 2000 follows the same numbers.
2006 was an important year for the wellness program at HP, when they got a major endorsement from their CEO. As a result of this, they took a detailed examination of their program as it was, and performed a consultant study and made a new proposal. As a result of this, they realized that it was a high stress industry and needed to tackle lifestyle diseases.

The Solution
After a very research and data based approach, they devised their "laser-focused plan." The idea of their plan was to increase produc-

tivity. Their program which is named "Winning with Wellness," was unveiled in 2010 with three pillars with the program will focus; these are physical, emotional and financial wellness. They examined the best practices used at various other companies and implemented them into their program. The revised program was originally launched into the US and then introduced globally. There was noticeable excitement and it quickly became a grassroots program.

The resources needed to accomplish this were varied. The first was a sustained financial commitment. This is to ensure the program is sustainable, and just a flash in the pan. Second was an inventory of all of their wellness centers, and to focus these resources into centers at strategic sites where the most people where, so they could be used by the most people. Also was the development of a web portal with challenges to drive engagement. Health meals were offered in the cafeteria.

In 2010, the program faced another overhaul with introduction of the three pillars. The pillars were originally brought into the US, and then progressed to five countries, and finally was brought to 34 countries. All of this happened within the span of twelve months. In 2011, an incentive structure was expanded upon, and the company began using biometrics. They have found that employees are engaged in the program, with 40,000 employees participating in their global wellness challenge which uses pedometers, and the team with the most steps wins. There is even C-Suite team. This is important, because to make these investments they needed passion and support from the top, and need a C-Suite that understands that is ok for employees to take time for themselves.

To determine that these were the best steps to take, HP conducted a lot of research. They determined they needed to boost participation after the launch of the program, and to do this they brought their website online, conducted health fairs, and health risk assessments. The personal dashboard website is an important part of their US program. Participants are given a pedometer and can track their steps online. They were able to track their personal progress and see the total progress of everyone participating. They were able to see in a video which was launched that all participants lost a total of 35,000 pounds, and walked around the Earth 30 times. This is crucial because it engaged employees.

The key decision factors to establish these programs were numerous. Smoking cessation and aid to help smokers quit was important. Financial management was an important factor as well; because of the stress money give everyone.

The Results

HP uses HRA and Biometrics to track everything, and has a survey which measures employee satisfaction with the program. This amount of data allows the leaders of the programs to what works and what does not, and allows them to see what the employees feel is effective or not. They did these surveys scientifically, with random sampling; and the fact that the employees were very candid about their responses was helpful. They were able to see the value the program created as well. The reduction in medical trend was outstanding; they saw the increased productivity they wanted with a decrease in absenteeism and presenteeism.

One of the programs that felt did not work was their complex biometric process. It was too difficult and not relevant for employees, and thus was not used. Another program which was revamped was their "Power of Pink" program which dealt with awareness and testing for breast cancer. The shortcoming of the program was not that it was ineffective, The Problem was that it was not comprehensive enough, and so extended it beyond breast cancer to awareness for all cancers. This program was then brought to the 34 countries the pillars were brought to. When the "Power of Pink" was brought to Ireland, it was the first employer program of its kind in the nation.

Some words of advice Elaine Beddome, VP of Global Benefits and Mobility at HP gives to programs are wise for programs large and small. The first is to be sustainable, as she says "you won't go to the moon in first year. " A program must think and act long term. The second is that analysis and measurement are important, and what you track should be followed. A third is a warning of whom you partner with, make sure you partner with and make sure they are capable of reaching the goals you want to reach. The next is that financial support from leaders is essential; money must be spent to make the program meaningful. Finally, a program must have visible wellness champions who make the participants believe they can achieve their goals.

CHAPTER 13
Wellness Program Communication

Driving Wellness Through Technology: Empowering Employees with the Right Information at the Right Time on the Right Device

By Michael Nadeau

Introduction

The technology explosion over the past 15 years has resulted in a fundamental shift in the way people communicate. The Internet and mobile phones have gone from an interesting novelty to an essential means of communication. Social networks allow people to know what their friends and connections are doing and thinking in real time. In a very short time, these technologies have changed from something we couldn't imagine to something many of us can't live without.

As the web has become a pervasive part of modern life, the ways that people find, consume and exchange information have evolved — especially with regard to personal health information. Today, 82 percent of adults are cell phone users and 43 percent have apps on their phones[97]. This explosive growth will continue to change the way people access personal health information. Already it has had a profound effect:

- **47 percent** of adults have used the Internet to get information about doctors or other health professionals.

- **38 percent** have accessed information about hospitals or other medical facilities.

- **33 percent** have accessed information about how to lose or control their weight[98].

As people change the way they access medical information, communication and collaboration methods have also changed dramatically. In the past, medical communication used to go only one direction — doctor to patient. For the patient, the experience was mostly a passive one. Medical care was something that happened to a patient.

No more. Today, patients are more actively involved consumers of healthcare, and most patients want to have a say in their care. Empowered by many technologies, we have seen the creation of a new type of patient — the e-Patient. The e-Patient is an active consumer of healthcare who is more likely to go online to search for a diagnosis, for understanding and for support. Technology is supporting e-Patients in their journey toward better health in a number of ways, including websites, online portals, mobile devices, apps and social networks.

For health and wellness organizations and employers who want to encourage better health, understanding the needs of the e-Patient is essential. The goal should be to provide the right information at the right time on the right device.

The Rise of the e-Patient

It can be hard to remember what life was like before the Internet, computers and mobile devices because they're now so ubiquitous. However, there was a world before Google, Facebook, WebMD, Wikipedia, iTunes, Amazon.com and the plethora of websites, devices, social networks and tools that we use to access information. We may take for granted this easy, immediate access to knowledge on demand, but once upon a time, information was scarce, expensive, institutionally oriented and designed for consumption. Now, the Internet has made information abundant, inexpensive, personalized and designed for participation.[99]

Today, information flows from online access. In the U.S., 79 percent of adults use the Internet and 63 percent of people have broadband connections at home[100]. These online connections are not confined to our homes and offices anymore. Eighty-five percent of people own a mobile phone[101], and 38 percent of these users are accessing the Internet from smart phones — a number that is rapidly growing. Powered by this on-demand access to technology, people are more comfortable than ever going out to access the exact information they need, when they need it. These engaged, empowered and networked people are e-Patients, and their numbers are growing as access to online and mobile technology increases.

For people who are facing a serious health condition, this access to information quickly becomes a lifeline. After receiving a diagnosis, the first thing these e-Patients want to do is go online for knowledge, comfort and reassurance. What they find online is a web of information and support:

- **60 percent** of e-Patients have engaged with some form of social media.

- **41 percent** have read someone else's commentary or experience about health or medical issues on an online news group, website, or blog.

- **24 percent** have consulted online rankings or reviews of hospitals/other medical facilities.

- **24 percent** have consulted rankings or reviews of doctors or other providers.

- **19 percent** have signed up to receive updates about health or medical issues.

- **13 percent** have listened to a podcast about health or medical issues.

If you ask a medical professional, one of the greatest concerns they have about patients going online for health information is the inconsistent quality of what is available. What e-Patients find is everything from world-class information from top providers to quackery. What e-Patients need is access to sources of good information from health professionals and the ability to interact with those professionals.

Online health portals, such as those available from a quality workplace wellness program, can provide a comprehensive, easy-to-use web interface where people can access reliable information. The best of these portals allow users to access biometric information, track personal goals and use educational health resources and tools. These portals can also offer secure, confidential messaging at any time between a member and a health professional.

Unfortunately, access to reliable health and wellness information is hardest to come by for those who need it the most. Adults in the U.S. who are living with chronic disease are significantly less likely than healthy adults to have access to the Internet (62 percent vs. 81 percent). The Internet access gap creates an online health information gap. However, lack of Internet access, not lack of interest in the topic, is the primary reason for the difference. Once online, having a chronic disease increases the probability that someone will take advantage of social media to share what they know and to learn from their peers[102]. Workplace wellness programs have a unique opportunity to close both the access and information gaps. By providing online access to reliable information through multiple applications and devices, wellness programs can reach both the highly able and engaged e-Patients and the underserved adults with chronic conditions.

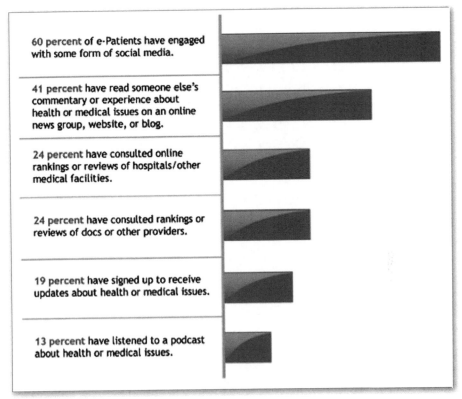

Figure 13.1

Mobile Health: There's an App for That.

The most important health decisions aren't made in the doctor's office. Instead, those crucial decisions take place in the pharmacy, in the grocery store aisle, at a restaurant or at home when a person is deciding whether or not to exercise. You can't call your doctor every time you need to decide what to eat for dinner[103].

Thanks to the growth in smart phone ownership and use, people are more empowered to make healthy decisions and to access health information anywhere, anytime. Two in five adults (40 percent) use the Internet, email or instant messaging on a mobile device, an increase from the 32 percent of adults who did so in 2009[104].As it has become easier to access the web from mobile devices, the use of mobile apps has also increased. Today, 35 percent of the entire U.S. population has a cell phone with an app.[105]

Apps can provide access to health information that makes it easier to eat healthy, count calories, manage weight, monitor exercise, quit smoking, handle stress, live with a chronic condition and make many other health decisions more effectively.

Mobile access also improves access to health information in minority communities. African- Americans and Latinos continue to outpace Caucasians in their use of data applications on handheld devices. The use of mobile apps provides these groups with access to health information that may not otherwise exist.[106]

Although young adults have the highest levels of mobile data application use among all age groups, use of mobile technology is not just a trend among young people. Utilization of these services is growing fast among 30 to 49 year-olds. Compared with 2009, cell phone owners ages 30-49 are significantly more likely today to use a range of mobile data applications on a handheld device.[107]

Preventable illnesses caused by lifestyle factors such as poor nutrition, lack of exercise, tobacco use and obesity are a major driver of healthcare costs in the U.S. today. Providing on-the-go access to health information is a powerful tool that can help people at risk of these conditions make better choices and successfully modify behavior.

The Power of Social Media: Giving People a Voice

For people who are experiencing a serious health condition or trying to make a significant lifestyle change to improve health, it's easy to feel isolated and alone. As a result, it's no surprise that people who are living with a chronic disease are more likely to reach out for support online.[108]

Even people who have the support of family and friends can benefit from interacting with people who are going through a similar experience. For these people, online social networking tools can provide a support system and allow:

- **One voice to be heard:** For people in the midst of health changes, articulating thoughts and feelings can create a sense of control and can actually be therapeutic. After people regain a sense of control, it's easier to take action and make changes necessary to improve personal health. Whether the forum is a blog, an online forum or some other online social channel, asking questions and expressing thoughts and fears can help people find important information and realize that they have access to support.

- **Many voices to be heard:** In his book *The Wisdom of Crowds*, James Surowiecki explains that groups of people are often smarter than the smartest people in them. When patients with the same chronic condition share observations with one another their collective wisdom can yield clinical insights well beyond any single patient or physician[109]. This is the idea behind crowd sourcing. Allowing users to rate everything from the helpfulness of user-provided answers to the quality of products and services benefits the entire community.

Although many people believe that social media use is only for young people, the reality is actually quite different. Social networking among Internet users ages 50 and older has nearly doubled — from 22 percent to 42 percent over the past year. Nearly half (47 percent) of Internet users ages 50-64 and one in four (26 percent) users age 65 and older now use social networking sites.

For young and old, these social networks can be powerful secret weapons to enable good health. Social networks enable virtual support networks that can combine virtual and real-world communities to provide a powerful support system. For example, a smoker who is fighting to quit may not have someone in the office to turn to for support, but online, entire communities exist to offer encouragement and tips.

Two activities stand out among people living with chronic disease: blogging and participating in online health discussions. Studies show that having a chronic disease significantly increases an Internet user's likelihood to say they work on a blog or contribute to an online discussion, a listserv, or other forums that help with personal issues or health problems. As one person told the Pew Research Center's Internet and American Life Project: "[An] online support group helped me learn about the disease and provided comfort in knowing that my symptoms were not 'just in my head,' and helped me take steps to adjust to living with a chronic condition."

For many people, these online interactions offer real-world benefits.

Best Practices for Connecting Employees with Wellness
For employers who want to use online communication channels to improve workplace wellness, consider the following recommendations:

- **Provide online workplace health portals with high-quality health information:** The workplace is actually the best place to provide health information because that is where your employees spend most of their working hours. If you offer a workplace wellness program, your partner should be able to provide access to up-to-date, accurate health information in a variety of formats for the benefit of your employees.

- **Be aware that your audience is bigger than you think it is:** Keep in mind the 80/20 rule: For every two people who post on an online forum, there are eight more people who will peruse the information today, tomorrow or next year. Your audience is far larger than the number of active participants.

- **Improve access to health experts:** Online and on-demand interactions via a health professional's portal can help employees get answers to health questions accurately and quickly. Plus, knowing that someone is there when questions arise improves engagement and compliance with wellness efforts.

- **Encourage users to participate:** To benefit from the wisdom of a crowd, you need a crowd. Provide employees with a forum and then encourage them to act as experts, filters and recommenders of what works (and what doesn't).

- **Embrace the move toward mobility:** As smart phone adoption increases, people will increasingly expect access to an app to provide what they want at the click of an icon. It's not enough for a wellness program to be online, it needs to be on the go. Mobile access to wellness information is quickly becoming an essential requirement of any program.

- **Provide multiple channels:** No one source works for everyone at all times. For an employee in the office looking for his or her biometric information, desktop access to a health portal may be enough. In the doctor's office, access to a mobile app is the only way to go. An employee looking to talk to others about high blood pressure might prefer to communicate on a social network rather than talk to people in the office.

- **Ask for help:** An employer shouldn't expect to have all the answers. Solicit feedback from employees and find out what your employees really want to use.

Conclusion

Online access to tools and technology can be a driver of health improvements for everyone in the workplace — from the most tech-savvy e-Patient to the online newbie. Providing multiple communication and support channels is essential, and Viverae is ready to help with several tools:

- **An online portal:** The Viverae Health Management System (VHMS) provides members with quick, secure access to personal health information such as biometric data and health score information, as well as a variety of tools and access to health coaches to support every employee's journey to wellness.

- **A mobile application:** Members can load Viverae's mobile application onto a smart phone to get access to their personal health information and important wellness tips on the go.

- **A social network:** Through VHMS, members can access a social network that offers online communities and expert advice that allow people to share their stories, ask for help and enjoy the support of others as they take active steps toward improving their health.

The workplace is a great place for wellness to start. Put the right tools in place and make it easier for employees to get healthy.

Resources

1   Purcell, Kristen; Entner, Roger; and Henderson, Nichole. The Rise of Apps Culture. The Pew Internet and American Life Project. September 14, 2010.

   http://pewinternet.org/Reports/2010/The-Rise-of-Apps-Culture/Overview.aspx

2   Raine, Lee. The Rise of the e-Patient. The Pew Internet and American Life Project. October 7, 2009.

   http://www.pewinternet.org/Presentations/2009/40-The-rise-of-the-e-patient.aspx

3   ibid

4   ibid

5   ibid

6   Fox, Susannah; and Purcell, Kristen. Chronic Disease and the Internet. The Pew Internet and American Life Project. September March 24, 2010.

   http://pewinternet.org/Reports/2010/Chronic-Disease.aspx

7   Purcell, Kristen. The Power of Mobile. The Pew Internet and American Life Project. September September 13, 2010.

8   Smith, Aaron. Mobile Access 2010. The Pew Internet and American Life Project. September July 7, 2010. http://www.pewinternet.org/Reports/2010/Mobile-Access-2010.aspx

9   Purcell, Kristen; Entner, Roger; and Henderson, Nichole. The Rise of Apps Culture. The Pew Internet and American Life Project. September 14, 2010.

   http://pewinternet.org/Reports/2010/The-Rise-of-Apps-Culture/Overview.aspx

10 ibid

11 ibid

12 Fox, Susannah; and Purcell, Kristen. Chronic Disease and the Internet.

Key Ideas

- The e-Patient is an active consumer of healthcare who is more likely to go online to search for a diagnosis, for understanding and for support

- Crowd sourcing; allowing users to rate everything from the helpfulness of user-provided answers to the quality of products and services benefits the entire community

- Social networking among Internet users ages 50 and older has nearly doubled — from 22 percent to 42 percent over the past year. Nearly half (47 percent) of Internet users ages 50-64 and one in four (26 percent) users age 65 and older now use social networking sites

Questions

1. The e-Patient is an inactive consumer of healthcare, more likely to visit a website for a diagnostic than a doctor.

    a. True

    b. False

2. Internet usage for people 50 and older has doubled over the past year

    a. True

    b. False

In Wellness Communication, Clarity is Key and Less Is More
By Shawn Connors

For years, most wellness communication had been riddled with corporate-speak and jargon instead of clear, concise language aimed at busy employees with short attention spans.

Before you draft emails, newsletters, posters and other ways to explain and promote your wellness program, remind yourself of three probable (and unfortunate) realities about your audience and your message:

- They don't really want it.

- They don't really have time for it.

- They didn't really ask for it.

With that in mind, informing employees about the advantages of participating in your wellness program might be your primary communication goal, but it shouldn't be your initial one. The original mission is to capture employees' attention in the first place. A good rule of thumb: You can't educate or motivate unless you captivate.

Savvy organizations accomplish this by creating wellness communication that is conversational and succinct. They deliver messages with tones and lengths that fly in the face of what other organizations consider to be "proper" and "official."

Clarity is Key: If Your Messages Aren't Obvious, They Can't Be Understood

Businesses that want to sound "official" usually end up sounding confusing or egotistical. The intent of their messages is lost in the delivery, usually because the messages have more to do with the sender (*"This is what we want, and this what we think"*) than with the receiver (*"Here is what you asked for, and this is how it applies to you"*).

Today, there's a Grand Canyon-sized gap between what companies want to say and how they choose to say it. One problem is most workplace communicators neglect to consider the importance of "voice" — the tone of their communication, as determined by their audience. Another reason is workplace communicators eschew clarity — the main ingredient of effective communication — because, well, they use words like "eschew" instead of "avoid."

The growing disconnect between what employers write or say and what employees read or hear has fueled the "plain language" movement in several industries, including healthcare. The problem in the medical field is understandable: Highly educated doctors often aim to *sound* highly educated and their vocabulary — much like the journals and books they read — are technical. A similar issue often affects company CEOs and presidents, who aim to sound business-like.

But if your wellness messages aren't obvious, they won't be understood or acted upon. In fact, they might not even be read or heard. This is especially true when a topic is viewed by employees as important but intricate (improving overall wellness, learning how to make exercise and healthy eating habitual, etc.).

As a workplace communicator, you might have the task of reaching a large variety of workers, including people who struggle to read, and those who can read but either don't take the time or simply tune out health information. It's an important challenge. In fact, the National Patient Safety Foundation says the biggest barriers to being healthy are not age, income, education level, race or ethnicity. Rather, studies indicate that the strongest predictor of a person's health status is his or her ability to understand and use health information.

"We can't keep focusing on our information instead of our readers," said Audrey Riffenburgh, founder and president of consultancy Plain Language Works, LLC. "Clear communication is about focusing on what your readers need to know and then delivering that by making sure messages are relevant and understandable. Putting that communication in plain language doesn't mean you're 'dumbing down' messages. It simply means you understand the importance of having employees *receive them.*"

Need to Get Clear? Avoid These Common Problems

1. *Getting technical and clinical.* Some organizations try to show off their intelligence by distributing long articles or emails filled with jargon. Keep your messages simple and understandable.

2. *Covering too much.* Say it quick, and make it stick. Listen to seasoned radio sources (politicians, book authors, activists, etc.) and notice how many of them are great at getting their points across in "sound bites." Decide on your main concept and focus on getting that message across. Then stop. Future messages should discuss related concepts.

3. *Failing to highlight important copy.* Cut the gist of your message down to an "elevator speech" you can describe in a sentence or two. Make those words the first ones readers see. Don't "bury" the point.

4. *Creating "brick walls" of text.* Don't make readers scroll down several screens to read an email, and don't pass out an important internal brochure that lacks illustrations, charts or tables. Include subheads, sidebars, pull quotes, boxes and the like whenever possible, especially when presenting an idea that can be better understood visually on first glance.

5. *Lecturing.* Provide take-away value. Remember, your audience is going to think, "So what?"

Less is More: Does Your Wellness Communication Pass the Scan Test?
The average attention span of Americans today is roughly the time it has taken you to read this sentence. "You only have a minute to gain their attention" is an incorrect maxim. You actually have about 2.7 seconds.

And then you have to keep their interest so they can act upon your communication? That's not easy. You are trying to reach employees at the same time they are updating a file while also instant messaging with a co-worker while also straightening up their desk while also listening to a conference call.

How can you get employees to *view* — let alone *read* — your wellness communication?

"If a worker views something for a few seconds, he or she should be able to describe at least the gist of what you're saying," said Alison Davis, CEO of employee communications firm Davis & Company, and coauthor of the book *Your Attention, Please: How to Appeal to Today's*

Distracted, Disengaged and Busy Audiences. "If that can't be done, your communication program is going to suffer a quick death."

Many employees turn a deaf ear to anything involving topics they don't understand fully. So when they see an email about important changes to the company's wellness plan, for example, their tendency is to delay reading it until they absolutely must.

"It's such an unkind reality — yet such a critical realization — to understand that most employees need to be told why they should care," said Sharon Long Baerny, principal of Seattle-based communications agency We Know Words. "Whatever you're communicating, it's much more important to you than it is to your recipients. To make your messages more effective, you must begin to think more like them."

The key is brevity. So, think of teasers and billboards. Make your messages easy and scannable. Cut your articles to a couple hundred words. Get your videos down to one minute, max. Stick to the main concept.

If you do, your emails, newsletters, and posters will come with *credibility*, not just copy. Employees might even start looking forward to receiving it. They'll realize something you already know: Your organization's wellness communication is well worth their time.

Need to Get Concise? Try These Tips
Truth is, people don't read. They scan. We are a populace versed in instant gratification.

Relish the role of making your wellness communication simple, not just essential. Here are four tips:

1. Use short sentences. Keep in mind how you would tell people if you were talking to them.

Instead of ... Joe utilized numerous strategies to achieve his goals of increasing his daily activity and decreasing his consumption of unhealthy foods.

Try ... Joe had two goals: adding activity to his day and eating less junk food. He tackled his goals in many ways.

2. *Be positive and inspirational.* You want to encourage healthy behavior. Be a cheerleader, not a scolder.

Instead of ... Smoking is bad for you. You should give up this unhealthy habit before it's too late!

Try ... Giving up smoking can help you to feel better and live longer. Why not give it a try? Here are some simple ideas that may work for you.

3. *Use bulleted lists when including steps or tips.* Organizing information into bulleted lists makes it easier to read and process.

Instead of ... During our next monthly meeting, we will be discussing changes to our program, in addition to new incentives and an update to our points system.

Try ... During our next monthly meeting, we will be talking about:

- Changes to our program
- New incentives
- Update to our points system

4. *Include actions to take or where to go for more information.* Don't leave readers hanging. If you're including a story, determine what you want your readers to do with the information. If you want them to sign up for a new weight-management program, tell them so and provide them with a link, e-mail, or location of where to sign up. You may also want to include a few steps they could take on their own to get started on managing their weight — a sneak peek of what to expect with the program.

Five Wellness Communication Assumptions to Avoid

1. Assuming you can get employees to act on your messages without telling them why and without asking them to act

2. Assuming employees will read, instead of simply scanning, your content

3. Assuming it's not worthwhile to encourage employees to make seemingly minor healthcare changes and choices

4. Assuming professional-sounding language is better than simple "plain speak" in your wellness communication

5. Assuming all employees absorb and retain communication in the same manner and prefer the same medium

Key Ideas

- Before you draft emails, newsletters, posters and other ways to explain and promote your wellness program, remind yourself of three probable (and unfortunate) realities about your audience and your message:

- They don't really want it.

- They don't really have time for it.

- They didn't really ask for it.

- Informing employees about the advantages of participating in your wellness program might be your primary communication goal, but it shouldn't be your initial one. The original mission is to capture employees' attention in the first place. A good rule of thumb: You can't educate or motivate unless you captivate

- One problem is most workplace communicators neglect to consider the importance of "voice" — the tone of their communication, as determined by their audience. Another reason is workplace communicators eschew clarity — the main ingredient of effective communication — because, well, they use words like "eschew" instead of "avoid"

- If your wellness messages aren't obvious, they won't be understood or acted upon. In fact, they might not even be read or heard

Questions

1. Informing employees about the advantages of your wellness programs should be your first communication goal.

   a. True

   b. False

2. What is "voice"?

   a. The tone of the communication as determined by the audience

   b. Whether the passage is informative, or whether it is intended to entertain

   c. Whether the passage is serious or comical

   d. None of the above

3. If wellness messages are not obvious they will not be understood, acted upon, or read.

   a. True

   b. False

CHAPTER 14
Small Group Wellness Programs

Wellness Programs for Small Businesses
By: Jonathan Edelheit and Renée-Marie Stephano

In the United States, small businesses are everywhere. A small business is defined as "a business independently owned and operated, is organized for profit, and is not dominant in its field" by the U.S. Small Business Administration, where the number of employees which qualifies a business as "small" varies by industry. These businesses represent 99.7 percent of employer firms, pay 44 percent of total U.S. private payroll, created 65 percent of new jobs over the last seventeen years, and employ half of all private sector employees[110]; these small businesses drive the economy. Small firms also hire 43 percent of high-tech workers, and produce 13 times more patients per employee then larger firms[111]; so they drive American innovation as well. In 2007, 59.9 million people were employed by small businesses. These people are a vital part of the American population, and the American economy.

Ensuring these people are taken care of, not just financially but physically and emotionally; is important to making sure they remain healthy, happy and productive. A simple way of doing this is through a wellness program. Programs like these are often seen as being in the realm of large corporations. Although this was once true, it is becoming less costly and easier to implement a program for small businesses. Many small businesses are actually seeing that their costs are shrinking because of their wellness plans. The large firms are able to see their return on investment easily, when they see less sick days and insurance claims, and in the increased productivity. Even for the large companies it takes a number of years for the return on investment to be calculated, time many small businesses do not have. Small businesses also suffer another setback; they do not have the large numbers to do effective studies on the return, although the same trends will be true for large and small populations.

In a summary of the challenges facing small business wellness programs, The Trust for America's Health along with the Small Business Majority "identifies challenges and opportunities to increase uptake of workplace wellness in the small businesses community[112]." They list a number of factors which "forms the contrast" between large and small businesses. One of these is the lack of data small businesses have access to, without an abundance of data it is difficult for a business to make an informed decision on whether or not a wellness program will benefit them. Another factor they list is a lack of awareness; simply put many business owners and employees do not know about wellness programs or the benefits they can bring. A final factor is the unpredictability of the number of employees working for a small business; because there are so many differences in the number of employees it is difficult to make a prototypical program which can be adapted for a business.[113] Until these shortcomings are addressed, it will continue to be difficult to effectively create a wellness programs for small businesses.

Small businesses are also at a disadvantage through the use of incentives[114]. Many larger companies offer their employees either a financial incentive, actual money, to reward and encourage participation. Some large companies also give a break on insurance premiums, which is difficult for small businesses because only half of all businesses with 3 – 9 employees offers health insurance, three fourths with 10 – 24 employees, ninety percent with 25 – 49, and ninety eight percent for employees with 200+ employees finding that overall small firms were almost twice as likely as large firms to not insure their employees[115]. Small companies cannot give a premium break to their employees if they have no health insurance. An interesting new incentive strategy small businesses are giving their employees is instead of offering cash they are giving their employees stock options[116]. It is innovative ideas like this one that will drive small businesses into the world of wellness.

With all of these problems facing small businesses, is it even possible for one to implement a wellness program? It is. There are a number of new government initiatives aimed at helping the country to become a healthier place, and wellness programs are one of the tools to help get the job done. The recent Supreme Court decision to uphold the Patient Protection and Affordable Care Act (PPACA) will make it easier for people to receive health insurance. The debated "Insurance Exchanges" will allow people who currently do not have insurance to get it, but along with this access to care are requirements that put the focus not on treatment but on prevention which is what wellness programs strive to do[117]. Another government plan targeted at prevention of illness is being ushered by the Centers for Disease Control and Prevention (CDC), named The National Healthy

Worksite Program which specifically targets small and midsize businesses "in implementing science and practice-based prevention and wellness strategies that will lead to specific, measureable health outcomes to reduce chronic disease rates.[118]" In order to help America become healthy once again, and to help stem the tide of rapidly growing healthcare costs, the U.S. government is using wellness programs to achieve this goal.

So now that the government is helping small businesses in wellness, what are some tips to creating an effective program? All good wellness programs have some features in common, these should be used to aid the development of any program be it large or small. First, a program should be tailored to the needs of your organization; a cookie cutter program will not be effective and will just be a waste of money. Second, they present to their employees amenities that are enjoyed by all employees regardless of fitness level; a service not used by large portions of your employees is also a waste of money. Third is the ability for the program to be usable in the employee's everyday life, with constant daily use the program is that much more effective. Finally, is an approach to not only benefit the physical wellbeing but mental wellbeing, as stated earlier a happy employee is a more productive employee. These four characteristics will help ensure the program is accomplishing its goals, and encouraging people to participate. [119]

Since the beginning of wellness programs, large companies were primarily the only ones to have these programs. They were able to see that these programs would bring about positive changes in their workforce, and they had the resources available to implement it. Now the tides are turning, the advantages that once only belonged to these large companies are beginning to make its way into the small business community. Although there are still difficulties that the small business must face, like research, and incentives, creative ideas to tackle these issues are beginning to take hold. With recent government programs to help these businesses in their endeavor to increase the health of their employees, the future looks even better. What was once a lofty, almost impossible, goal for small businesses is becoming a reality, and with it comes the advantages a healthy workforce brings; increased productivity for the company, and longer happier life for the employee.

Key Ideas:

- Small businesses represent 99.7 percent of employer firms, pay 44 percent of total U.S. private payroll, created 65 percent of new job over the last seventeen years, and employ half of all private sector employees.

- Small firms hire 43 percent of high-tech workers, and produce 13 times more patients per employee then larger firms.

- There are a number of new government initiatives aimed at helping the country to become a healthier place, and wellness programs are one of the tools to help get the job done.

- All good wellness programs have some features in common, these should be used to aid the development of any program be it large or small.

- First, a program should be tailored to the needs of your organization; a cookie cutter program will not be effective and just be a waste of money.

- Second, they present to their employees amenities that are enjoyed by all employees regardless of fitness level; a service not used by large portions of your employees is also a waste of money.

- Third is the ability for the program to be usable in the employee's everyday life, with constant daily use the program is that much more effective.

- Finally, is an approach to not only benefit the physical wellbeing but mental wellbeing, as stated earlier a happy employee is a more productive employee. These four characteristics will help ensure the program is accomplishing it goals, and encouraging people to participate.

Questions:

1. Small and large businesses produce the same amount of patients.

   a. True

   b. False

2. Half of all private sector employees work for small businesses.

   a. True

   b. False

3. Which government agency is helping small business wellness programs?

   a. FEMA

   b. HHS

   c. SSA

   d. CDC

Case Study: Success of a Small Business Wellness Program
By Renée-Marie Stephano

Introduction and Background
The Materials Distribution Agency (MDA) is an agency of the provincial government of Manitoba. They are mandated to operate like a private business and make a profit. They distribute janitorial and stationary supplies to the government, and medical supplies to citizens. They are a small company with 90 employees in the Manitoba region of Canada. The median age of employees is 45, with 45 percent being male, and 55 percent being female. Their program is administered by a large health program.

The Problem
The MDA being a Canadian operation works under different circumstances than US businesses. The costs of health are borne mostly by the provinces and not the employers. Thus the drive for a wellness program was not to reduce healthcare costs but to engage employees. The drive for a wellness program began when they moved into a new office and warehouse. A proposal for a small exercise room was given to management which was accepted.

MDA administered a health risk assessment to identify the key problems of their workforce. They found physical inactivity was the largest issue they faced followed by tobacco use. Other issues they face are musculoskeletal problems and absenteeism.

The Solution
To begin the weight room they bought a treadmill, a stationary bike, and a weight machine. The room quickly became popular among the workers. Since the initial investment they have purchased an elliptical machine, free weights, a Bosu ball and mats. Whoever enters the room must record their name and which machine they used. Aside from gym equipment, they purchased a PlayStation 2 videogame system with a Dance Dance Revolution game. This opens the door for people who do not want to use exercise equipment to still have a chance to work up a sweat. They even have competitions every winter which includes 10 people. Another game they use is ping pong. They purchased the ping pong table four years ago and hold tournaments for singles and doubles.

The wellness committee has created a schedule of activities and a budget to use for these programs. Some of the highlights include a wellness fair in April, Golf outings in July and August, Healthy Work Month in October, and the afore mentioned DDR and ping pong tournaments in January and February. The health fairs are a big hit with DDR and ping pong demonstrations, and presentations from physiotherapists, dieticians, practitioners of Chinese Medicine, naturopaths, dentists, employees assistance, the lung association and from the provincial benefits plan. Healthy snacks are given out.

The Results

The employees express great satisfaction in the program. They enjoy that the recreational activities bring the employees together and allows them to get to know people they would not normally associate with. The employees like the stress relief benefits of the ping pong table. They have seen a reduction in the number of absenteeism, but tracking that specifically to wellness program is difficult to do. The wellness program is part of the company's business plan and annual reports, and is thus integral to the agency.

The provincial government has praised their program, and was nominated as a leader in wellness. The wellness committee was even nominated for an internal to government Service Quality award for innovation. Slowly the program is moving into social media to promote their health fairs and to post the winners of their various tournaments.

The largest obstacles in their way were the fact that the senior bureaucrats, while being pro-wellness, did not approve of the public knowledge that the MDA purchased the equipment, but with the recent success of the program this idea has changed. The other is the thought from management that the only thing people should be doing during the work day is working, and this will only change with time.

Joel Hershfield the Manager of Finance and Technology and the Healthy Workplace Coordinator has a word for advice for small companies like this. The first is to get all area of the organization involved. The second is to ensure senior management is not only onboard but participates also. The next is that there is such thing as over communicating your programs and activities. Also is the reminder to be passionate about wellness, if you are passionate then it will rub-off on others. Finally it is to seek out information from others who have done this through things like LinkedIn, and simultaneously do not be afraid to try something new.

CHAPTER 15
Fully Insured vs. Self-Funded

The Difference Between Fully Insured and Self-Funded
By: Jonathan Edelheit and Renée-Marie Stephano

There is some debate as to whether or not businesses which are fully insured should implement wellness programs. At face value the argument against it is sound. "Because we are not self-funded we are not taking on the risk of our employee's poor health so there is no need, plus it will cost too much" is the summary of the argument. But recent research is increasingly showing that this is not the case, besides obvious things like a healthier workforce, what are the reasons a fully insured employer should implement a wellness program? This chapter will seek to answer this question.

To answer this however, another question must be answered first and this; are insurers embracing or not fully embracing wellness programs? It seems like a solution which provides a real benefit, the employees are healthy, the employer is happy, and the insurer is saving money by not covering as many insurance claims. But, of course, offering comprehensive wellness programs cost money and adding a comprehensive wellness program could add to the cost of the health plan, which could make that insurer less desirable, or it simply cuts into the insurers profits too much. In the highly competitive area of insurance, differences in prices can be the reason why an employer chooses one insurer over another.

This is not to say that all insurance providers offer limited to no wellness programs. They do. Many offer services like web portals, which allow employees to log and track their health and to see the gains they are making. This can team with programs some insurer's offer where they sponsor health clubs and offer credit to people who use the clubs often. Tobacco cessation programs are also becoming popular among insurers, where the insurer helps pay the costs of office visits and prescription drugs which aid in quitting.

So to move back to the original question what, if any, are the potential benefits to a fully insured program for implementing a wellness program? Even though it may seem like the insurer is taking all of the risk for the health (or lack thereof) of your employees there are several factors of employee health which impact the price of even a fully-insured program. For instance, insurers will adjust premiums based on the employer's claims experience as more and more employees join the company plan. This means that an unhealthy workforce will be charged more by their insurer. This scenario does not mention that if an employer's claims come in higher than the insurer predicted, the insurer will get their money back through premiums in the next year.

So it is clear that insurance companies will in fact charge employers more money for unhealthy populations. This makes sense though, insurance companies exist to make money for their shareholders. These direct costs of insurance are only part of the wellness picture, the not so obvious benefits of healthy employees are crucial to fully understanding the benefits of a wellness program.

Healthier workers are not only making less claims from living a healthier lifestyle, they are also taking less sick days and thus are in the office more. This decrease of absenteeism, workers being absent from work, and the decrease of presenteeism, workers coming to work sick and not working at their full potential and getting their coworkers sick, can greatly increase or decrease the productivity for an office. This is especially true of small offices which are the ones most likely to be fully insured. If one person is out sick in a ten person business, that is 10 percent of the workforce out of the office and at least 10 percent less productive. Another not so obvious factor is the boost of morale a healthy workforce, there are many studies showing the positive effects of exercise and proper diet on creating a positive attitude, and happy employees are more productive employees. Creating and maintaining a wellness program also shows your employees that you are concerned with their health and wellbeing, and this creates not only happiness about the company but a loyalty to the company.

Thus the benefits of initiating a wellness plan are both monetary and emotional. It is the combination of these two effects where the benefits really shine. They combine to bring out the best of a business, less money spent on healthcare and more gained through increased productivity. Although many insurers offer programs which help employee wellness, they do not have the same effect a concentrated comprehensive wellness program. By keeping employees healthy, even a fully insured company will lower direct medical costs through lowering premiums. The added bonus is in the indirect costs, less employee absenteeism and ultimately improved health and happiness. The influence of these indirect benefits cannot be simply written off, the boost they can provide a small company are immense and will offset the costs associated with a wellness program.

Case Study: Giving Wellness an Education
By Renée-Marie Stephano

Background and Introduction

The Miami-Dade Public School System is the fourth largest school system in the United States, with over 345,000 students, and 45,000 employees approximately 28,000 of which are teachers. Although the program does not extend to the students; keeping the teachers happy and healthy is an important aspect of ensuring the children receive the best education they can. Keeping the teachers well so they can teach the kids is the primary purpose of this program.

The Program

The program arose in 2010 after the school district transitioned from a fully insured to a self-funded insurance policy. There are many facets of the program. One of which, named 'Fit for Work' revolves around "knowing your numbers" which involves biometric screening. At a number of locations they have started walking programs.

Another aspect of the program is a comprehensive flu shot drive. This is important because of the numbers of employees and children; and children are notorious for getting the flu. This is part of their commitment to keep the teachers and children in school getting an education and not sick at home.

One of the large issues is the fact that the Miami-Dade public schools are so spread out. There are over 450 locations, and thus is difficult to have a wellness coordinator at each of these locations. Instead they have divided up the district into regions; South, South Central, Central, North and North Central, and focuses on regional activities.

These regional activities are varied. They range from the Mercedes Benz Corporate Run, to a 'fitness day' health fair sponsored by the superintendent. Another event they are planning is another health fair, but not only for employees but for the employee's spouses and children. The idea is to make a fun day at the park for families with a focus on health. By getting employees and their families involved it increases the health of everyone. Because the schools are the largest employer in Miami-Dade, by looking at families this will have a lasting impact on the community.

CHAPTER 16
Other Important Information

At Risk: Why Corporations Can't Ignore Non-Movers
By Amanda Carlson-Phillips, and Dr. Roy Sugarman

At many companies across America, the wellness conversation and leading question is the same: wellness programs make healthy people healthier and fit people more fit, but can they impact our at-risk non-mover population in a meaningful way? We believe that impacting non-movers is not only critical to short- and long-term cost savings, but the only way to truly create a paradigm for wellness that includes everyone. Recent findings show that half of the U.S. population spends little or nothing on healthcare, while 5 percent of the population spends almost half of the total amount.[120] A recent *Wall Street Journal* article estimated the additional expense for obese employees averages $1,429[121], medical costs for obese employees are up to 117 percent higher than costs for their non-obese counterparts[122], and treatment of cardiovascular disease (the leading cause of premature, permanent workforce disabilities in America [123]) accounts for $1 of every $6 spent on healthcare in the United States.[124] These are costs and statistics organizations simply can't ignore if they want to remain competitive globally.

For companies to maintain a competitive advantage they need to make wellness a top priority. Studies have shown that wellness programs have a proven ROI advantage, and companies that invest $1 in wellness see a $3 return in healthcare costs.[125] By investing in their human capital through integrated wellness programming that provides employees with innovative, proactive health strategies, companies will begin to impact their at-risk employees and families in a meaningful way, reducing their overall costs and fostering improved performance and productivity company-wide.

When it comes to making healthy behavioral improvements, many inactive employees find themselves running in the same circle, never veering off the path to make sustainable advancement with their goal.

For many employees and employers, weight loss is the primary marker of the success or failure of a wellness program. However, research is finding that achieving a healthy body fat percentage through the integration of nutrition and exercise, and improving actual cardiovascular fitness, may have the greatest potential in reducing cardiovascular disease risk. Current research supports the contention that cardiovascular fitness is more closely linked to cardiovascular disease than actual physical activity.[126] Therefore, it has been suggested that individuals who improve their actual cardiovascular fitness levels (rather than just increasing their actual physical activity level) will decrease their relative risk to cardiovascular disease risk factors.[127]

What we want employees and employers to understand is that wellness isn't simply about weight loss or preventing disease; it is about improving behaviors that help employees create more energy, reach their goals and live better outside of work. For employees to succeed in their health journey, they need to focus on all aspects of health. At Core Performance, our proven system is rooted in behavioral health strategies across four health fundamentals – mindset, movement, nutrition and recovery. We believe when these four areas are implemented together in a wellness program, they successfully optimize health and performance for each individual.

One piece of feedback we have heard frequently from clients is that you cannot impact non-movers. The truth is that non-movers need simple, proven strategies to improve their lives. Our team not only believes at-risk individuals can be engaged to change, we have proved it with leading companies like Intel. At their Chandler, AZ campus, Intel commissioned an IRB-approved research study to examine the impact our programming had on their employees. In 14 weeks, the Core Performance program participants, two-thirds of whom were non-movers, received integrated nutrition and fitness support and achieved the following results with a commitment of less than three hours per week:

- Cholesterol reduction averaging 5 percent

- Average fat loss of 14 lbs

- A 19 percent increase in VO2 capacity (measure of cardiovascular health and fitness)

- A 30 percent overall reduction in the number of individuals categorized as "at risk" based on their lipid profile

Additionally, a leading U.S. supplier of healthcare information technology solutions commissioned Core Performance to help improve overall employee health and wellbeing. The program was designed to engage employees in best practices across mindset, nutrition, movement and recovery, and focused on fat loss and exercise rather than weight loss. After three months of participation, employees achieved the following results:

- 67 percent increase in productivity at work

- 86 percent increase in energy levels

- 75 percent increase in confidence

- 84 percent increase in positive attitude

- 79 percent renewal rate

- 9 percent decrease in body fat for non-movers (3 percent decrease for movers)

- 17 lbs fat loss for non-movers (6 lbs loss for movers)

- 14 lbs gain in muscle mass for non-movers (4 lbs gain for movers)

- 36 percent improvement in flexibility and agility for non-movers (41 percent for movers)

After six months of participation employees collectively lost a total of 138 pounds; but what is really impressive and important to consider is that these employees lost over twice that amount in total fat, losing a total of 382 pounds of fat. Furthermore, only 25 percent of participants at the start of the program were considered to be in excellent fitness condition. By the end of the program that figure doubled to 50 percent.

This data, along with the results from Intel, prove that weight loss isn't the only factor that quantifies the success of a program or an individual. Programming that goes beyond the myopic focus of weight loss and instead centers on fat loss, fitness and other markers of vitality has a significant impact on individuals likely to develop chronic conditions like diabetes and heart disease. This data also shows the quantifiable impact programming can have on a sample employee population, which typically is a mix of active employees and non-movers.

Science and applied research tells us that non-movers need the following to improve on the wellness spectrum: a compelling reason

I'd do anything to lose 10lbs, except eat healthy and work out.

your e cards
someecards.com

A simple explanation of why many fad diets and trendy exercise programs don't produce long-lasting results.

to change (the WHY), an integrated program to support them every step of the way (the WHAT) and experts to help them with additional motivation and education (the HOW). Below we will outline the importance of these three elements, and also provide tips for how you, as an employer, can implement programming that is actionable, engaging and successful for this population.

Start with the WHY by identifying the "IT" factor
People start moving when they find a compelling reason to do so, but choosing to lead an active lifestyle must be rooted in an individual's own aspirations, not because someone else thinks the person needs to be more fit or active. Many employees realize they "should" get healthier, but never get started on a better journey to health. So the question becomes: how do we get them motivated to engage in a healthy lifestyle change?

Identify the "IT" factor – For wellness to reach your at-risk population, employees need to first identify what they perceive as their goal. Many might visit a gym and say they would like to lose weight, so a nutritionist or coach will design a program around weight loss. While a weight-loss program might work for a few months, the simple goal of weight loss is not enough and is unlikely to stick with that employee for the long haul. For employees to reach their goals, they need to understand what truly drives them, what they want for themselves in terms of better health and what we call at Core Performance "identifying their 'IT.'" Our philosophy of identifying an individual's "IT" digs deep, utilizing motivational interviewing and cognitive psychology to help people create roots with their goal. We continually ask people the question, "why?" to find those deeper reasons; and while identifying the "IT" requires time and soul search-ing, the actual "IT" itself is a simple, one-to-two sentence statement. So if your employees want to lose weight, is it because they want more energy for their kids, to be productive at work or does it go beyond that (e.g., "I want to lose weight so I can enjoy time with my family and provide for my children.")? Whatever their motivator is, identifying the "IT" by asking a series of questions and pinpointing what is truly important is critical towards getting these employees to think differently about their own health.

Tip: Employees will never get started on a better journey towards health if they don't find a compelling reason. Start by evaluating "why is IT" with these exercises:

a. Create a questionnaire that helps employees evaluate where they are on the health spectrum and where there is room to upgrade.

b. Conduct motivational interviews with your employees and ask questions that help address the root of their goal.

Establish the WHAT with work-life integrated programming
Many employers think impacting non-movers can't be achieved, but our research shows these employees will engage if they are provided with integrated programming that provides support, clear instruc-tion and a sense of community. If employees believe that wellness is something they can include in their current lifestyle and not just another item on their growing list of responsibilities, they are more likely to be excited about making a change. Making simple changes like upgrading a daily ritual with respect to exercise and diet in a small, manageable manner allows employees to see benefits quickly; but it also lets them feel good about their own successes, creating an "upward spiral" of healthy behaviors and leading employees to

become autonomous with their health. When employees engage in integrated programming that supports their goals, they can begin to realize what they can do to make their "IT" a reality, and trust that it can be achievable. Below we've outlined the top five tenets that lead to successful program integration with non-movers.

Strategic Switching – Research shows that employees are more successful when they replace a bad habit with a better one. The best place to start is to have individuals focus on one ritual, such as "I will park the car farther away from work to gain a few extra steps in my day" or "I will choose a side salad instead of french fries" – these changes upgrade daily routines in simple ways and encourage individuals to continuously make improvements with everyday activities.

Tip: Ask employees to write down one habit they will replace with an upgraded ritual. Start by creating small groups with similar goals and routines to build community towards this goal.

- *Next time your team heads out to a company lunch, make a point to order healthy appetizers to share.*

- *Try a walking meeting outside instead of sitting in the conference room.*

- *Get a group of people who arrive at the same time to park farther from the building entrance. That way they have a buddy to share the distance with.*

Increase the fun factor – No one likes to add another dreaded item to a "to-do" list. Instead of making employees feel like wellness is yet another chore in their hectic lives, find creative ways to engage. For example, instead of posters outlining why drinking calories is bad for you, put together a contest in which employees guess which sugar-sweetened beverage contains the greatest amount of sugar and reward participants with healthy prizes such as water bottles and reusable grocery bags. Sheraton Hotels made fitness a corporate initiative by setting a Guinness World Record for the largest resistance band workout, encouraging employees to join in on a group workout in Midtown Manhattan with key Sheraton executives. Instead of wagging a finger to promote wellness, focus on cultural norms that work within your organization and use those guiding principles to build relatedness and community around wellness.

Tip: Design wellness activities that work for your organization. Whatever field your business is in, it's critical to design initiatives that your employees can relate to and have fun with:

- *If you're in the financial industry consider an activity that emphasizes numbers such as setting a company goal for miles walked in a month.*

- *If your field is more creative, set up a Facebook page that advertises new events and contests.*

- *Integrate knowledge and behaviors. For example, each month have employees participate in a knowledge quiz (e.g., choosing the healthiest of 3 brands of yogurt), and conduct monthly drawings for those who were correct and reward them with discounts on the highlighted item (yogurt) in the café.*

Master a healthy habit – For many non-movers, exercising has likely been a negative experience for them, so providing them with strategies they can master in a short period of time is a catalyst for change for this population. When at-risk individuals master simple strategies, this generates a sense of autonomy that drives engagement. This also allows individuals who are non-movers to avoid the intimidation factor of a gym, and create habits out of no-sweat movements they can do at work or anywhere at any time. Providing non-movers with simple strategies they can control and be successful with will ensure that non-movers continue to build past their mastery to learn new behaviors and movements, and expand their habits to include more active and healthy activities.

Tip: Consider using a nutritionist or coach to help employees master movements:

- *A nutritionist can help employees conquer a healthy recipe or upgrade one unhealthy dietary habit.*

- *Use trainers to help non-movers master 3-5 functional movements. For example, get your call center employees to master five movements to improve their posture and minimize aches and pains or have warehouse employees master 2-3 stretches they do each day before and after a shift.*

Think of food as fuel – According to the CDC, one in three American adults is obese[128], while 50 percent of the U.S. population lives with at least one chronic disease.[129] Poor nutrition is a leading cause of the rates of chronic illnesses such as heart disease, obesity, diabetes and many other preventable health-related issues. Fundamentally, many employees know that a diet high in saturated fat and sugary drinks isn't good for them; but do they understand that the way we eat has a direct impact on the way we feel? It is not about dieting to be "good or bad", "healthy or unhealthy", it is about eating in a way that provides your body with the nutrients, hydration and energy it needs to perform at its best. Encourage non-movers to start thinking of food as fuel, a way to feed the brain and fuel the body. When employees start to view food as a path to enhanced productivity, they can start to make healthier food choices, whether it's switching to a high fiber cereal in the morning, substituting a large soda for a cup of water or choosing to eat a piece of fruit with a handful of nuts over a donut. This increased awareness and mindfulness about what they are eating will compound over time into a large sum of healthy eating habits. Guiding employees down a path to upgrading current diet behaviors and to view food as fuel is an effective way to build a more positive attitude toward healthy nutrition.

Tip: Start in the cafeteria. Employees can choose to make better choices about nutrition, but it is also critical that employers offer healthier food choices at work and improve the quality of employees' daily nutrition intake.

- *Hire a nutritionist to upgrade current cafeteria offerings and create an environment that increases the likelihood for employees to make better choices (e.g., provide both brown and white rice, or offer healthier side dishes like steamed vegetables or a fruit cup, and strategically place healthier items in the café).*

- *Create an integrated, yet simple system that helps the employee take "knowing to doing" in the cafeterias. Go beyond just labeling the calories and add some value with the signage. Quick tips, serving sizes, fun facts or the use of colored labels to help employees identify healthy choices from less healthy ones.*

Choose your adventure – At Core Performance we believe that individuals are the experts when it comes to themselves and know best what their daily routine is like – what works and what doesn't. All of us want to know that our actions direct our lives in a meaningful way, so allowing employees to pursue their own path to a certain degree is integral to increased engagement and to the long-term success and sustainability of a wellness program. So, rather than forcing every company division to sign up for a group workout experience, allow individual employees to self-select healthy tracks that work for them. Once a non-mover identifies "IT," and has the tools to upgrade his or her exercise and diet behaviors, providing that person a sense of self-empowerment to choose healthy routes will ultimately increase the individual's drive to improve. This will result in a greater level of engagement and ensure the longevity and success of the program.

Tip: Let employees choose what works for them to build autonomy and lasting engagement.

- *Try a hands-on healthy cooking demo to show employees that nutritious food can taste great*

- *Host a relaxation workshop on active recovery for employees on the go, or an aches and pains activity focused on minimizing daily pain for warehouse workers.*

Provide the HOW with onsite nutritionists and coaches to deliver continued education

Having onsite support in nutrition and fitness provides ongoing motivation, education, information and support for employees in a meaningful way. This level of integration can help employees make the transition from knowing what they should do to having the skills to actually do it. Non-movers need an expert or team of experts to help collate the information for them and get them on a healthier track. We've learned that personalized support is effective at impacting this population. Because wellness is a lifelong journey, not a single destination, providing individuals at risk with experts they can talk to and learn from is critical for them to upgrade behaviors and change their mindset for the long haul.

Below we've illustrated activities that an onsite nutritionist and trainer can provide to your program.

Lunch and Learns – Weekly webinars or onsite meetings led by either a nutritionist or trainer drive awareness and interest in healthy living while educating and empowering employees to be proactive about their health. We've found that "lunch and learns" are an effective tool to encourage and engage people who otherwise might be too intimidated to visit a gym to learn more. However, it's imperative that "lunch and learns" address all levels of wellness, not just diet and exercise, for employees to understand and integrate all aspects of health into their life.

Tip: Design "lunch and learns" around the time of year and the four key elements to wellness – mindset, movement, nutrition and recovery.

- *For example, topics for summer "lunch and learns" might include healthy hydration, how to eat right at the ball game or amusement part and guidance on what to buy organic.*

- *Get your leadership involved—encourage your C-suite to select a topic and host one of the lunch and learns so employees know attendance is encouraged and that wellness is a top priority*

Onsite Evaluations – Onsite assessments take place at your company before, during and after wellness initiatives to evaluate employee progress and quantifiably assess what your wellness program has achieved. They utilize a variety of protocols designed to identify injury risks and other inhibitors to wellness, vitality and performance. Traditional wellness screenings give basic, but dated fitness assessments. Many non-movers already know they need to eat better and exercise more, but offering an onsite movement and nutrition evaluation combined with strategic takeaways is incredibly efficient for three reasons: 1. Onsite evaluations make it easier for employees to participate without interfering with their personal time. 2. Employees are likely to engage in an evaluation more than once if offered at work. 3. Next steps can be immediately identified, providing non-movers with strategic educational and motivational next-step solutions that can help them achieve their "IT."

Tip: For non-movers, it's particularly important that these assessments do not discourage employees, but rather provide them with the "what" (detailed information about their current health) and the "so what" (here is what you can do to change those numbers in a proactive way). One strategy we often use to contextualize results is sharing that the evaluation is simply the starting point on the road map and now they have the map to get where they want to go—this eliminates the feeling of "getting a bad report card" with a "knowing-to-doing" transition.

We can begin to change the conversation about wellness and reduce the percentage of employees categorized "at risk" if more companies start thinking about smart, integrated wellness strategies that specifically engage non-movers – the WHY, the WHAT and the HOW. The cost of ignoring this population is significant–and growing. The American Heart Association reported that the costs of heart disease in America will triple between now and 2030, to more than $800 billion a year[130]. Overlooking non-movers comes with a price–financially and emotionally–if these individuals feel isolated from company initiatives. Employees become even less engaged and empowered to make a change, decreasing their productivity levels, increasing their sick days and escalating your corporate healthcare costs. Companies will continue to pay if they exclude non-movers in their wellness initiatives, and those who do include at-risk employees will significantly increase their competitive advantage. Non-movers are notably absent in their workforce wellness programming and if they feel ignored, they will become even less willing to apply simple, actionable strategies they can apply to their current lifestyle to enhance their productivity in work and improve their performance in the game of life.

Transforming the Landscape: How You Can Impact Your Company's Non-Movers

Historically, companies have viewed engaging non-movers as an uphill battle. However, with healthcare costs rising and disease risks skyrocketing, it's more important than ever that employers find meaningful ways to engage at-risk populations with integrated programming to improve how they look, feel and perform every day. We've outlined research demonstrating how companies like Intel have invested and succeeded in impacting non-movers, provided context on the criteria it takes to move the needle at your company and included some tips on designing a program for non-movers that intersects with your organization's culture, provides consistent and ongoing support, allows for some degree of employee choice and leverages best practices from both research and proven experience.

We believe that by helping your employees identify what deeply motivates them, providing them with an assessment of where they are on their journey to better health, then matching that information with skill development to actually make those changes and plans actionable, you can significantly reduce healthcare costs, increase productivity and improve the culture of wellness at your company. Whether you choose to start small with monthly lunch and learns and fitness classes or adopt a comprehensive solution with personalized nutrition and training support, we believe that for companies and employees alike, having the confidence to take the first step is critical in the journey to achieving your goals.

Key Ideas

- A recent Wall Street Journal article estimated the additional expense for obese employees averages $1,429 , medical costs for obese employees are up to 117 percent higher than costs for their non-obese counterparts , and treatment of cardiovascular disease (the leading cause of premature, permanent workforce disabilities in America) accounts for $1 of every $6 spent on healthcare in the United States.

- Wellness isn't simply about weight loss or preventing disease; it is about improving behaviors that help employees create more energy, reach their goals and live better outside of work.

- The actual "IT" itself is a simple, one-to-two sentence statement

- Our research shows these employees will engage if they are provided with integrated programming that provides support, clear instruction and a sense of community

- The best place to start is to have individuals focus on one ritual

- Encourage non-movers to start thinking of food as fuel, a way to feed the brain and fuel the body

Questions

1. Wellness is only about weight loss and preventing disease.

    a. True

    b. False

2. Employees need integrated programming that provides support, clear instruction and _____ to engage.

    a. A sense of purpose

    b. A sense of knowledge

    c. A sense of community

    d. A sense of incentive

3. Food is not fuel for the body and brain, but a reward fro hard work.

    a. True

    b. False

Corporate Wellness and Stress: A Workable Solution
By Dr. David Koivuranta

Stress is a powerful word. It has the ability of bringing to mind the things we least enjoy in our lives. Sometimes these thoughts about stress occur on a conscious level, other times it's a stress that is acting under the surface of our awareness. The stress of facing another Monday at work, the stress of meeting a deadline, the stress of working through lunch again, the stress of that extra 30 pounds we're carrying around the midline and all the stress of those physical, chemical and emotional challenges in our lives are ever-present and relentless. Just like gravity, whether or not you believe in it, whether or not you are aware of it, it's having an impact on your life.

We are somewhat aware that stress is present in many aspects of what we do every day. Being aware of those stresses creates one of two possible scenarios: it allows us to respond in a positive and proactive way or it allows us to react to those responses by reflex. Our bodies, based on habits or programs we have developed since birth, often deal with subconscious stresses reflexively. These reflexes either support good health and wellness or they sabotage those same efforts. Through inspection and some sleuthing, it can be determined if these reflexes exist and whether or not they are supportive of our efforts to live a good life. If they are not, they must be brought to conscious awareness and re-trained.

Conscious awareness of stress allows for real-time responses by individual choice to ensure that the desired outcome in any situation is created, expected and accepted so we can move past the stress. This positive and proactive awareness allows us to live in alignment with how we want to see each day, each year and, ultimately, our whole life unfold and progress. Being empowered to operate in this fashion has health, work, career, relationship, spiritual and plentiful other benefits.

Ultimately, it's totally possible to live and work positively with stress.

In the workplace, fostering an understanding that stress is ever-present sets the foundation for accepting stress as a factor in productivity, morale, turnover and other tangible or intangible parameters. A company or organization that supports systems and procedures that empower employees to deal with stressful situations or challenges in day-to-day operations will thrive. Having no such systems or procedures in place can undermine the company's goals, objectives, vision and mission.

The first step in this process is determining the causes and sources of potential stress. Ergonomic stress for computer users or assembly line workers is a daily challenge. Chemical stress for those handling hazardous materials or for those with few nutritious options for lunch is a problem. Emotional stress from issues relating to management, providers, suppliers, clients and customers is certainly abundant. Quite often, it is possible to determine these sources by way of employee surveys, performance evaluations and third-party consultations, observations or audits.

When the causes and sources have been identified, they can often be prioritized based on prevalence or potential workplace impact. Those factors that show up most often, or stand to interfere the most with performance standards or fiscal goals, can be narrowed so that a focused protocol can be created to help circumvent any negative impact they may have. Ergonomic intervention, material handling instruction, complaint resolution and inter-worker relationship building are all effective protocol categories that can change the very fabric of a company when it comes to the common stresses that affect every nook and cranny of everyday operations.

Although there are solutions that can be created through changes to business operations and procedures regarding stress problems, it still leaves the weakest component -- the human component -- unaddressed. Luckily, humans are uniquely equipped to handle stressful situations. Regardless of the source, stress is something with which we are designed to co-exist.

There is a common, fundamental solution to all sources of stress. It comes from the body's natural ability to adapt and deal with stress. In times of conflict resolution or solving problems, our inborn ability to handle crisis is a powerful tool. This ability comes from our fight or flight system regulated by our nervous system. If, for example, we encountered a tiger (stress), our body would instantly engage in reflexes that increase our heart rate and breathing so that we can get away from the tiger. Once we are away from the tiger, our heart rate and breathing return to normal and we can go about our normal routine again. This is a very helpful system that is designed to resolve challenges in our environment, both internally and externally.

Here's a valuable question: What if we couldn't get away from the tiger? Our body would continue to react with a heightened response until one of two things happens. Either the tiger "gets us" or the body shuts down and fails as it succumbs to the ongoing struggle to escape the tiger. The purpose of describing this situation is to emphasize that our bodies can excellently handle short-term stresses and challenges. It's the long-term, relentless stresses that can really cause problems.

The interesting thing is that all of this stress is perceived. Stress does not actually exist. It's an interpretation. Although most of us would find being in the same room as a tiger very stressful, there are those who would relish the challenge of taming that wild beast. In that case, that person would have controlled their perception and their physiological response wouldn't be one of fight or flight, but rather one of focused intent to deal with the situation. Their breathing may still go up, as will their heart rate, but it would serve to allow them the wherewithal to interact with the tiger.

The problem in society, including our workplaces, is that many stresses are long- term or chronic stresses. They do not just come and go, and they are often not something from which you can run away. They are present every day, every week and every month in our personal and professional routines. Deadlines, angry customers, overbearing managers, frustrating colleagues... the list of what we perceive as a stress can be lengthy. It may not be a tiger, but it is perceived as a stress nonetheless and our bodies will react exactly the same way.

The body does not know the difference between a physical, chemical or emotional stress. It reacts virtually identically for each stress. And if that stress does not disappear or if it is not perceived or looked at differently, the stress response continues indefinitely, whether you are aware of it or not. One of the ways your body will react to stress is to release stress hormones (e.g. cortisol and epinephrine) from your adrenal glands. These chemicals are part of the endocrine response that helps to raise heart rate, increase breathing, make you more alert and help you feel less pain thanks to our body's endorphins. This endocrine response is also tied into and controlled by your nervous system. Various areas of your brain are involved with the stress response and they are keenly based on your perception of the environment, internally and externally.

What this means is that whether you are aware of it or not, any unresolved stress in your life will constantly keep your body under a stress response. The negative side effects of this unresolved stress are numerous. In times of stress, like escaping the tiger, your immune system, your digestive system and your reproductive systems, for example, are suppressed. They are not important to have active at times of fight or flight. And in the short term, this is ok, until the stress is escaped or resolved and those systems can then come back online. With chronic stress, the outcome can be much different and much worse.

Let's take a common everyday stress and see how the body may be reacting to it. Let's say that we work at a computer all day with poor ergonomics and bad habits. We're at an internal cubicle with no windows and fluorescent lighting. We have been working on a huge account that was due two weeks ago, and due to various challenges, the deadline continues to be extended with definite pressure from our supervisors and our employer. The air is recycled and dry, and because the people closer to the windows are hot during the day from the sun, the air conditioning keeps the interior of the space very cold. Each day we arrive at work knowing what troubles are ahead of us and then every day we leave late knowing that we have to come back the next day to the same struggles.

Some common side effects from this stressful environment include headaches, back pain, frequent head colds, stomach aches, intestinal distress, high blood pressure, weight gain, depression, loss of energy and focus and decreased sleep. This happens due to the indirect and direct changes to your autonomic nervous system, the system that controls your organs, glands and blood vessels. The stresses put an emphasis on your body towards energy creation and conflict resolution. To do that well, your body puts less effort into maintaining your immune system, digestive system and reproductive organs. And that makes you feel unwell.

Stress is a factor in all the leading causes of death and morbidity in North America: heart disease, cancer, stroke and diabetes. It is not because stress is stress, but because it creates a real physiological problem in your body that is not supportive of health and wellness. Stress is real; and the perception of stress, either consciously or subconsciously, will lead to a stress response. The degree of this stress response and its various outcomes, good or bad are under our control. In other words, even though we acknowledge stress as an important factor that affects our health and our life, we often characterize it as something that we cannot change. This is in fact what is killing us. This is why we often remark, "My work is killing me!"

It is not true that we cannot do much about it. We have choices. If we took the cubicle scenario mentioned earlier and decided we wanted to change what was happening, we could. An ergonomic assessment would help ensure that we had the right furniture and hardware to carry out our deskwork. Furthermore, a good ergonomist would let you know that it is all about your habits and your awareness that will save you time and discomfort while working at the computer. We drink enough water during the day to make sure we're not thirsty, we wear or keep a sweater at hand to deal with the cold air and we consider using indirect lighting at our desk to combat the fluorescent light bulbs. We might even request that the operations manager install some full spectrum bulbs that we pay for ourselves...a great investment.

We approach our supervisor and/or manager and we create a new strategy to deal with this account. We ask to take the lead on the project so that we can focus our efforts on controlling the desired outcome instead of dealing with the missteps and uncoordinated efforts of the team. We get to work 30 minutes earlier, after a thought-out breakfast, with our homemade lunch in hand, ready to stay on top of this situation. We take the proper time to rest and consume our food during our lunch break. This supplies us with ample energy and positive spirits to complete the task at hand. Scheduled rest periods allow us to be more productive and get more done with good quality even though we aren't working "around the clock".

It may sound too good to be true. If it does, you may already be headed down a path of chronic stress that you may or may not be aware of. And it will have health implications. Succumbing to the mindset that we don't have options or control is a leading contributor to stress having a negative impact in our lives and leads to disease. Having or creating a work environment that also leads employees to feel the same way creates the same results. Only, it also has negative business implications that directly relate to absenteeism, presenteeism, morale, retention, direct and indirect costs, and increased short- and long-term insurance or disability claims.

So what do we do? Where do we start? The first step is to clearly acknowledge that stress is a big problem in the workplace. Having an awareness of this fact and understanding its relevance fosters an appreciation for its potential impact and the benefits of a plan to correct it.

Secondly, it is valuable to underline the key stresses that your workforce is exposed to. From supervisors, managers and executives to front-line staff and sales, a brief survey would surely uncover some of the bigger concerns. An outside third party would help to discover key stresses by way of observation, interview and investigation. This data and information is the foundation for making key changes to policies, procedures and protocols.

Next, create a new thread in the fabric of the company that is dedicated to supporting a wellness and preventive approach to stress. It is one thing to accept the fact that stress exists and to find out the key areas where stress exists, but it is an entirely different effort to make this a key underlying premise to the vision, mission and goals of the company. From the top down, stress management, business operations and employee wellness must be a top priority for the company.

Now that a commitment has been made and the research has been done, begin rolling out solutions that support positive outcomes in all the key areas of stress. Physical, chemical and emotional (human) solutions exist to every problem; quite often, the same people who are able to point out the problems are the very ones who have the most innovative and effective ways of solving those issues. Third-party companies that can roll out company-wide initiatives based on proven methods of stress reduction also exist.

Finally, monitor the feedback from employees, track the company's performance and measure the results. Commonly, sales will increase and revenue will grow simply because of the efficiency and proficiency unearthed by a system with less negative stress. In business, efficiency and proficiency are the rule. Be great at what you do and do it in a timely fashion. Stress interferes with both of these factors. Reducing stress and providing for a stress-reducing environment in the workplace will bring real positive results.

Stress is inevitable, but its impact and the outcomes in business are by our choosing and under our control. With a little bit of effort and awareness, stress can be the impetus to improve what we do in the workplace and how we do it in. Congratulations for taking the time and initiative to make stress a workable solution.

Consumerism in Healthcare: From "A" to "Ism"
By: Amit K. Gupta

Employers are tasked with the responsibility to deliver healthcare to employees based on promises made decades ago. Accordingly, they are the purse holders in the healthcare delivery chain, owning the decision power over employee healthcare. As each stakeholder in the delivery chain—including the employer—sets their own rules, choices narrow for employees. They have no control over what services are covered under a plan. They do not set the rules for what is reimbursable from a Health Reimbursement Account (HRA) nor for what is qualified under a Health Savings Account (HSA). They are not involved in deciding which costs will be visible to them (e.g., co-pays, deductibles) and which costs will be hidden and paid for by the insuring health plan. They are told which doctors they can see readily and which doctors require a special request for a visit. They are guided to use generic drugs over branded medications, or to get an ultrasound before a more costly imaging procedure such as a CT scan or MRI, and often only after preauthorization.

Already difficult for consumers to understand, the healthcare maze has been further complicated by employers, and often in the name of consumerism. If co-pays for brand name drugs are too small to make an impact on cost savings, we go raise them. If consumers can't see the cost difference between generic and brand name drugs, we make a tool to show them the difference, hoping they'll actually use the tool. If no one enrolls in an employer-offered health and wellness program for smoking cessation and weight loss, we add incentives to the same program and change nothing else. Unfortunately, these adjustments only reach so far when we try to fix what isn't working well.

Are we asking the right questions, and solving the right problems?
To truly push a cultural transformation in healthcare, we have to start solving the right problems, and we need to do this by asking the right questions. In the grand scale of things, does it really matter how the Flexible Spending Account (FSA) and HSA function together? Or, is it really the principle that is more important, where consumers are the owners of a healthcare account and the employers act as co-contributors to cover healthcare expenses that the consumers have deemed necessary for themselves? Is the problem

that not everyone has health insurance coverage and should? Or, is it a problem of healthcare access, availability and cost transparency from providers, which prevents consumers from choosing whom they go to, when, and how much they pay in a free market, with or without health insurance? It is the lack of a solution to this latter problem, not a lack of health insurance coverage, that makes people seek emergency room visits.

When it comes to health and wellness programs and the use of incentives, we have also focused on the wrong solutions. Although we have bridged the gaps in technology by offering online portals, only a small percentage of employees use them. We have added incentives to health and wellness programs to make them more palatable, but these incentives last only for several months, making their value 'negligible' from an employee's perspective. As a result, many consumers still haven't changed their healthcare behavior. However, the problem isn't with the incentives, the technology or even the consumer, but rather with the structure of the incentives programs and with what the health industry deems as "best practice" when offering these programs—best practices that were not devised using any consumer input.

We envy the technologies that have found a way to engage consumers for several hours a day, be it Facebook, Twitter or Pinterest. Why haven't we? Isn't healthcare important? What's our "fix"? Is it to follow the pack, and put social newsfeeds, walls and friend connections in employee portals that only 1 percent of employees or plan members use?

While all these efforts are admirable and show that the industry is trying to make a change, it also shows the lack of understanding about what it means to own something from a consumer point of view. What are some solutions to the healthcare conundrum that involve a true degree of consumerism? Could the next best fix be mobile apps or social gaming?

Before we answer some of these questions, let's first discuss consumerism.

The Four Pillars of Consumerism
Allowing consumers to own their health is deeply rooted in four

pillars of human psychology: belief, trust, freedom of choice and building self-expertise.

Belief

The underlying factors necessary for a consumer to believe in his or her own health include self-motivation, an external support system, proven results shown by others and an easy-to-do, easy-to-understand stepwise program for achieving results.

Consumers who don't believe in their own health will fall through the cracks, end up with chronic illnesses and cost thousands in healthcare dollars. The truth is, if a person does not believe enough in their own health to take care of it until push comes to shove, there is nothing that the healthcare industry can offer to improve health engagement, produce better health outcomes or save employers on costs. The healthcare industry can help instill a better belief system in consumers, but not by taking on the decision-making responsibility on their behalf.

Imagine a program called "Cheers." Based on consumers' targeted health needs—weight loss, for example—a five-step program is available. The program has a coach, who is responsible for calling upon the consumers, engaging them in a motivating discussion and getting them to sign up. Furthermore, for each of the five steps, the consumer is free to choose friends who can accompany him or her in completing those steps. These are the support group members who will cheer the consumer on as he or she follows the program. The coach will measure the consumer's progress and record it in an easy-to-use, consumer-accessible technology system. Support group members can also log on to share their motivating comments or verify the activities of the consumer. At the end of the program, the employer can reward the consumer, who is their employee. Rewards can include gift cards, travel benefits, office privileges, lower health plan costs in the next enrollment period and more. If the program is fun and has worked for others (and is therefore "proven"), then the consumer's belief in it will be high. Notice that this is an example of a social media-based solution that enables consumers to own their health.

Trust

Although we might be connected to everyone in the world within six degrees, trust doesn't go beyond two degrees. When it comes to health, this means that closest friends and family most often represent the first degree of trust, and a long-term family doctor is likely to represent the second degree of trust. Therefore, it is pointless for an employer or health plan to attempt to gain a consumer's trust, especially when it is obvious to most consumers that employers and health plans have other motives. Recently, even Facebook faced criticism when the company automatically promoted products that a user "liked" to that user's friend circle—along with the user's picture and "endorsement"—without obtaining the user's official permission for such promotion, thereby violating the social trust that exists between the user and his or her friends.

When corporate interests do not align readily with consumer interests, what can companies do to gain at least a little trust from consumers?

Anything health-related that an employer offers employees today has to be maintained within a wall of privacy, both for legal reasons and to allay employee fears about employers knowing their personal health information. Respecting consumer privacy is critical to building trust.

Also important for building trust is permission (e.g., enabling patients to give specific permission on how their health records are used and with whom they are shared).

The most important factor for gaining trust, however, is to *give* trust. The value of giving trust cannot be stressed enough. Take the case of incentives. Almost all health programs are structured to provide an incentive at the back end of the program, where once the program is finished (or a result is obtained), the incentive is earned. We in the healthcare industry expect results and outcomes; therefore, we think in those terms. Consumers, however, seek a lot more than just results. Consumers seek achievements.

Imagine a program called "Fame." In this program, the employer grants $500 to each employee—not after program completion and not based on results, but up front. The employees are instructed that they are completely free to do whatever they want with that $500. However, it is recommended that they use it for accomplishing something related to their healthcare. The employees are free to choose their own health accomplishments and the respective programs to achieve these accomplishments on their own, with their own research. Only caveat is that they must document the entire story of their accomplishment in a special online diary. If they are successful in their accomplishment, their story can be published in a new book called "101 Stories of Life-Changing Healthcare Experiences."

Consumers will submit their stories, such as "How I Lost 10 lbs with Yoga in 2 Weeks" to "Hop-skipping is My New Favorite Cardio Workout." If their story is selected, they will become an "ambassador" who teaches others about how to achieve the same results. The book will be published annually and given to all employees during health plan enrollment. Maybe the employer will also provide a bonus reward to the ambassadors for their extra time. This will not only help build a culture of better health, but it also goes a long way in building a trustful relationship with employees. Not many expect an employer to trustfully hand out $500 to let employees spend at their discretion.

Freedom of Choice

Trust and freedom go hand in hand. To date, the providers, health plans and employers have all struggled with each other to gain control of healthcare decision-making. In this struggle, the ones who have done well are the vendors, who will sell their product to whoever holds the cards at the moment. Consumers have mostly stayed out of the struggle, seeking their own alternatives and knowing that no matter who had control, it wouldn't be beneficial for them.

Is it possible for the health industry to give real freedom of choice (i.e., the freedom to choose one's own health plan or to not have a health plan at all) to consumers? The freedom to directly contract with doctors for the services one needs under a direct primary care or concierge medicine model, or using HSA dollars for direct care are other potential alternatives. What about the freedom to decide that an MRI is better suited for them than an ultrasound, and their freedom to pay the difference in cost because they'd rather have that MRI? Or the freedom to get one's own lipid profile test done from a lab, rather than requiring a doctor visit first at a higher overall cost?

Consumers feel that they lack freedom of choice in their health-care decision making for many reasons, from laws and regulations and the restrictive design of plans and benefits to the lack of direct access to providers and the lack of consumer price transparency.

Most consumers therefore abide by the rules, but exercise freedom outside of the industry, by doing their own research or accessing independent online services. It will be difficult for the healthcare industry to build a culture of consumerism unless they truly learn to give consumers freedom of choice and decision making.

Imagine a marketplace called "Freedom Health." In this market, the doctors post their own services or bundles of services as "plans." A person can buy any service whenever they need one. The bundled service plans purchased are either prepaid or subscribed to. Every health service or plan has a price posted. A person might have full health coverage and use the market for further convenience, have a high-deductible plan and use the market for their primary 'below the deductible' care or be uninsured, in which case they have come to the right place!

Anyone who cares only about annual physicals and a few labs for maintaining proper health can subscribe to a basic wellness plan. Consumers who want every screening done systematically every year may be interested in a comprehensive plan. An athlete may want cholesterol, lipid profile and hormone-level lab tests. Someone else may want a quick online teleconsultation for a cold, with an antibiotic prescription. A diabetic consumer may even subscribe with a practice for a direct diabetes care plan that includes home visits.

The market has something for everyone, including doctors and practices that provide the services in their area. Doctors receive ratings by the consumers they treat. Consumers can make appointments right online. Their health record is updated directly by the doctor they visited for the services. The market is online and mobile phone access is available 24/7.

Employers can contribute to an account for their employees, who can then use the funds as they please in the marketplace, avoiding unnecessary office visits, ER visits and redundant tests.

This is freedom of choice, where the cost savings will come from price competition between physicians and practices in each region. Price transparency is built into the entire model rather than being a 'transparency tool' for projecting out-of-pockets costs under a health plan. In fact, this model can even drive greater innovation in product designs and plan offerings directly from providers. All this is achieved with one simple goal in mind: in consumerism, the patient owns his or her health and is free to choose.

Expertise

In every industry, consumers, as buyers of services, build a level of expertise as they compare services, prices and merchants. They research and understand what they want to buy and how it will help them before they make their purchase. Consumers share their expertise and experience with friends and family. Becoming an expert on a subject matter, by self-research, self-understanding and self-achievement, then sharing the gained experience with others, is an inherent need within all consumers. For example, if a person lost 15 pounds in one month using a new spectacular diet he or she found, that person will be eager to tell everyone about it. Self-found authoritative status builds social reputation and credibility among peers. Given the reach of the Internet, a person's peer network can include online forums, communities and social media websites such as Facebook and Twitter.

From an employer's perspective, helping to build consumer expertise as part of the consumerism strategy is critical. Don't think about how *you* can better provide the expertise to guide consumers. Think how you can let consumers discover for themselves what benefits them, what is more cost-effective for them and who the best providers are for their care needs.

Pre-negotiated provider discounts and access controls were valid ways in the past. However, in the face of rapidly rising costs, if consumerism is to really take off, a truly free-form consumer healthcare marketplace should be given a chance to establish market-driven price pressures on provider costs through competition. In this marketplace, consumers should be allowed to build their own expertise in managing their health with guidance from providers and other consumers who have shown various healthcare achievements.

*Imagine a consumer-driven health system called "Expert Health." In this system, consumers are provided both **incentive funds** and **healthcare savings account funds** up front with each enrollment. Catastrophic health coverage remains in place at a higher deductible.*

Consumers set their own goals to achieve certain health results, be it weight loss, better diabetes management, learning to eat better, exercising more or a combination of goals based on their own personal needs.

The consumers shop in a marketplace for health services directly from providers. The market defines "providers" as more than just physicians. It includes merchants such as Weight Watchers, nutrition counselors, personal trainers, experts in diabetes care and alternative health providers.

Expert Health allows patients to build their story of how they achieved their health goal(s). Consumers self-document which services they purchased, what providers they went to, what advice they found most useful and which health programs they found on their own that delivered the best results. If they positively achieved their goals, they become an expert in Expert Health and the incentive funds are released to them. They can 'make public' their story, and that story becomes a product to which other consumers can subscribe and follow.

Given that all services, programs, providers, providers' advice and resultant health metrics are embedded within the stories of consumers, it is easy for anyone to follow along, reducing redundancy in the health system. These achievements by consumers may even give rise to new standards and protocols. This is just one example of a market-driven expert health system.

Consumerism Movement and its Stages: A Summary

I have shared a vision of consumerism. But how do you make it happen? What are the stages? What are the gaps in your overall healthcare strategy?

Stage 1

This stage began more than a decade ago, when health plans and employers alike began implementing member portals, complete with health information, medication cost comparison tools, provider cost and quality comparison tools and out-of-pocket cost analyzers that members could use during enrollment to determine their cost exposure under traditional managed care plans. WebMD, Rxaminer, Subimo and HealthShare Technology were among the leaders at this stage.

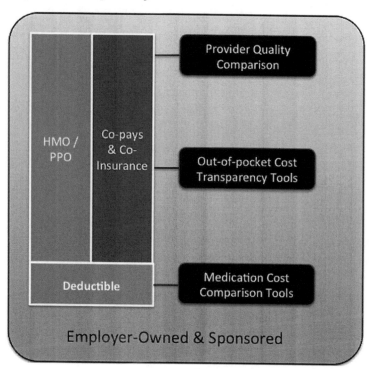

Provider Quality Comparison

HMO / PPO

Co-pays & Co-Insurance

Out-of-pocket Cost Transparency Tools

Deductible

Medication Cost Comparison Tools

Employer-Owned & Sponsored

If you are an employer at this stage, you have not adopted consumerism to its fullest extent. Consider stages 2 and 3.

Stage 2

This is the stage where most employers are today with their consumerism strategy, the promise of "consumer-directed healthcare" (CDH). Leaders in CDH, such as Definity Health, Lumenos and CareGain, defined the market for healthcare account administration early on. HRA, HSA and FSA combinations took hold of the market. Multipursing became a buzzword, allowing various services to come out of different account structures. Debit card platforms from MBI, Metavante and Evolution Benefits expanded to include multipursing and auto-substantiation of services at the point-of-service, especially pharmacy. Member portals were expanded to combine healthcare account management, debit card transactions, substantiation functions and decision support tools.

Innovative large employers began experimenting with HRA/HSA combination plans. Some added incentives, where employees received HSA contributions as an incentive for following through with and completing various employer-directed health programs.

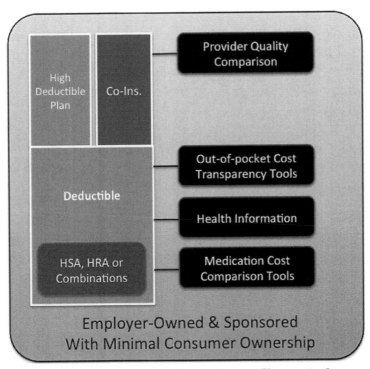

While this progress is commendable, it is still an employer-owned and controlled form of consumerism. In an effort to introduce consumerism, we may have possibly added further complexity as well. Employers may wish to consider stage 3.

Stage 3

Consumerism has to be simple and owned by the consumer. This stage offers a vision of a true healthcare marketplace; where there is a role for incentives and a role for healthcare accounts; where employers receive the ROI for their contributions into health accounts and incentive funds; where health plans continue to offer catastrophic coverage, provider discounts and administration. The only difference is that consumers are now 100 percent responsible for managing their healthcare at the 'first-dollar coverage.' For most, this is approximately the first $2,500 of healthcare spending per person.

Figure 16.4 Goes Here

HealthTap offers consumers a place to get their questions answered directly by providers. Healthper offers a social gaming model for health engagement, breaking down health programs into daily actions that are associated with Groupon-style deals and employer rewards. Keas allows employees of a company to form a team and compete with other employers' teams - a team competition model. Health plans have also stepped in with social gaming. Humana Games offers an online game with healthy activities.

Direct primary care practices and concierge medicine models are allowing doctors to directly contract with consumers for primary and specialty care. Qliance, Iora Health, MedLion and MD VIP are examples of practices that directly contract with patients. Meanwhile, KlearHealth became the first to offer a free-form marketplace, allowing doctors across the country to offer services and bundled plans direct to consumers, whether the consumers are insured, have high-deductible or consumer-directed plan, or are uninsured. On KlearHealth, patients can contract directly with providers online and self-pay, including from their HSAs.

Conclusion

The healthcare industry has truly advanced over the last decade. Employers have many options, whether they wish to be paternalistic and guide their employees to become healthcare consumers using employer-offered technologies, tools and programs; or whether they wish to really push employees towards a free-form marketplace model, where the employee owns all of his or her healthcare and is in charge of all decision making while the employer simply contributes towards a portion of the costs.

Healthcare consumerism will progress, and consumers will drive the need for a marketplace. The marketplace may even move towards becoming global rather than regional, with the growth of healthcare tourism markets. It's important for each employer to assess where they stand in the healthcare consumerism movement, and how to best leverage it for their employees. Whether an employer is driven by innovation or by cost pressures, there are plenty of technologies, solutions and vendors now available to help create the right model for each employer's needs.

Key Ideas

- To truly push a cultural transformation in healthcare, we have to start solving the right problems, and we need to do this by asking the right questions.

- Allowing consumers to own their health is deeply rooted in four pillars of human psychology: belief, trust, freedom of choice and building self-expertise.

- The most important factor for gaining trust, however, is to give trust.

Questions

1. What is missing from the following list of the four pillars of human psychology: Belief,_____, Freedom of Choice, and Self-expertise?

   a. Trust

   b. Action

   c. Entertainment

   d. Knowledge

2. The most important factor for gaining, is to demand trust.

   a. True

   b. False

3. What is meant by "consumerism"?

   a. The wasteful spending on healthcare by the consumers

   b. A plan to get healthcare decisions to be made by the consumer

   c. Large companies targeting consumers to buy their products.

   d. None of the above

Catalytic Innovation for Transformational Leadership
By Dr. Rick. J. Botelho

Executive Summary

Catalytic innovations are defined as socio-psychological interventions that work for positive change, such as motivating healthy habits. They are convenient, inexpensive, easy-to-use and beneficial to diverse populations. Hi-tech and empathic solutions expand the reach and enhance effectiveness of such innovations. To accelerate the scale-up and impact of these innovations, we can use blended learning methods (including social media and Health 2.0 online learning programs) to take advantage of the greatest untapped resource in healthcare: namely, students, employees, health consumers and patients of healthcare. Catalytic innovations that empower 4p-patients/consumers (Prepared, Proactive, Proficient and Partnering) enhance the engagement and participation rates in health promotion programs. Family & Peer Health Coaching programs (F-PHC) are for patients and led by patients. These programs use low-cost, self-reflective learning exercises to set up ongoing coaching experiences. Learning organizations (such as Employee wellness programs, Accountable Care Organizations and Patient-centered Medical Homes) can implement F-PHC programs. To cultivate such organizations, we need to build social networks of transformational leadership development that provide the stewardships for implementing F-PHC programs in health education, clinical and work settings. These programs use low-cost, self-reflective learning exercises to set up ongoing coaching experiences. Our learning organizations will create professional movements that improve the health habits of practitioners and staff within the education, health and work sectors. In turn, our learning organizations can disseminate F-PHC programs to patients and their families. Alignment of our educational institutions, clinical organizations and worksite settings will generate the momentum to create professional movements for health. In turn, these professional movements can cultivate learning communities to generate social movements for health. Ideally, professional and social movements will work synergistically together to reverse the epidemics of unhealthy habits and reduce mounting burdens of chronic diseases.

Health Coach Buddy Program: Catalytic Innovation for Transformational Leadership

Our short-sighted, divergent and mal-aligned worldviews about health, disease and science have created toxic environments and cultures detrimental to healthy living. These negative social influences have created epidemics of unhealthy habits and mass-produced diseases on scales unprecedented in the history of humankind.

Our disease-producing cultures prevent us from generating meaningful dialogues and mounting effective counter-measures to work against the negative social influences that created these behavioral epidemics and mounting burdens of chronic diseases. To build health-promoting cultures and environments, we need relevant and reliable complex process innovations working ecologically at multiple levels to generate upward spirals of positive social influences that overcome these negative social influences.[131]In essence, we need to create a culture shift in our communities where people make healthy changes, demand healthier choices, support policies to make these choices available, and establish a culture where we make health an easy choice.[132]

To reverse these epidemics, we need Health in All Policies (HiAP) to align inter-sectorial action that involves the political, public policy, educational, employment and health sectors.[133] To implement such policy initiatives, we also need transformational leadership to disseminate complex process innovations working at multiple levels. Along with these macro- and meso-level interventions, we need micro-level behavioral change innovations to reverse these epidemics and associated chronic diseases.[134] Together, these multi-level interventions can work synergistically to unravel the psychosocial genome of unhealthy habits.

Table 1: A Multi-level Synergistic Approach	
Macro-Level	Develop political support and dynamic public policies that generate professional and social movements that promote healthy habits
Meso-Level	Cultivate learning organizations and communities to disseminate behavior change programs
Micro-Level	Experience behavior change learning processes and implement health behavior change programs for practitioners, staff, patients & their families

We can use complexity sciences to address the ecological challenges of disseminating dynamic process innovations that sustain behavior change at individualized, organizational and population-based levels.[135,136,137,138,139,140,141,142] To facilitate such large-scale change, we need to understand the limitations of the biomedical paradigm and evidence-based medicine, so that we can disseminate innovative learning platforms about health behavior change that facilitate productive dialogues among providers, patients and purchasers in worksite, community and healthcare settings.

Understand the Limitations of Evidence-Based Medicine
Evidence-based interventions do not work for the vast majority of patients in changing their unhealthy habits. Brief interventions address surface change (e.g. educating patients about the risks of their unhealthy habits and eliciting their good intentions to change). Good intentions are typically short-lived, because individuals maximize the short-term emotional rewards and minimize the long-term benefits.

Evidence-based guidelines are too simplistic for addressing the ecological, non-linear dynamics of behavioral epidemics Furthermore, current public policies, re-imbursement methods and clinical models do not support the systematic implementation of evidence-based interventions for behavior change in healthcare settings.[143,144,145,146,147,148] Consequently, brief interventions are of marginal impact at population-based levels.

Overcome the Limitations of Evidence-based Guidelines
The learning experience of using Family and Peer Health Coaching (F-PHC) programs can help you understand why evidence-based guidelines inadequately address the complexities of behavior change.[149,150] Researchers generate objective data to predict the impact of a particular intervention on the average patient. This (outside-in) scientific evidence cannot provide any specific guidance on what will work for any particular individual.

Experiential learning methods build on the strengths of evidence-based guidelines and overcome the limitations of evidence-based interventions that address predominantly surface change (see table 2).

Table 2: Address Surface Change
Increase knowledge
Declare good intentions
Set goals
Develop instrumental skills
Create action plans

To develop your own personal evidence, you can use F-PHC programs to go beyond surface change by exploring and making deep change (see table 3). In effect, you become the researcher of your behavior change. In other words, you select and discover which theories, models and constructs that meet your needs, in contrast to traditional research methods where individual subjects fit into the theories, models and constructs pre-selected by the principle investigator of the study.

The F-PHC process provides a menu of self-reflective learning exercises, based on a wide variety of theories, models and constructs. This learning process involves journaling responses to these learning exercises. In effect, you conduct the equivalent of a semi-structured interview on yourself, prior to the process of engaging in a series of coaching session with a family member or peer.

Table 3: Explore Deep Change
Change perceptions about benefits, risks & harms
Reduce emotional resistance
Increase motivation
Address discrepancies in values
Explore motives (why change?)
Develop emotional self-regulation skills
Enhance self-efficacy (confidence & ability)
Generate passion & commitment to change
Develop discipline to change
Develop coping skills
Use your faith to change
Inspire & create hope to change

Develop new coping skills
Improve time management skills
Enhance problem-solving skills
Cultivate resilience
Build healthy identities
Clarify and understand your worldview

The F-PHC programs involve collaborating and coaching each other over time in how to improve our health habits. This learning process activates us to cultivate wisdom about making deep change and developing our own personal evidence about change.

With this paradigm shift from scientific to personal evidence (see table 4), we become the principal investigator, researcher and author of our own behavior change. We discover our own solutions for change.[151]

Table 4: A Paradigm Shift	
Scientific Evidence	*Personal Evidence*
Evidence-based guidelines	Experiential based learning processes
Health education and advice	Catalytic innovations
Static content interventions	Dynamic complex process interventions
Surface change	Deep change
Expert research model	Cultivated wisdom from experience
Rigid hierarchical organizations	Learning organizations & communities
Health promotion initiatives	Professional & social movements

Thus, evidence-based interventions only help practitioners raise the floor of their organizational performance. In contrast, we can develop our own personal evidence to help healthcare settings break through the ceiling of our organizational performance.

Identify Worldview Limitations about the Complexities of Health
The medical worldview of health is the absence of disease. Closed-

minded worldviews about health limit our capabilities and restrict our capacities to reverse the epidemics of unhealthy habits and the growing mountains of chronic diseases. Health goes well beyond treating the pathological malfunctioning of the mind-body machine, or a broken cog in the wheel.

Health is much more than preventing diseases. To go beyond the medical model of disease, we can use the ecological model of health. This involves moving beyond the scientific worldview of positivism, so that we can more effectively address the complexities of facilitating behavior change at multiple levels.

In 1948, the World Health Organization (WHO) defined health as "a state of complete physical, mental and social well-being, and not merely the absence of disease or infirmity."[152] This landmark definition expanded our worldview about health well beyond the medical model of disease.

However, this static and individualistic definition has many limitations in addressing the complex dynamics of health, because the etiology of health is much more socio-environmental and socio-psychological than an individualistic phenomenon. Health is social.[153] We must pay robust attention to the social and behavioral factors that support health promotion and workforce well-being.

The development of optimal health is contingent on both individual and social learning processes that predominantly occur outside of the health sector. This raises questions about how healthcare and health should be conceptualized and defined.[154,155] Healthcare is a human right.[156] But the multi-dimensional concept of health is not a right, because healthcare plays only a minor role in the development of health.

Expand Our Conceptual Understandings About Health

An ethical, dynamic and evolving model of health incorporates a blend of scientific worldviews and constructs to address the ecological complexities of facilitating changes at multiple levels. The psycho-social-spiritual worldview of health includes concepts, such as well-being (positive emotions, engagement, relationship, meaning and achievement); social coherence and the development of resilience, character strengths and virtues (see table 1).[157] Individuals can improve their health and self-care of diseases by cultivating the development of any combination of the following skills:

- Experience and maintain happiness despite negative circumstances

- Develop autonomy, resilience and social coherence [158,159,160,161]

- Cultivate activation, vitality, intrinsic motivation and self-efficacy [162,163,164,165,166,167,168]

- Inspire pursuit of virtues such as open-mindedness, equanimity, inclusiveness

- Self-regulate emotions and controlling behaviors[169,170,171,172]

- Self-control over desires and destructive impulses[173,174,175]

- Manage polarities between individual and community values[176]

- Amelioration of flaws and closed-mindedness

Health is a shared responsibility that involves individuals, families and communities cultivating healthy environments and cultures with the goals of promoting healthy habits and well-being. This social conceptualization of health includes both individual and group happiness. Health is an individual, community and cultural journey of spiritual and psychological development toward higher levels of consciousness, well-being, happiness, virtues and functioning.

Overcome Toxic Environments and Disease-producing Cultures
Individuals, communities and cultures can use this dynamic model of health to overcome negative social influences created by our toxic environments and disease-producing cultures. These negative influences work against implementing complex process innovations that are essential for reversing these epidemics. We first need to understand the magnitude of our resistance against addressing these challenges before we can cultivate the open-mindedness and motivation needed to effectively implement macro-, meso- and micro-level innovations. Multi-level, synergistic actions will transform our:

- Disease-producing cultures and toxic environments that generate negative social influences and encourage unhealthy decision-making toward

- Health-promoting cultures and environments that create positive social influences and foster healthy decision-making

- Clinical and organizational inertia that limits our capacities to work on these complex challenges arises from our limited scientific worldview of health, the lack of catalytic innovations within healthcare and poorly prepared transformational leaders

Create Catalytic Innovations

Catalytic innovations are defined as socio-psychological interventions that are convenient, inexpensive, easy-to-use and beneficial to diverse populations. "Catalytic" is a metaphor for positive, pro-active social contagion for personal health improvements. As patients, we are the greatest untapped resources within our healthcare system. These innovations tap into these latent resources and thereby expand the reach of these needed programs more effectively and efficiently. They provide good-enough solutions to the over-, under- and non-served populations. The widespread adoption of these innovations fosters dissemination through a process of self-organizing replication and scaling up of needed services to over-, under- and non-served populations. These innovations catalyze large scale, socio-psychological changes that promote health, happiness and well-being.

The F-PHC program is an example of a catalytic innovation: a longitudinal process curriculum that complements health promotion, disease prevention and disease management programs, within and beyond our healthcare delivery systems. We need such collaborative learning platforms to discover and develop our own personal evidence about deep change.

Catalytic innovations that activate and empower *"4p-patients"* (prepared, proactive, proficient and partnering) enhance participation rates in professional and social movements. To integrate learning innovations about health into all sectors of society, we need longitudinal, lifelong health literacy curricula that help us develop appropriate health and disease management skills at all educational levels and life stages.[177,178,179,180,181] As patients, we can document the outcomes of our learning processes (such as F-PHC) in computerized personalized health records (PHR) that interface with our electronic medical records.

F-PHC programs are based on a central tenet of transformational leadership. Micro-level change begins from within, inspires others to do the same and emanates outwards to create meso-level and macro-level changes. Such bottom-up approaches must work synergistically with top-down strategies of building social networks of transformational leadership development. This leadership challenge involves expanding, aligning and converging our diverse worldviews about health, disease and science. In other words, macro-level influences facilitate meso-level and micro-level changes to accelerate the dissemination process.

The monumental challenge of disseminating personal transformation processes requires highly scalable learning platforms to build social movements. Such movements have the potential power to reverse the rising tides of these behavioral epidemics. To do this, we can learn from the grandfather of social movements.

"I have only three enemies. My favorite enemy, the one most easily influenced for the better, is the British Empire. My second enemy, the Indian people, is far more difficult. But my most formidable opponent is a man named Mohandas K. Gandhi. With him, I seem to have very little influence."
Mohandas K. Gandhi

The non-violent social movement mobilized and inspired by Gandhi galvanized the Indian people to generate political forces that undermined and overthrew the exploitation and benevolence of British colonialism. Today, we face the tyranny of disease-promoting cultures and toxic cultures, enabled by the sovereignty of the biomedical paradigm that monopolizes the vast majority of healthcare resources to the detriment of individualized and population-based health promotion. Furthermore, the U.S. medical care system wastes an estimated $700 billion dollars a year. We need a paradigm shift from disease care to health care, so that we can use our limited resources in lean ways, eliminate waste and vastly improve the value delivered by our yet-to-be developed healthcare system based on disruptive and catalytic innovations.

The implementation of catalytic innovations needs continuous improvement and evaluation in practice and community settings. [182],[183],[184] Participatory research methodologies and systemic realist reviews provide ways to refine catalytic innovations iteratively over time and add rigor in evaluating dynamic, complex process innovations for cultivating healthy habits. [185,186,187,188,189,190,191,192,193,194,195,196,197,198]

Experience the F-PHC Learning Process

The F-PHC learning process begins with you by developing your own personal evidence about deep change. Counseling and coaching techniques have been converted into a menu of self-reflective learning exercises for behavior change tasks (see table 3). In effect, these exercises de-professionalize these techniques for everyday life. In other words, you conduct an interview on yourself.

Each task has a menu of self-reflective learning exercises that break down and simplifies the complex process of change. You can use whatever learning exercises that you need in order to discover your shortest path to healthy habits. These exercises will evoke internal dialogues to enhance your self-awareness about how your thoughts, feelings, perceptions, motives and values influence your resistance and motivation to change.

Table 5: Behavior Change Tasks
1. Explore goal-setting
2. Address discrepancies in values
3. Explore your issues about change
4. Lower your resistance to change
5. Increase your motivation to change
6. Develop specific skills
7. Work on small-step & idea goals for change
8. Prevent lapses and relapses

To facilitate healthy behavior change, you can reflect about, and make journal notes in response to the learning exercises. Such self-reflection can help you make sense of your learning experiences. To make better sense of your learning experiences, you can discuss them with others and coach each other. Such self-reflection and collaboration can help you transform your unhealthy habits into healthy ones.

By collaborating with others and becoming the principal investigator, researcher and author of your own behavior change, you discover what works for you. Depending on your changing needs over time, you can work through your resistance and ambivalence to change, and make deep change by completing any of the following tasks and self-reflective learning exercises associated with these tasks.

Task 1 helps you explore the cognitive and emotional implications of setting your small-step and ideal goals for change. Goal-setting, without understanding how you feel about your goals, can be a setup for repeated failures. Learning exercises will help you understand more about the limitations of rational problem-solving and the use of action plans—setting goals and selecting methods to achieve those goals. Furthermore, you can also learn more about how your:

- Confidence, ability, passion and commitment affect your prospects of change

- Accountability and discipline affect your ability to maintain change.

In so doing, you will understand more about your personal challenges of working on health behavior change.

Task 2 helps you rank/order your values in ways that clarify the discrepancies between what you say and what you do. You are invited to reflect on these discrepancies in terms of what you think, how you feel and what you want to do about them. After reflecting about and discussing your discrepancies with your peer or family health coach, you can generate your ideas about what will inspire you to "walk your talk" and make meaningful change.

Task 3 helps you further explore deep change. What is holding you back, and what pushes you forward? To explore and understand these dynamics, you can assess your:

- Resistance and motivation based on what you think and how you feel

- Competing priorities and energy level

- Blend of motives

Such a multidimensional assessment can help identify where you need to focus your energy on making deep change.

Task 4 helps you recognize how you can underestimate your emotional resistance in ways that jeopardize your prospects of change. You will learn more about your feelings and how they affect your behavior. Learning how to lower your emotional resistance can set the stage for developing effective motivation to change.

Task 5 provides multiple options for increasing your motivation. You can discover which of these options work best for you:

- Focus your time and effort more effectively on change

- Make your values work for you

- Enhance your faith to change

- Change unhelpful beliefs into helpful ones

- Strengthen your freely chosen motives to change

- Overcome your rationalizations for not changing

- Be hopeful and have positive expectations about change

Task 6 identifies specific emotional skills that you may need to make deep change. You may have to:

- Overcome your addictive tendencies

- Enhance your coping and emotional regulation skills

- Improve your problem-solving and time management skills

- Change from an unhealthy to a healthy identity

Task 7 helps you take action steps toward your goals. Self-reflective learning can be an ongoing circular process between setting goals and selecting appropriate learning methods. Based on your learning experiences, you can develop effective methods for putting your goals into action.

Task 8 identifies what you can do to prevent relapses, such as

- Identifying your temptations, emotional triggers and high-risk situations for lapses

- Addressing your urges and cravings to overeat, smoke, drink alcohol and/or use drugs.

You can re-program the autopilot of your unhealthy habits into a healthy one. With this explicit process, the change process becomes more transparent to you, your peers and your family members.

F-PHC Guidelines
It is important to know what to avoid in your coaching relationships (see table 6). You may violate the first two guidelines, provided that you are invited to do so by your coachee.

Table 6: The Don'ts of F-PHC
Give advice or suggestions*
Offer solutions*
Work harder than the coachee
Become more invested in improving outcomes than the coachee
Impose your agenda
Ask leading questions
Overuse closed-ended questions
Define their issues, problems and dilemmas from your perspective
Fix their problem
Self-disclose without a clear purpose

These learning exercises prepare you for the family and peer coaching (F-PHC) sessions. The F-PHC guidelines set the stage to:

Engage in change dialogues within your coach-coachee relationships
Provide feedback to each other about enhancing your coaching skills
Like any other new skill, it takes time and practice to enhance your skills. When you do your first coaching session, you can break up the sessions into the three phases using the 1-2-1 time frame: spend twice as much time in the middle phase as the as the beginning and closure phases, for example, 5-10-5 minutes. The closing phase often gets shortchanged.

The purpose of the first "practice" session is to give the coach the experience of using the guideline questions. Take a 5-minute break after each phase to assess your reactions to using the guidelines.

What worked well? Generate some ideas about what questions or statements might work better.

When you do the role-reversal of your F-PHC session, you can do a "practice session" or do a real session without any breaks in 10-20 minutes. If you do a real session, only use the questions that make the session work. As you become more familiar with the process, you will use fewer questions, listen more attentively and use reflective statements.

Table 7(i): The Do's of F-PHC
Beginning Phase
Invite reflections—*What did you learn from doing the exercises?*
Clarify issues and dilemmas—*What do you think that you need to work on?*
Evoke emotional self-reflection—*What do you feel about what you just said?*
Elicit and validate emotional responses—*Sounds like you are feeling (identify positive feelings about changing) or (or identify a negative feeling about not changing)…*
Ask focused, open-ended questions—*How important is it for you to work on your…. (state an identified issue) right now?*

Table 7(ii): The Do's of F-PHC
Middle Phase
Comment on real-time issues about ambivalence—*You are talking about change but you don't seem really invested in it?*
Refocus on change—*How can you focus on what it would take to change?*
Gently challenge assumptions—*Maybe now is not the best time to change, but it could also be the best time, too.*
Generate new perspectives & possibilities—*If you make a change now at this difficult time, you are more likely to stay on track when you go through other stressful periods in your life.*

Generate new ideas to change—*How can you overcome what's holding you back so that you can move yourself forward?*

Work through strengths—*What strengths & successes can you draw on to help you change?*

Create tolerable intensity—*What can help you build up your motivation to change?*

Reframe issues from negative to positive perspective—*Failures are just learning opportunities toward success.*

Table 7(iii): The Do's of F-PHC
Closing Phase

Assess change—*What do you think about the progress that you have made?*

Ask problem-solving questions—*What will help increase your commitment to change?*

Ask solution-based questions—*What will it take for you to achieve your goals?*

Invite feedback about what was helpful—*What did you find helpful about this coaching session?*

Cultivate Social Network of Transformational Leadership Development

The overarching purpose of this guidebook is to cultivate social networks of transformational leadership development that create the capabilities and capacities to galvanize and mainstream the dissemination of F-PHC programs. This leadership dissemination process is distinct from the charismatic or personality cult movements. These personality-centered social movements are so dependent on the individual leaders that the cause of social movement undergoes a demise after the leader dies or disengages from the cause of the social movement. In contrast, people-centered social movements develop continuous succession plans for future leaders, based on measuring the longitudinal impact of the F-PHC learning processes on outcomes.

The primary goal of this transformational leadership development process is to facilitate the implementation of self-management and behavior change programs (such as F-PHC) into educational institutions, healthcare settings, work sites and communities. The initial focus is on developing professional movements for practitioners and staff working in educational organizations and clinical settings. In other words, practitioners and staff learn how to improve their own health habits before they help their patients do the same. However, the health sector has only a small impact of improving the overall health of the populations. Nonetheless, the health sector can develop professional movements that leverage other sectors to develop social movements for health.

The primary audience for the F-PHC learning process is for:

- Aspiring leaders and trainers (patients, practitioners and staff)

- Lay peer health coach trainers, health coaches and wellness coaches

- Educational leadership/management teams (faculty, trainers & students)

- Change management teams (behavior change facilitators, practitioners & staff)

- Change leadership teams (change agents, champions & executive leaders)

- Executive leadership coaches to change management-leadership teams

Transformational change begins from within: an inside-out learning approach. After all, how can you change others, if you cannot change yourself? The experiential learning processes of F-PHC programs can help you:

- Change your unhealthy habits as you help others do the same

- Begin your journey as a transformational leader to whatever level you aspire to

Transformational leaders accelerate the implementation rates of F-PHC programs by supporting healthcare professionals, behavior change facilitators, practitioners, staff and students to create learning organizations and communities about behavior change. In complementary top-down approaches, we can use social media to develop social networks that create positive influences from the bottom up to counteract these negative influences. Social media and online learning platforms will help to:

- Facilitate crowding-sourcing to develop healthier habits

- Galvanize a shared purpose to promote healthy habits

- Adopting learning innovations for the common good

- Create online learning communities

We need to promote, motivate and inspire healthy habits at multiple levels, from individuals to cultures. Participatory health involves an individual and collaborative process of telling, writing and reflecting about our health stories in ways that improve our own health habits and well-being. The creation of wisdom learning communities will facilitate the process of making health improvements at individual, family, organizational, community and cultural levels.

Transformational leadership is essential for facilitating major socio-psychological and socio-cultural change.[199] In other words, these leaders use positive social influences, supports and networks to facilitate individual, organization and community change, using inside-out experiential learning processes. To integrate behavior change learning innovations into all sectors of society, we need transformational leaders at all levels of our organizations and communities. The systems integration of broad-based leadership across organizations and communities is essential for enhancing the performance of our health promotion, disease prevention and disease management programs within and beyond our healthcare delivery systems.

To integrate catalytic innovations about healthy behavioral change into all sectors of society, we also need longitudinal, lifelong health literacy curricula that help us develop appropriate health and disease management skills at all educational levels and life stages. We can document and journal the outcomes of our learning processes in our computerized personalized health record (PHR) for interfacing our electronic medical records. These curricula, combined with the proactive use of the PHR, support the lifelong learning process of healthy behavior change.

Frameworks 1 and 2 provide ways to reflect about how open-minded and close-minded worldviews respectively enhance or hinder our sustainable personal, professional and leadership development (SPPLD) processes. All individuals, groups and communities are dynamically changing, in terms of their degrees of open- versus closed-mindedness and their profiles of virtues and flaws. The challenges of addressing virtues and flaws operate at intrapersonal and interpersonal levels within our organizations and communities. To what extent do virtues triumph over flaws, or flaws prevail over virtues?

Transformational leaders inspire individuals to take on these challenges, work for the greater good and bring out the best in others. Such transformation begins with oneself. Personal development is at the heart, mind and soul of this learning process. After all, how can we help others change if we cannot change ourselves? How can we foster greater open-mindedness and work more effectively with a diversity of worldviews?

The SPPLD frameworks of open-mindedness and closed-mindedness provide contrasting perspectives on different levels of ethical consciousness. Virtuous spirituality (see SPPLD framework 1) uses healthy memes (such as the Hindu swastika, which means "well-bring" in Sanskrit) and holistic metaphors, such as health is an organic garden. The effective use of memes and metaphors fosters cohesion, inclusion, healing, trust and equanimity in ways that cultivate open-minded worldviews. In turn, our worldview helps us develop healthy identities, resilience and beliefs in ways that foster positive assumptions, perceptions, biases, thoughts and feelings.

SPPLD Framework 1: Reflecting about Open-minded Worldviews

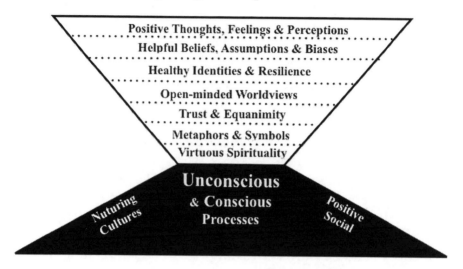

Flawed spirituality generates negative memes (such as the Nazi swastika) and inappropriate metaphors (health is a machine) that foster separation, fragmentation, alienation, suffering, fear and emotional reactivity. Our emotional reactivity fosters closed-mindedness and inhibits our capacities to elicit and receive needed feedback for our ongoing development. In turn, closed-minded worldviews create negative assumptions, thoughts and feelings, distorted perceptions and prejudices that create flawed belief systems and unhealthy identities.

SPPLD Framework 2: Reflecting about Closed-minded Worldviews

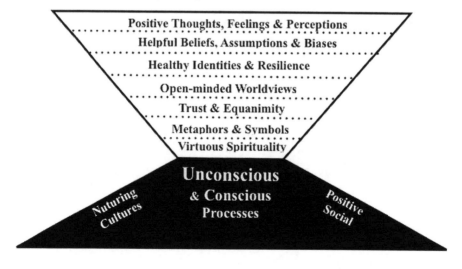

A dynamic polarity between open- and closed-mindedness is in all of us, and in our group dynamics within organizations and communities, to varying degrees. This battle between open-minded and closed-minded worldviews can:

- Descend destructively into downward spirals of negative social influences

- Create stalemate between negative and positive social influences

- Ascend constructively into upward spirals of positive social influences

When we move toward greater open-mindedness, we enhance our abilities to be more inclusive, understand more about our differences in worldviews, engage in more meaningful dialogues about aligning and converge our diverse worldviews. This learning process can galvanize our actions for the greater good of all.

A task for transformational leaders at all levels within organizations and communities is to share their learning experiences about fostering virtues and addressing flaws. Such acts of courage involve sharing our strengths and vulnerabilities. Effective leaders manage the polarity dynamics between the flaws and virtues of our diverse worldviews in ways to:

- Create upward spirals of positive social influences, cultivate virtues and minimize our flaws

- Prevent downward spirals of negative social influences that exacerbate flaws and undermine our virtues.

- An understanding about the polarity dynamics between open-mindedness and closed-mindedness, in relation to enhancing virtues and exacerbating flaws, is critically important to fostering transformational leadership development.

Call for Action
How can you develop as a proactive, collaborative experiential learner, in terms of health behavior change and leadership development? To cultivate such an identity, you can:

- Seek new learning opportunities to reflect about your behavior change

- Share learning experiences about changing your unhealthy habits

- Trust the collaborative learning process of enhancing your coaching skills

- Foster the circular process of feedback dialogues about behavior change

- Support and learn from each other's failures and successes

The web site (www.familyandpeerhealthcoaching.com) provides additional resources, such as information about the F-PHC guidebooks, evocations and podcasts that you can share with family members, friends and colleagues. In sharing these resources, your actions may contribute toward a virtuous cascade of positive social influences by helping to:

- Enhance the health of your family

- Foster positive peer coaching relationships

- Create learning communities

- Build social movements

These horizontal and bottom-up approaches will help to disseminate F-PHC programs and promote healthy habits.

Furthermore, you can also share podcasts and this guidebook with leaders, change agents and champions who work for different stakeholders: such as educational organizations, healthcare settings, corporations, companies, community organizations, funding agencies and foundations that are interested in implementing low-cost learning innovations. Again, your contributions could generate an additional cascade of positive social influence by helping to:

- Activate change management teams to implement F-PHC programs

- Create learning organizations

- Cultivate transformational leadership development networks

- Build professional movements

In so doing, your actions may contribute toward top-down strategies to promoting healthy habits.

The development of a collaborative learning identity is essential for growth, maturation and progress as a transformational leader. This transformational leadership guide can help you initiate a lifelong journey of learning how to implement and disseminate F-PHC programs in ways that create learning organizations and communities. Mobilizing and aligning guiding coalitions of learning organizations and communities can generate the momentum needed to build professional and social movements that promote healthy habits.

Build Catalytic Innovations on Evolving Initiatives
The evolving development of the patient-centered medical home (PCMH) and accountable care organizations (ACOs) will provide greater leadership opportunities and organizational supports to promote healthy behavior change and self-care of acute and chronic diseases.[200,201,202,203,204] The Triple Aim also aspires to address these monumental challenges by:

- Enhancing patient experiences

- Improving population-based outcomes and

- Reducing per-capita costs.[205]

We need such innovations to build on the National Committee for Quality Assurance (NCQA) certification process for the PCMH.[21,206,207] The effective adoption of catalytic innovations will also benefit from building on, and developing synergy with, preexisting and new models of care, such as the community-oriented primary care and the chronic care model.[208,209,210,211,212,213,214]

Ideally, leaders should create learning communities that integrate catalytic innovations into their community capacity-building initiatives. Leaders can create opportunities for skills and leadership development with career trajectory pathways, using asset-based approaches, linking to networks and partnerships with multi-communication channels and foster participatory decision-making processes in order to create meaningful, learning communities. These development processes are enhanced by having a shared vision with clear goals, conducting need assessments, generating commitment to action, developing process- and outcome-monitoring protocols and adopting dissemination methods and sustainability strategies.[60] Our healthcare systems have yet to learn how to leverage community engagement and mobilization to accelerate inter-sectorial progress toward health equity by coordinating political, advocacy, public policy, economic, educational, social and health improvement initiatives.

Catalytic innovations are essential for promoting healthy behaviors and self-care of chronic diseases, within and beyond the health sectors.[215] Long-term investments are needed to develop, test, refine, evaluate and disseminate scalable, dynamic and complex process learning interventions.

Behaviorists Drive Workforce Wellbeing Success
By Edward J. Haaz, Steffany Haaz, and David M. Spratt

Introduction
There is a growing body of evidence suggesting that working Americans desire good health, financial security and work-life fulfillment—all of which will help them better achieve both their personal and professional goals. But few employers have made "workforce wellbeing" programs that encompass these objectives a top corporate priority. The same can be said about creating a culture that values employees enough to invest in their health. The upshot is that these efforts will pay off in terms of lower healthcare costs, as well as higher levels of employee engagement, satisfaction, productivity and retention. These are the keys to a competitive advantage.

People today are forced to make hundreds of daily choices, which is a stressful and tiring proposition. Employers could assist in unburdening employees from decision fatigue by making healthy choices the default choice that's woven into the fabric of their corporate culture—thus, creating a "culture of health" that encourages healthy behaviors. While employers must understand that some employees will struggle to achieve their wellness objectives much more than others because of various factors, there may be challenges in the process of shifting workplace norms to accomplish key workforce wellbeing objectives.

People naturally resist change, which initially is perceived as a threat to the status quo. This perception can be altered as long as people recognize how any change in their behavior can be beneficial. Corporations are much like individuals in that they, too, resist change, but those that refuse to disrupt the status quo for the sake of preserving harmony will pay a high price for enabling unhealthy behaviors. What's needed is a partnership approach from the top down that empowers healthy behavior from the bottom up. It's up to the executive leadership to assemble a grassroots initiative team that makes employees aware of cognitive dissonance, which Merriam-Webster defines as "psychological conflict resulting from incongruous beliefs and attitudes held simultaneously." This effort will help people make necessary changes to live healthier.

Why Education Alone Isn't Enough

The linchpin of any worksite wellness initiative is a meaningful behavior-modification strategy that recognizes the many factors influencing the desire to improve one's health. Providing credible educational materials through a number of communication channels is essential for any workforce wellbeing initiative. Such an effort should address employee wellness beyond physical health or traditional medicine. But it is not enough to simply make information available. In fact, when used as the sole source of health promotion, education can actually serve as a control group to evaluating the effectiveness of various clinical interventions that are implemented as part of a more comprehensive approach.

Knowledge is power, but it cannot guarantee results. After conducting health-risk assessments (HRAs) on more than 10,000 participants in wellness programs, we have heard countless stories about people acknowledging the need to change, but failing to take action. The fact is, people must first believe they can change in order for behavioral modification to work. They need to feel empowered to change and motivated to make better decisions about their health.

Under the Theory of Planned Behavior, a theoretical model of health behavior, it's also important to consider how one's knowledge, attitudes and beliefs impact health status. The Ecological Model also suggests that a variety of factors outside of the individual play a role in influencing health behaviors. These include the interpersonal influences of relatives, friends, co-workers, social networks and institutions, and the community at large. Within an even broader context, public policy also influences the way people act. In order to help employees take action, employers can help reduce or eliminate barriers that stand in the way of change and offer meaningful guidance, while honoring individual or cultural values and beliefs.

Workforce wellbeing programs help raise awareness about the need to maintain good health. People are more likely to improve health behaviors if they sense there is a problem or behavior that requires change. They must then interpret the impact of the problem, decide what plan of action to take and make the change that's needed. This is followed by the behaviors that sustain the desired change. The trouble with most traditional programs is that they fail to recognize this decision-making process and understand that an individual's readiness to change both influences where they are and the likelihood of moving to the next stage. Employers can utilize tools and customized programs that help guide individuals through each action step. A highly personalized portal and action plan featuring targeted content geared toward each individual's disease risks, behaviors and readiness to change can help to promote positive behaviors.

While there are automated and computerized programs that respond to individual readiness to change, there has been an overreliance on technology, with employees increasingly asked to point and click their way through a virtually infinite amount of information. Employees may not actually read or understand those materials. Despite the growing popularity of social networking to help people achieve their wellness goals, any online connections being made are not an adequate substitute for face-to-face interaction. Texting, tagging and tweeting with strangers about lowering one's cholesterol or improving body mass index results isn't the same as having a meaningful dialogue with a health coach, doctor or trusted friend or mentor in person. In short, the high-touch approach will usually trump a high-tech approach.

A similar concern is whether people will find adequate information and motivation through their social connections or a primary care physician (PCP). As many as 35 percent of the employees we have encountered do not have a family physician or only visit their doctor when they're sick. The annual visit is an incredibly important element of preventive medicine and health information that is often missed. The most logical place to ensure everyone has chosen a PCP may very well be during an onsite biometric screening event. The VP of HR for one of our manufacturing clients strongly believes that no one should ever be left "medically homeless" (i.e., without a PCP), since a family doctor can detect serious health problems early and help manage chronic illnesses.

The Power of Face Time

One shortcoming of the traditional model of HRAs is that self-reported information is skewed by a lack of complete honesty in their responses. There's a tendency to write what's expected. If people know they should be going to the gym three or four times a week, they're going to get as close to those numbers as possible. But having an actual conversation with a healthcare practitioner can help motivate people to tell the truth. When someone verbalizes their answers, they can hear themselves thinking as part of a more multi-dimensional process that activates the other side of their brain compared with responding in writing to a question about their health. The traditional HRA is not often a consciousness-raising experience. Simply put: employers who insist on a traditional HRA might pay a higher price down the road when workforce wellbeing results fall short of expectations.

One effective resource toward workforce wellbeing is the use of behaviorists in combination with physicians, nurses, nutritionists and health educators to better support meaningful behavior change at both the individual and corporate level. It's a natural extension of corporate wellness objectives that becomes better understood as the behaviorist guides employees along the path to achieving and maintaining good health.

According to industry researchers, an effective way to encourage participation in the HRA and biometric screenings is through the use of cash or cash "value" incentives such as health insurance premium differentials. These incentives should change from year to year so that they're not viewed as an entitlement and the reward must be commensurate with the effort that is put forth. For example, the second-year incentive could include separate and cumulative incentives for participating in the HRA and biometrics, as well as opting in to coaching or participating in specified wellness programs. There is also an intrinsic motivation associated with improved health and quality of life. If achieving even the most incremental goals serves to make people feel better day in, day out then it will be easier to effect change. Additionally, it is crucial to secure a commitment to the program from key stakeholders who might include union leaders, managers, corporate executives and well-respected co-workers. Positive experiences spread like wildfire and encourage increased participation from one year to the next.

While most executives and HR professionals may not think their organization can afford to conduct face-to-face health assessments during their onsite biometric screening event, the same argument can be made for failing to take this more robust approach. Meeting face-to-face at the worksite with a trusted physician and behaviorist who take an evidence-based approach is the best possible employee engagement model—one that can produce an engagement rate that's three times higher than traditional outbound telephonic approaches.[216] Behavioral coaching is more likely to succeed with an unlimited number of sessions and ability for program participants to contact their coach at any time. Sessions may average 10 minutes for a routine follow-up and 30-45 minutes for more extended counseling or coaching. Any outcomes from behavioral health risk coaching can be measured by year-over-year changes in each individual risk profile, as well as an aggregate risk profile of participants. Each year, clinical improvement and compliance related to targeted risk factors are measured.

The Need for Bold Choices

Some forward-thinking companies have taken a brave stance by implementing strong policies, such as banning tobacco use on the worksite property. Some smokers initially perceive it as an invasion of their privacy, but we have found that as many as 90 percent of those same people are usually deeply grateful about three months after the program is put into place—admitting that without such a push, they never would have seriously attempted to kick the habit.

The lesson for employers is that any substantive moves associated with changing employee behaviors could cause some unrest in the workplace, but they also can produce compelling results. It's not only the right thing to do—there's also a business imperative involved. If executives seek to maximize shareholder value, then it stands to reason that healthy employees have a better chance of being more productive than unhealthy employees and, therefore, more helpful to the bottom line. Here's another way of viewing the issue in the C-Suite: Commanding officers are supposed to care about the health and wellbeing of their soldiers, especially in the heat of the battle, so why should it be any different in the workplace?

There are countless other wellness examples to consider. Employers who are truly serious about promoting nutrition, for instance, will make sure healthy choices in the cafeteria are less expensive than unhealthy choices (e.g., a salad vs. fried entrée)—even if it means helping subsidize the cost of meals and snacks. It's also important to have meetings with healthy choices, such as fruit instead of doughnuts, and encourage employees to take the stairs rather than the elevator, or walk during work breaks.

These policies send a consistent message about the company's values and are in keeping with the notion of establishing a "culture of health." It's worth noting that employers can reduce employee health risks by as much as 5 percent annually when more cultural elements are incorporated into best practices for worksite wellness programs.[217] The result is 2.5 times higher than standard practices.[218] One recent analysis also showed a $3.27 reduction in medical costs and $2.73 reduction in absenteeism for every dollar spent on these programs.[219]

From a Culture of Safety to Better Health

In establishing a worksite culture of health, employers can borrow from the notion of a "culture of safety" as an important reference point. No one would ever think of walking out on a manufacturing floor without wearing their safety equipment. Wearing a pair of safety glasses, earplugs, hair net, special boots or gloves was once seen as an imposition. But employers realized many years ago that it wasn't a personal choice; it was a company choice because the company also suffered just as much (if not more than) as injured workers. The employee wellness movement is similar to the safety movement; at their core, both are about fostering a symbiotic relationship between the employer and employee, rooted in concern for one's personal wellbeing and the desire to assemble a high-performance workforce.

Ten years ago, a manufacturing client of ours decided to build on its culture of safety by adopting a culture of health. The thinking was that if employees were expected to use protective equipment and maintain plant equipment, then why not expend the same effort maintaining their own body through preventive medicine and healthy lifestyles? Perhaps not surprisingly, this effort has helped substantially reduce healthcare costs and improve clinical outcomes.

There are numerous critical stakeholders involved in workforce wellbeing programs, particularly in a manufacturing setting. One such entity is organized labor, whose membership pays dues to the union and helps generate revenue for the employer—as long as they're healthy. This places additional dollars on the table for collective bargaining, while lower healthcare costs help free up dollars for worker salaries. When unions embrace a culture of health's value proposition, then they are able to develop a powerful partnership with employers in pursuit of the same goals and solutions, which can help counteract any acrimony over salaries, benefits and working conditions.

The Complete Health Equation

Embracing a "whole person" approach to good health involves physical and mental/emotional health components that influence each other. It's not enough to focus on lowering an employee's cholesterol level without also considering how the individual is sleeping, relating to a spouse, caring for a sick child, exercising, building financial security and handling stress. How can we expect anyone, from rank-and-file employees to top executives, to function at a high level unless their employer is taking a holistic view of their work and life challenges?

Emotional and behavioral health have increasingly become more acceptable as points of meaningful discussion in the corporate arena, particularly since the 9/11 terror attacks, when virtually every workplace recognized that the nation's collective psyche had been seriously jolted. There is still some stigma associated with seeking treatment for mental health or substance abuse issues, but there is less resistance to addressing the emotional challenges that affect people on a day-to-day basis. Physical and emotional energy, along with a sharp intellect, are required in order for the mind, body and spirit to operate at their peak performance. Executives need to learn what world-class athletes already know; recovering energy is as important as expending it. But this thinking also must trickle down to every level of the workplace. It is just as important for line workers to be fully engaged at home and work and making healthy choices along the way.

The whole person approach builds on basic education to include little-known details that may get lost in the information overload of today's time-challenged society. It's no longer enough to shout from the mountaintop that abstaining from tobacco products, alcoholic beverages and foods high in trans fats will help prevent chronic diseases such as diabetes, or suggest that beans, brown rice, cinnamon, garlic and oats can help lower cholesterol. It's also not enough to say that regular cardiovascular workouts help the heart and blood pressure without incorporating that key information into the daily activities of people making lifestyle choices. Employers need to realize there's much more to worksite wellness than simply helping someone quit smoking or drinking, lose weight or exercise more. The workforce wellbeing movement digs much deeper than a purely physical realm or traditional treatment, linking behavior changes to a cultural shift.

Understanding—and Transcending—ROI

There's no shortage of anecdotal evidence that corporate wellness programs can deliver a return on investment (ROI) over the long run. Coming up with accurate or reliable short- and mid-term diagnostic measures of continuous population health improvement isn't so clear-cut; some employers use this ambiguity as an excuse for not implementing a program. The process is complicated and employers should expect somewhat of a lag before they begin to see substantive clinical changes in their employee population because of the time it takes to adopt healthy behaviors. It is also important to expect a lag between the behavior change and a clinical outcome.

The chief executive of one client of ours said he believes healthy people are more productive and unhealthy people are likely to be less productive. But when asked if he would devote less than 1 percent of the company's total medical spending to employee wellness, his reply was: "Well, I don't know. What's the return?" HR departments have long been under enormous pressure to speak the language of business, which includes justifying virtually every line-item expense. And while measurement is important, employers who pursue wellness are doing the right thing for the right reason. The bottom line may not change quickly, but it is only one factor that can show measurable change over time. Additionally, not all changes are easily measured, but anecdotal changes in the lives of employees have a far-reaching impact that shouldn't be left out of the equation.

It's perfectly reasonable to equate healthy employees with a healthy bottom line, but there's much more to this connection when viewed within a larger, whole-person context. Employees who are motivated to achieve their personal best in both work and life obviously offer employers a better chance of fielding a high-performance workforce in an increasingly competitive business climate, which can help deliver higher profits. They also will remain more loyal to an employer they feel cares about them, and in some cases, took aggressive steps that ultimately saved their lives. It starts with a serious commitment to healthier living that makes people feel better, live with greater passion and happiness and have greater belief in their potential for future growth.

C-suites everywhere are feeling enormous pressure to rein in health-care costs once and for all. Their best hope is to focus on the root cause of these escalating expenses, which are preventable diseases such as heart disease, stroke, diabetes, hypertension and asthma. Many of these illnesses are fueled by unhealthy living, including a national obesity epidemic that is driving up costs and undermining health. Research has shown that the high prevalence of co-morbidities requires a focus on members with the greatest risk rather than specific disease categories.

Establishing a cost-avoidance strategy will help employers bend the trend on healthcare costs by reducing health risks and increasing productivity. Two key components include rigorous measures featuring a scorecard-driven approach and value-based purchasing of healthcare services.

Employers who take these steps can achieve high-value workforce wellbeing outcomes that offer them a clear competitive advantage, irrespective of ROI. The idea behind a worksite culture of health, whose prevalence across the corporate landscape is largely unknown, is to promote patterns of healthy behaviors that are supported by organizational and environmental policies.[220] There simply isn't enough statistical evidence for HR professionals to argue the business case for creating a healthy worksite culture or identifying effective strategies toward attaining this goal.[221] There also are few standard tools that determine what constitutes a healthy culture or track cultural change.[222]

One leading industry observer who has published several articles on workforce wellbeing recommends using an "optimal lifestyle metric" to measure simultaneous adherence to several positive health behaviors.[223] As part of that effort, employers would educate their workforce about the impact of healthy behaviors on medical costs and health status to help raise awareness about the importance of wellness. Also, employees are urged to establish priorities by focusing on a behavior they feel is realistic and enjoyable before adding others to the mix along the way to maintaining good habits. If walking for an hour or more five days a week is simply too much, then it's important to start with a much more attainable goal and build from there.

There are several key drivers to benchmarking workforce wellbeing. One is to expand the focus of sick care to integrated population health management, with an emphasis on helping those with chronic conditions and disabilities to make appropriate care choices. Another is to engage employees and their spouses in early detection and prevention programs that reward them for making smarter care choices. At some point, it is ideal to include spouses in a workforce wellbeing program, since they are also "covered lives" and employee engagement rates tend to be higher with their involvement.

Workforce wellbeing initiatives shouldn't break budgets, but they are an essential ingredient in any HR budget, considering the fact that employee healthcare is one of the largest costs of doing business. And they will surely bend the cost curve. The executive of a client company admitted that the initial motivation for implementing a workforce wellbeing program was to lower the cost of healthcare, but he also learned early on in the process that the company was actually saving lives—a far more powerful and valuable motivation than simply securing the best possible ROI.

Conclusion
The only way for employees to become world-class performers who provide a clear competitive advantage is if they're able to function at their highest possible level. In order for that to happen, employers must embrace a more aggressive approach that transforms one-dimensional worksite wellness programs into comprehensive workforce wellbeing initiatives. It starts with establishing a culture of health that also incorporates an evidence-based, whole-person approach to help employees achieve optimal health and a solid work-life balance. Critical to this effort is the ongoing use of a behaviorist who helps employees to achieve and maintain a healthier lifestyle. The behaviorist provides ongoing assistance that sustains the changes desired by the individual as well as the organization. Another critical component in ensuring success with behavior modification is having appropriate incentives in place. While securing ROI is a worthy goal, employers must remember that it's difficult to quantify. A healthier workforce will eventually lead to a healthier bottom line at a time when employee healthcare benefits represent one of the biggest costs of doing business.

Key Ideas:

- People naturally resist change, which initially is perceived as a threat to the status quo.

- It's up to the executive leadership to assemble a grassroots initiative team that makes employees aware of cognitive dissonance, which Merriam-Webster defines as "psychological conflict resulting from incongruous beliefs and attitudes held simultaneously." This effort will help people make necessary changes to live healthier.

- Under the Theory of Planned Behavior, a theoretical model of health behavior, it's also important to consider how one's knowledge, attitudes and beliefs impact health status.

- The traditional HRA is not often a consciousness-raising experience. Simply put: employers who insist on a traditional HRA might pay a higher price down the road when workforce wellbeing results fall short of expectations.

- One effective resource toward workforce wellbeing is the use of behaviorists in combination with physicians, nurses, nutritionists and health educators to better support meaningful behavior change

- incentives should change from year to year so that they're not viewed as an entitlement and the reward must be commensurate with the effort that is put forth

- The behaviorist provides ongoing assistance that sustains the changes desired by the individual as well as the organization

Questions

1. What is cogitative dissonance

    a. The inability to create an original idea

    b. The inability to think of a word

    c. The conflict from holding mutually exclusive beliefs simultaneously

    d. None of the above

2. What is the Theory of Planned Behavior?

    a. A theoretical model of health behavior

    b. A theoretical model of planning events

    c. The theory which states that people prefer planning ahead of time

    d. The theory that states t hat all «planned behavior» is predetermined by a number of factors

3. Behaviorists should be used in conjunction with physicians, nurses, nutritionists, and health educators.

    a. True

    b. False

How Personality, Generational, and Gender Styles Dictate the Design, Selection, Implementation and Management of Wellness Programs for Increased Corporate Performance
By Lynne M. White

Corporate wellness programs fail for many reasons, but, ironically, most of the top reasons--not having interest, assuming one size fits all, not having enough wellness activities, and lack of reinforcement--are directly linked to your employee population's makeup. Truth be told, it's because most companies have little idea who their employee population is from the standpoint of what makes them tick, what they like or don't' like, what their stressors or motivators are, why they engage or don't engage, how they want to be communicated with and so on.

So how does a company get knowledge on those insights and influencers quickly and at a reasonable cost before embarking on a health and wellness program? By integrating the mix of personality types, generational nuances and gender subtleties of your employee population to learn the influences from their psychological, emotional, intellectual, behavior, universal human drivers, and group dynamics. These wellness variables dramatically dictate which program elements to use and the most effective ways to implement and manage it for daily integration that generates profitable results.

Personality Types
Personalities are as unique as fingerprints, but there are universal similarities and likenesses that create groups that provide invaluable insights for wellness success. Developing a more accurate and precise assessment of your employee population personalities will show key influences that motivate worker behaviors, especially around your health and wellness program.

The goal of the personality assessment is to determine the primary personality styles of your employee population. For example, a driver personality is typically money-motivated and is quick at decision making.

One of the simplest and most direct best practices in capturing a high-level understanding of your employee population personalities is to conduct a personality assessment. With many personality instruments and tools on the market, like Meyers-Briggs and DISC, it can be overwhelming. There is no need to choose a sophisticated, comprehensive or costly personality tool in this methodology. Apply the KISS method to your selection process; make it fun and go for ease, speed and affordability.

Consider tools that use simple 5th to 7th grade-level language, primary colors from childhood that foster positive emotions, as well as easy ways to quickly "see" a personality on someone. For example, The PACE Palette uses the primary colors of green, red, yellow and blue with very simple attributes that are quickly identifiable in someone. The DISC Assessment is another direct, simple and easy-to-apply tool with great assessment summaries. From these, derive the key attributes of your employee population and sub-population personalities and build your wellness program accordingly.

Generational Nuances
It is a well-known fact that we are at a time in business where there are four generations of people in the workplace. Each comes from very different times, ways of living, external influences, values and a myriad of other items that make up the human being in that generation. By going beyond the surface and researching each generation's influencers, you gain powerful insights into the source of their beliefs, perspectives and ways of functioning in your work environment, individually and collectively. This is one of the keys, as it tells you what you need to build into your wellness program to achieve the highest adoption, utilization and results possible.

For example, communicating a wellness program face-to-face to a Traditionalist Generation worker and via online mechanisms to a Generation Y worker will typically give you a much higher likelihood of success with each. If you were to use a "one-size-fits-all" style of communication and put them in a single company-wide webinar announcing the wellness program, it would likely be met with tepid interest from each generation. You will see why as you scan **Table 1** – Generational Nuances Sample – in the following pages. It is a generation composite sample to get you started on capturing and understanding generational nuances. You are encouraged to conduct your own research.

Table 1 – Generational Nuances Sample

Generation	TRADITIONALISTS	BABY BOOMERS	GENERATION X	MILLENNIALS (GEN Y)
Age Range (varies)	Born 1925-1945	Born 1946 – 1964	Born 1965 – 1980	Born 1981 to 1997
Upbringing Influencers	grew up in tough times; The Great Depression, World War II, Elvis, Frank Sinatra, microwaves, pressures to confirm, many rules, known as "The Silent Generation", very private	grew up in improving times; Vietnam War, Woodstock, Watergate, television, civil rights and women's rights movement, rock and roll, protests/riots, space exploration, racial divides, first me generation, fewer rules, stay-at-home moms with nurturing environments	Grew up in a poor economy, expanded technology, Chernobyl, Lockerby, cable, digital, fax, pagers, palm pilots, missing children on milk cartons, computers in the classroom, latchkey children, increasing day care; feel they are being penalized for the excesses of their parents	grew up in tranquil and prosperous times, diversity, everything and anything goes, the Internet, school shootings, corporate financial scandals, 9-11 terrorist attack, Columbine, information age, invention of social media
Root Fear	The world is not safe	My world is not safe	My family is not safe	I am not safe
Core Values	dedication, sacrifice, hard work, conformity, law and order, patience, duty before pleasure, adherence to rules, honor, compete and stand out	strong ideals and traditions, very family-oriented, personal gratification, health and wellness, personal growth, work, involvement, team-oriented, getting ahead	diversity, thinks globally, balanced, fun, likes informality, self-reliant, dry humor, artful, likes to experiment, lives in the present, independence, security	confidence, sociability, morality, diversity, technoliteracy, street smarts, style conscious, live first, work second, friends, creativity, saving the world, simplicity, balanced

Generational Personality Traits & Characteristics	traditionalist, adaptive, conservative, loyal, conformists, past-oriented, belief in logic - not magic, patriotic, appreciate discipline, hardworking, self-denial, social, financially conservative	liberal, idealistic, driven, optimistic, soul-searchers, willing to "go the extra mile," break the rules, time stressed, politically correct	reactive, pessimistic, skeptical risk-takers, bosses as colleagues, expects immediate results, selfish, pragmatics, self-sufficient, flexible, skeptical of institutions, entrepreneurial, more independent, questions everything, globally concerned	Need for speed and thrill, optimistic, prefer collective action, tenacious, not loyal; disrespectful, confident, worldly, self-sufficient, impatient, team centric, socially and politically conscious
Mantra(s)	WE, Do the right thing, make a difference	US, We're going to fix everything; we're tired, but we're still rebels "I made a difference"	I, Show me the money	ALL, Whatever
Life Approach	Stand fast; Be responsible; Do the right thing	Stand up; Compete and stand out; Make a difference	Stand back; Take care of #1; Watch which way the wind blows; Be ready to move on	Stand with a group; Stick together; Talk it over; Share
Technology	technophobe	late adopter	early adopter	technophile
Environment	stable	dynamic	flexible	fun
Work Meaning	an inevitable obliga-	an exciting adventure,	a difficult challenge, why does	A way to make a difference;

Work Ethic	tion, punch the clock, retirement for some loyal and dedicated, hard workers because it's the right thing to do	hard workers in order to climb the ladder, driven, they don't like rules for the sake of rule and buck the system in such cases; thrive on possibility and change; work hard to gain the success they enjoy	hard worker for work/life balance, balanced, entrepreneur style, invest in own development rather than company, works hard but seeks more efficient ways to work, so they have time for fun	eager, but anxious Is it 5pm? I have a life
Authority	great deal of respect for authority	love-hate; questions authority; eager to get rid of command and control style of previous generation	unimpressed; dislike closesupervision,	seeks autonomy, respectful of traditionalists
Leadership & Management Style	• do as I say, not as I do • don't ask questions • hierarchical thinking	• consensus • pushing more and more • "What does it take to succeed?" view • Lead, follow, or get out of the way	• I handle it...you handle it • Comes from "What does it take to be left alone?" view • Just do the job.	• Collaborative leadership style • Comes from "What does it take to make it work?" view • You help me, I'll help you.
Worker Style	• disciplined, loyal • word is their bond • information flows top down • hard time with	• highly competitive • recognize how unique I am • respond to people and the situation	• Skeptic style is waiting for you to "try" to take advantage" and is ready to vote with their feet • Balance style wants meaning-	• they are the herd animal and need to be with the group. • work best in environments with others

younger generations	• violate my expectations and I'll get verbal • Overachiever style is responsible and takes home work • Ready to retire style is entitled and feels they have "done" their time"	• ful work balanced with their meaningful life and will stick if the work offers "rewards" • everything is relative, nothing is permanent	• not happy when left to their own devices • do not want to be treated as "kids"
Relationships	• word is their bond, so do what you say • organizational charts are adhered to and are expected to be followed	• show me generation • accept people on equal basis • people must perform to a standard • embrace team work • value peer competition	• reluctance to commit • need constant feedback as they use it to adapt to situations	• often thinks and decides communally • mutual respect • work with people you like and in a meaningful way
How to Make Them Mad	waste their time, don't follow the rules, buck structures	letter of the law, don't give them the "big picture", imply they aren't different or unique, not offer to help	misuse authority, waste time be inflexible, micromanage, reject change	be closed-minded, don't train them, imply they are "kids", not delegate, be slow in responding to questions
Triggers	• slow to accept change • careers identify who they are • don't waste their time	• respond to "feel good" scenarios as the believe they are entitled to it • wants to be treated as individuals • time is valuable, and	• reactive and find fault with Baby Boomers for their uncertain lifestyles • relate primarily to their own generation • trust no one, especially those	• willing to accept responsibility for correcting the improprieties of their predecessor generations • focuses on their own plan for their future

Buying, Adoption, Utilization Behaviors	• loyalty-based product buying behaviors • buy to satisfy their basic conservative values	• don't' follow the rules • too open and not private
	• recognition like money, title or acclaim (i.e. enhance their status) • personal gratification and recognition • opportunities to show off • political, social or environmental statements • present options • give details and be prepared to give details	• they seek things that give instant gratification and deep personal fulfillment • push recycling • willing to pay a little more for socially and ecologically positioned items or causes • sharing is fine, but no group projects
		• older than them • repulsed by hype and insincerity, and they can spot it quickly • side emotionally with the common person and will buy things that help elevate the ordinary • cause sensitive and often galvanize to support common problems
		• like a challenge and flexibility • work/life balance with clear goals • give them ways to own time and solve their own problems • value access to information and lots of it • ask for feedback and give them regular feedback • cause-related marketing appeals to this group • if your message is true, they enthusiastically adopt things
		• seek solutions • show mutual respect • give them the space and time to learn and make a decision • do what the group or their posse says to do • how will it preserve the community
		• seek their feedback • use humor and create fun learning environments • encourage them to take risks, break the rules • use movement, color, graphics, sound, and a guarantee • solve real problems quickly and completely • help stay in touch and in control • encourage and foster community behavior

Communication Preferences & Information Flow	PREFER: • face-to-face, formal typed or hand-written communications • private nature • focus on words DISLIKE: • mostly anything not in person or phone such as email, fax, text, and cell phone • NOTE: cell phones are used mostly for emergency calls	PREFER: • telephone, face-to-face, fax, or email • group and/or team meetings and a lot of them • cell phones are for talking (not necessarily for texting) • guarded when giving and receiving information • direct, open communication that avoids being controlling • focus on body language DISLIKE: • social networking sites • blogging • texting • being controlled	PREFER: • heavy email • let them choose the communication and how often they use it • expects key information to be passed through a portal, hub and spokes model • prefers one-on-one or to be alone • speak in sound bites to keep their attention • strive to keep them in the loop DISLIKE: • face-to-face, formal letter writing or team discussions • struggle with communicating up or down a generation • a few barriers with social networks	PREFER: • IM/text messaging • online social networks • email (but only for work or school) • informational flow that is fluid and far less structured • lean toward an open and collaborative communication method and style • use action words DISLIKE: • face-to-face, telephone, professional or even casual letter writing • being talked down to

Sources & Notes:

Cox-Otto, Pamela. (n.d.). *Generational Struggles Inside The Workplace.* Retrieved from http://www.interactcom.com/presentations/Entrepreneur_keynote.pdf

Tips to Improve Interaction Among the Generations. (n.d.). National Oceanographic and Atmospheric Association Office of Diversity. Retrieved from http://mysdcc.sdccd.edu/Norfolk_Training/Instructor_Info/Training_Tips_and_Info/COMMUNICATION/Done/intergencomm.htm

Gender Subtleties

Embrace that men and women are profoundly differently, especially in business. Deepening your knowledge of the subtleties between the genders is invaluable in guiding your wellness program in all aspects. For example, as a generalization, most men are fact-based and women are emotion-based. Using facts around the wellness program will gain men's trust and interest quickly, while women will need to connect emotionally to the wellness program for the greatest likelihood of adoption and utilization. Flipping the approaches or generalizing one approach to both genders would be a significant degradation in the adoption and utilization percentages.

Table 2 – Gender Subtitles Sample – will get you started with the insights and influences of the genders. However, you are encouraged to do some legwork and create your own. You can learn a great deal more gleaming over oodles of information and it doesn't take much time to create a sufficient profile.

Table 2 – Gender Subtleties Sample

Men	Women
· Hierarchical, Directive, Transactional · Outcome oriented · Don't ask to participate, just jump in · Perspective is one up or one down in relation to others · Survival based, view things as life or death · Underlying state of constant War or Battle mode · Need to "preserve independence and avoid failure" · Provider, protector, procreator functioning in the world · Appeal to their instinctual nature · View other men as "get my back" or "they out to kill me" · Simply, single focused · Compartmental thinking and discussion style · Fact-based · Less forgiving and patient than women · Command and control style · Communication is function and has a purpose, asserting · Survival marketing is effective	· Participative, supportive, and interactive · Process oriented · Ask to participate, give-n-take · Do their homework · Time, work effectiveness, self-improvement and fitness are important to women · They like a network of connections · Decide quickly whether to buy or pass on an offer · Price sensitive and are usually good savers · Focused marketing. · Intuition and influence style · Communication is a means of expression, collaborative · Nurturer based, all about enhancing everything · Multitasked, multi-focused · Emotion-based · Growing self-identity and independence · Seeking ways to balance career and family

Sources:

Armstrong, Alison. (n.d.). *The PAX Programs.* Retrieved from www.paxprograms.com

Glaser, Connie. (n.d.). *Bridging the Gender Communications Gap.* Retried from: http://www.connieglaser.com/article-archives/gender_communications_gap.html

White, Lynne. (2012). Lynne M. White Corporation. Field Observations.

The Mix (Putting It All Together)

The great benefit now comes in developing an understanding of how the mix of these three comprises your employee population. Overlay the personality types, generational nuances and gender subtleties and you will begin to uncover key strategies and aspects that are critical to your wellness program. For instance, you may notice that having a unique communication plan for each generation at the initial program launch is important. Following up with mixed generational communications in a phased approach would be a valuable addition to your wellness communication strategy. Perhaps you'll see that the activities need to be more diverse, because a driver-based, female baby boomer is motivated differently than a fun-based, female millennial, who is motivated differently than a cause-based male traditionalist. Whatever surfaces, you will be well armed with critical success data for your program design, marketing and communication, behavioral economics, employee motivation, engagement tools, employee education and enrollment methods to dramatically increase the success of your health and wellness program.

Key Ideas

- By integrating the mix of personality types, generational nuances and gender subtleties of your employee population to learn the influencers from their psychological, emotional, intellectual, behavior, universal human drivers, and group dynamics. These wellness variables dramatically dictate which program elements to use and the most effective ways to implement and manage it for daily integration that generates profitable results.

- If you were to use a "one-size-fits-all" style of communication and put them in a single company-wide webinar announcing the wellness program, it would likely be met with tepid interest from each generation.

- you may notice that having a unique communication plan for each generation at the initial program launch is important

Questions

1. Fill in the blank: a "one-size-fits-all" style of communication and put them in a single company-wide webinar announcing the wellness program, it would likely be met with _____ interest from each generation.

   a. Enthusiastic

   b. Tepid

   c. Frightened

   d. Eager

2. Having a unique communication plan for each generation at the initial program launch is not important.

   a. True

   b. False

Personal Financial Wellness & Organizational Health
By Paul Squires and Richard Lofredo

As this book makes abundantly clear, over the past two decades, health wellness services and benefits have become a common feature of most Fortune 500 companies. Enlightened leaders in these and other companies understand that physically healthy employees have less sick time, take fewer disability days, keep health insurance premiums down, and are less likely to have serious, debilitating and expensive illnesses. These enlightened leaders have been rewarded for their spending on physical health. Studies indicate that a corporate leader can expect a return of $3 in healthcare cost reductions for every dollar spent on wellness, according to the Wellness Council of America. Further, according to a Hewitt Associates study, in the US, national healthcare costs rose at a rate of about 9 percent in 2009. However, in that same year, companies such as Motorola, who have provided comprehensive corporate wellness programs for many years, saw increases of only 2.4 percent.

Less clear is the impact of personal financial wellness on an organization's employees and business success. However, researchers and corporate leaders have begun to recognize that employees who are financially stable and healthy are more productive, more engaged in their work, experience less stress and, consequently, are more physically healthy.

Personal financial wellness refers to employees who have the knowledge, confidence and motivation to proactively manage their personal finances to achieve their goals. This includes mastering key concepts, making wise selections about benefits, having a positive cash flow, saving for college and retirement, and achieving the peace of mind that comes with financial wellness. Personal financial wellness is the new challenge for corporate wellness. The research is new and the need is compelling. A few forward-thinking leaders (e.g., IBM and Meredith Publishing) have stepped up to the challenge and implemented comprehensive programs to assist their employees. All signs indicate that personal financial wellness is "the next big thing" in corporate wellness.

This chapter addresses personal financial wellness from a business leader's perspective; it describes the nature and scope of the problem among employees, the impact of poor employee financial wellness on productivity and employee engagement, and describes the costs, in behavioral and monetary terms, to organizations that fail to address the problem. The chapter describes how business leaders can measure and know the extent of the financial wellness problem in their organization and how they can estimate the monetary impact on their business. The chapter provides steps and guidelines for taking corrective action. A case study illustrating the diagnosis, remediation and program evaluation (including ROI) is presented. In short, the purpose of this chapter is to explain the relationships among employee personal financial wellness, health wellness, employee engagement and business success.

Scope of the Personal Financial Wellness Challenge
While the current financial crisis was exceeded in severity only by the Great Depression of the 1930s and matched by the financial crisis of the late 1970s and early 1980s, it is among the three worst in the last 100 years. If ever there was an appropriate time to focus on personal financial wellness that time is now. Personal financial wellness is sometimes a problem for top-earning, senior leaders but the challenge is primarily with employees at middle management levels and below. Researchers (Garman, Leech, & Gable, 1996) estimate that at any one time 15 percent or more of an employer's workforce is struggling with personal finance wellness. In financially challenging times such as the present, the percentage is higher. Consider some personal finance facts. For most employees, their home is their most valuable asset. In the recent economic downturn home values decreased by more than 20 percent on average in the US. For the hardest hit states, Florida, California, Arizona, Michigan, and Nevada, the percentage is higher, with Nevada topping the list at a crushing 53 percent (Chart 1). Financial experts (CoreLogic, 2011) estimate that nearly 25 percent of home owners are "under water" which means their mortgage is greater than the value of their home. Employees who purchased a home between 2000 and 2008 and whose down payment was less than 20 percent are likely to be under water. You can expect that 25 percent of your workforce is under water. In some states the portion of homeowners who are under water is significantly greater (Chart 2), with Nevada again topping the list with a shocking 65 percent.

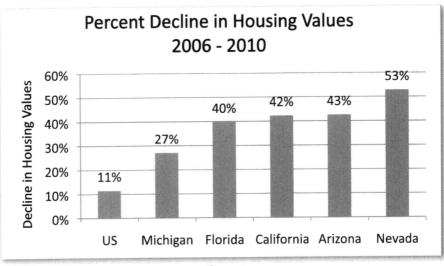

Chart 1

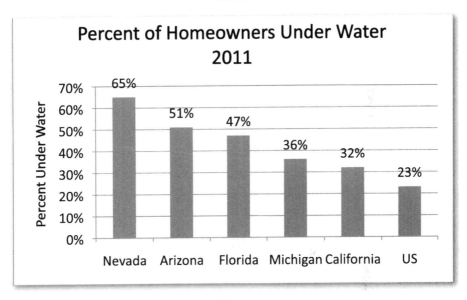

Chart 2

The drop in housing values has a direct impact on employees and employers. For example, if an employer wishes to promote a top-performing employee to a new position and it requires the employee to relocate, the top performer may not be able to afford the move or the promotion because he or she is deeply under water.

The personal financial wellness picture doesn't improve much when we look at other aspects of employees' personal finances. Historically in the US the average household rate of savings is about 8 percent[224]. Between 1972 and 1984 the average savings rate was 9.8 percent. In the last dozen years (2000 – 2011) the savings rate has been unusually low. It averaged 3.6 percent. There were some years in which the savings rate was less than 2 percent (2001, 2004) and it was negative in 2005, people spent more than they earned (Garner, 2006). These latter groups lived on credit cards and borrowed money by leveraging the equity in their homes. What's going on?

The failure to save today cannot be attributed to economic bad times. In Chart 3 are two graphs. Each presents a comparison of savings rates for two time periods, separated by 20 years, one generation. One graph compares two time periods for economic Bad Times (1979-1982 vs. 2008-2011) and the other graph compares two time periods for economic Good Times (1985-1988 vs. 2004-2007).

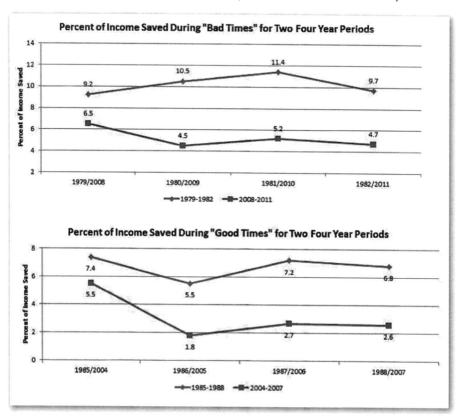

It's clear from these graphs that employees save less today, regardless of the economic conditions. Something changed over the past 20 years.

Not only are employees saving less, they are going into greater debt. The percentage of households that held second mortgages rose from 2.5 percent in 2000 to 12.5 percent in 2006. Credit card debt rose by 59 percent from 2000 to its peak of $957.5 billion in 2008 (FSB G.19 Report). Credit card debt can be devastating for households that fail to manage it well. Nearly half of all households do not carry any credit card debt, but for those households that do have credit card debt the statistics are worrisome. For those who do carry credit card debt, the average outstanding debt for households was $10,679 at the end of 2008. One year earlier, that average was $10,637. (Source: Nilson Report, April 2009). This is an astonishing amount when one considers average household incomes.

During this same period when debt was growing, real growth in income was flat and has declined since 2008. Currently, the average household income, adjusted for inflation, is $49,300. This is equal to the average household income in 1996 and represents a decline of $4,000 compared to 2000. The failure of household income to grow during the past decade is a fact for all income groups. While the inflation rate has been low, so have pay increases. When you compare the flat income growth experienced by most employees to the substantial increase in their household debt, you get a picture of the declining health of employees' personal financial wellness (Source: US Census Bureau).

The Federal Reserve Board tracks and reports quarterly household mortgage and consumer debt as a percentage of household disposable income (http://www.federalreserve.gov/releases/housedebt/). Between 1990 and 1999 the average household debt declined 4.5 percent, but in the next eight years it increased 17.6 percent. In other words, households were carrying significantly more mortgage and consumer debt as a percentage of their disposable income. It is not surprising then that the rate of personal bankruptcy has risen from 5 percent to 10 percent between 2006 and 2012.

Impact of Personal Financial Wellness in the Workplace

If you consider the personal financial wellness of the majority of your workforce, the picture is not a pretty one. If your workforce is representative of the population at large--and it probably is--then significant numbers of your employees have lost 25 percent or more of the equity in their homes and 20 percent are under water. Consequently, many of them cannot relocate if the business needs them to do so. Large numbers of your employees are not fully participating in the company 401K plan, nor are they saving for their retirement. While many employees have healthy DTIs, an employer can be sure that 15-20 percent of their workforce has debt service ratios that are well over the recommended levels. For these employees, their ability to remain free from debilitating stress, remain engaged in their work and maintain acceptable levels of productivity are significantly reduced. For these employees the financial stress and strain is unhealthy. There are direct costs due to poor personal financial wellness. Researchers have demonstrated that there are significant costs to a business when the personal financial wellness of a portion of their employees is suffering.

Stress

One cost is associated with the effects of stress. According to an annual survey of adults in the US conducted by the American Psychological Association (APA, 2011), money (75 percent), work (70 percent) and the economy (67 percent) continue to be the three most frequently cited causes of stress. These sources of stress have been on the top of employees' lists for the past five years. While small amounts of stress can be motivating, for most employees financial stress has deleterious effects. According to the APA survey the most common effects of stress are irritability or anger (42 percent); fatigue (37 percent); lack of interest, motivation or energy (35 percent); headaches (32 percent); and upset stomachs (24 percent). To make matters worse, employees do not cope well with stress. Many survey respondents reported engaging in behaviors that will exacerbate their financial woes, including drinking alcohol (18 percent), shopping (18 percent), smoking (16 percent), gambling (4 percent), and some were unable to do any activities at all (8 percent). So stress creates two costs for employers, one related to the negative effects of stress on physical health and the other is the impact of stress on employee engagement.

Engagement, Organizational Citizenship Behavior (OCB), reduced retirements

Every employer wants a fully engaged workforce. That's common sense. But for many years employee engagement was just a nice phrase to include in the CEO's speech or in the annual report. No one really agreed about what it meant, how much it mattered to business success or, more importantly how to increase it. Fortunately, organizational researchers in recent years have found answers to these questions. Now more business leaders are taking employee engagement seriously, and for good reason. Research indicates that the bottom-line impact and competitive advantages for companies with high levels of employee engagement are substantial.

Employee engagement is a connection between the employee and the organization. The organization might be a department, a group within a department or the overall business. It is cognitive and emotional – that is, engaged employees believe in the vision and goals of the organization. They believe the organization supports them in their efforts to achieve the organization's goals. Engaged employees have positive emotions about their goals, their efforts in achieving the goals and about the team and leader with whom they work to achieve these goals.

Leaders are critical to achieving employee engagement because it is through them that the organization's vision, goals, policies, programs and practices – the organizational culture – are created and sustained. Leaders who create a culture that builds employee engagement enjoy many benefits, including greater productivity at the individual and firm level, lower levels of turnover, higher levels of customer satisfaction and greater amounts of "organizational good citizen behavior." These benefits directly impact the bottom line of the business. One study of the impact of employee engagement among 700 mid-to-large US businesses found that companies with a business culture that supports employee engagement had 17 percent higher sales (DiBenedetto & Jones, 2012). Another study of the accuracy of business analysts' predictions of a company's profitability (they are very accurate) indicated that the analysts routinely under-predicted by 7 percent the profitability of organizations with high employee engagement and over-predicted profitability of companies with low employee engagement by 7 percent. Finally, the Gallup Organization has conducted over a thousand studies of organizations' employee engagement and its impact on the organization. The researchers, Harter, Schmidt, & Hayes (2002) concluded that higher employee engagement yielded a $960,000 per year per business unit increase in productivity and significantly lower employee turnover for companies with high or low base rates of turnover.

Results and benefits such as these are the reason that informed leaders implement policies, programs and practices that increase employee engagement. While there are excellent summaries of actions leaders can take to increase employee engagement (Harter, et. al., 2002), one purpose of this chapter is to describe the benefits of employee engagement gained through programs that improve employees' personal financial wellness. For example, in one such study of a medium-sized high technology firm the researchers gathered personal financial wellness data and data on four indicators of employee engagement - absenteeism, turnover, withdrawing effort and lateness. Results indicated that the company's productivity was lower by 16.5 percent due to the loss of engagement among those employees who were struggling with their personal finances (Sagie, Birati, and Tziner, 2002). In another study of several dozen retail companies, a one-point increase in employee engagement increased monthly sales by $200,000 per store. For 10 stores over one year the revenue gain is $24 million.

In addition to the costs associated with reduced employee engagement, employers incur direct costs when their employees' personal financial wellness declines. These direct costs include higher employer FICA payments because employees are not participating in 401K plans at all or at high levels. Consequently, employees are not deferring taxable income and the employer and employee must pay FICA on dollars that could have been avoided if contributions to 401K plans were higher. Employers incur additional direct costs due to increased administrative expenses associated with wage garnishments, requests for cash advances, loans from savings plans and requests to work overtime. Financially stressed employees find ways to work overtime, some portion of which may benefit the employee more than the employer.

One additional cost to the employer is the impact on retirement. Employees who are eligible to retire and wish to retire but cannot afford to do so can be an expense to the business. A Federal Reserve survey of consumer finances in 2007 found that only about half of the families surveyed had saved any money in a retirement account, and the median amount of retirement savings for those who had saved money for retirement was $45,000. Employees who wish to retire but cannot are at higher risk of disengaging from work. Often their health is poorer. Those who are 65 and over spend 36 percent of the US healthcare dollars while they comprise only 13 percent of the population. In dollars, they spend four times as much on healthcare as does a worker in the 19-64 age bracket. So while retirement-eligible workers may possess a lot of knowledge and experience, they increase a company's healthcare premiums because of their high level of consumption of healthcare services.

Case Study:
Meredith Corporation

The Meredith Corporation is a media and marketing company with businesses centering on publishing, television broadcasting, and marketing. It is based in Des Moines, Iowa and employs 3,300 employees across 18 locations in multiple states.

According to Meredith President and Chief Executive Officer Steve Lacy, "The primary goal of Meredith's wellness initiative is to help our employees enjoy a long and healthy life, right now and during retirement. We expanded our wellness program beyond health-related initiatives to include financial wellness. By providing employees financial information, resources and tools, we hope they are financially fit, in addition to being physically fit, at retirement."

Meredith's financial wellness program provided employees with financial tools, financial knowledge and decision making skills needed to achieve their financial health and more fully use company-sponsored benefit programs. The program included weekly worksite workshops, online financial education, personalized one-on-one financial planning sessions and an annual Personal Financial Wellness Checkup. Over 1,100 employees took advantage of the program services. The programs enabled participating employees to improve monthly cash flow, save for long-term goals, manage financial risk more effectively and help them invest wisely.

Results from the Meredith Financial Wellness program were measured on three levels: (1) participant satisfaction, (2) behavior change and (3) financial measures (401k and employee stock purchase plan contributions). The following is a list of highlights of the program's effectiveness. Overall, the return on investment was slightly greater than 3:1.

- 71.4 percent of employees completed the Personal Financial Wellness Checkup

- 35.0 percent of employees participated in one or more financial wellness workshops

- Average Financial Wellness Score (1-10) improved from 6.0 in 2010 to 6.6 in 2011

- Financial distress scores were reduced from 21.9 percent in 2010 to 12.9 percent in 2011

- The portion of participants with low savings rates was reduced from 48.2 percent in 2010 to 39.7 percent in 2011

- Participation in the Meredith 401(k) program improved from 84.6 percent in 2010 to 94.6 percent in 2011

What can an employer do?

Changing behavior is challenging. Whether it is exercising more, managing time better, eating more healthy foods or saving more for retirement, changing behavior isn't easy. The obvious action an employer can take to change employees' financial behavior is to assist in their personal financial education. Financial wellness is enhanced when employees attain higher levels of financial knowledge. The Meredith case study is an excellent example of the benefits of educating employees about important financial concepts such as cash flow, budgeting and compound interest, to name a few. As a result, companies that implement financial education programs reduce employee financial distress, increase employee engagement, and reduce direct costs associated with low levels of financial wellness.

But experience demonstrates that while financial knowledge alone can bring about behavior change, for some it is not enough. We all know that eating more calories than we burn off each day is the reason why over half of Americans are overweight or obese. But the problem is getting worse, not better. Or consider that half of the US population accounts for 97 percent of the $1.5 trillion in healthcare costs each year. And for this half, the vast majority of health problems are self-inflicted due to poor health habits. So the psychology of behavior change is an important component of improving one's wellness, including employees' personal financial wellness. In order to have the greatest impact on employees' financial wellness, a program of instruction that teaches the correct financial concepts **and** teaches behavior change skills is needed.

Let's first discuss finance knowledge. Finance is a large and sometimes intimidating topic. Teaching the right stuff is important for the success of a personal financial wellness program. Many employers believe they provide sufficient personal financial wellness training when the company that administers the 401K plan delivers a program about retirement. Doubtless some useful information is provided, but too often the instruction is focused only on retirement and, worse still, the instructor is a salesperson promoting the services that benefit the 401K administrator's bottom line and not that of the employees or the company. A better choice is to have a clear idea of what personal financial wellness competency looks like and to offer an educational program that addresses all of the elements of that competency model. One such personal financial wellness competency model is contained in the competency list below. Employees who have mastered these topics at a basic to moderate level are financially competent.

Competency Model List

1. Personal Financial Data

2. Cash Flow

3. Taxes

4. Retirement

5. Company Benefits

6. Inflation

7. Buying a Home

8. Support of Elderly Parent

9. Invest in Land

10. Major Purchase (e.g., Car, Boat)

One challenge is that each employee has a different level of financial knowledge. They don't know their strengths and weaknesses. People in general overestimate their mastery of a knowledge domain

– they know less than they think they know. There are few studies that examine the level of financial literacy in the US population. The JumpStart organization tests high school and college students' financial literacy (Mandel, 2008). In their 2008 testing their average score is 48 percent and 62 percent - solid Fs!

A best practice for increasing employees' self-awareness of their financial knowledge is to administer a test of personal finance knowledge that is based upon a personal financial wellness competency model similar to the one above. Employees who take such a test will then be aware of their personal strengths and areas in need of improvement. With this self-awareness, employees can focus their time, efforts, and select the courses most suited to their personal financial wellness development needs.

The second component of behavior change is self-management skills. As stated by renowned psychologist Albert Bandura, "Self-management is good medicine. If the huge benefits of these few habits were put into a pill it would be declared a scientific milestone in the field of medicine." Self-management competence is mastery of a set of interconnected psychological principles and a set of interconnected skills for proactively managing one's own beliefs, images, behavior and emotions in a manner that facilitates achievement of desired goals. Those who have mastered self-management are open to feedback, self-aware and introspective. They are aware of the beliefs, images, behavior and emotions that inhibit their success and they set goals and take actions to change the beliefs, images, behavior and emotions that interfere with success.

For example, a head of household participating in a personal financial wellness program was quite certain that she could not afford to pay off the credit card bills in full each month. She possessed requisite personal financial wellness knowledge – she understood credit scores, cash flow and the time value of money, for example. But she believed that her needs and the needs of her family were not predictable or controllable. As a result, she used credit cards to give herself a sense of control. She continued to accumulate debt because most months she could not pay much more than the minimum amount due. On several occasions she had attempted to cut back on expenses during a month and save $1,000 to pay off the credit card balances. These efforts failed. This experience undermined her confidence in managing her finances and reinforced her belief that her cash flow was not manageable without using credit cards.

This example is an excellent illustration of an occasion in which financial knowledge did not result in behavior change. This woman knew the importance of cash flow management but believed it was only achievable by means of credit cards – an unhealthy solution. She, like many who struggle with behavior change, lacked the self-management skills needed to change her behavior and achieve her goals. For her, three key self-management skill deficiencies were openness to feedback, mastery goal orientation and personal control. More specifically, she did not question her credit card approach and was not, at least initially, open to alternative approaches. She felt that there were too many unexpected expenses that were beyond her control and she set herself up for failure by setting a goal to save $1,000 per month. That goal was unrealistic. After a time she agreed to set an initial goal of saving just $50 per month. This was successful. In time a larger savings goal of $200 per month was set because it was feasible and moved her more rapidly toward a positive cash flow. This gradual approach was only possible when she accepted the belief that small steps and improvements are better than big steps (an example of the psychological principle called mastery goal orientation). Steady improvement builds task confidence and a sense of personal control. She needed to be open to feedback that monthly expenses are within her control, not perfectly but certainly enough to eventually eliminate the use of credit cards. The moral of her story is that self-management skills matter. Combined with financial knowledge, self-management skills will significantly increase employees' likelihood of achieving personal financial wellness.

The application of self-management to personal financial wellness is new. The value of self-management has been demonstrated time and again with school children, athletes and for physical health wellness. For example, school children who possess a goal mastery orientation are more successful in school. They experience less anxiety in the learning situation, they are not seriously set back by failure, they try harder, more often monitor their progress and are not afraid to try challenging learning tasks (Dweck, 1988). The same is true for athletes of all ages. In one study (Squires, Harris, & Mintz, 2010), college and high school athletes who had a strong sense of personal control and a mastery goal orientation (small feasible steps are better than large very challenging steps) performed better in practice situations and in the game or competition, as independently rated by their coaches. There is a great deal of evidence for the importance of self-management skills for good health. For example, a study of middle-aged and older adults (Infurna, Gerstorf, & Zarit, 2011) identified that personal control was a key predictor of health at both stages of life and differentiated healthy from unhealthy lifestyle habits. In short, self-management skills are critical to behavior change.

A final point about self-management skills is the importance of openness to feedback and self-awareness. The possibility of behavior change starts with awareness of the need to change (Prochaska, 2000[225]). For some employees the biggest impediment to behavior change is acquiring accurate and honest feedback about their personal financial wellness or lack of it. The subject of personal finances can be emotional, stressful and even embarrassing. For many, their beliefs about their own self-worth are tied into their personal financial wellness. Others overestimate their level of financial knowledge. In the spirit of mastery goal orientation, for some employees simply improving how they gather and genuinely listen to feedback about their personal financial habits is a worthy first goal on their path to behavior change and greater financial wellness.

Calculating ROI

Determining the benefits in dollars of a personal financial wellness program is a useful exercise. It provides objective, factual information about the value of the effort and expenses of personal financial wellness. This can be a very challenging task but with a few simplifying and reasonable assumptions we can make the task much easier without unduly sacrificing accuracy. There are three elements to the calculation. After each element is calculated separately we can add up the elements to obtain the value in dollars of the personal financial wellness program. We then simply subtract the cost of the program to obtain the ROI.

The first ROI element is money associated with employees' failure to save money in 401K accounts, flexible spending accounts or health savings accounts. This is the easy data to collect. Employers pay extra FICA expenses because employees don't participate in these deferred income plans. When employees contribute to these accounts, they reduce employer and employee taxes. The company saves 7.65 cents for each dollar employees place in these accounts. For a company of 1,000 employees in which 15 percent are not contributing due to financial distress, that's an immediate savings to the employer of $30,600 per year (Table 2).

Regarding employee engagement, the second ROI element, there are two ways to estimate this. First, you can apply the rule of thumb that for every 100 employees on the payroll your company loses 22.5 person days of productivity per year due to financial distress (Garman, 2003). Then do the arithmetic. Multiply the average daily worker productivity by the person days lost to obtain the amount of lost productivity in dollars. For a 1,000-person company there are 225 person days of productivity lost each year. A modest average daily worker productivity is $3,600. Combining these results comes to about $800,000 in lost productivity per year. After five years, that's a loss of $4 million (Table 2).

Researchers who study workforce productivity use a technique called **utility analysis** to measure, in dollars, the impact of training programs and similar employee interventions. This is the second method to calculate the ROI of employee engagement. In a nutshell, the key steps in a utility analysis are to first estimate, in dollars, the difference in productivity between an average worker – 50th percentile - and an above-average worker – say someone in the 85th percentile. Typically, this amount is 40 percent of the average salary for a job. Call this the revenue impact of the job. Then estimate the percentage of the job's revenue impact that will be positively impacted by the training. Conservatively speaking, a training program will provide a positive impact of an amount equal to 10 percent of the job's revenue impact. Multiply these two estimates (10 percent of the 40 percent); these are the dollars gained for a single employee. If there are 1,000 employees participating in the personal financial wellness program, then multiply the dollars gained per employee by 1,000. Finally, make adjustments for training costs to get a solid estimate of ROI.

The third ROI element relates to employees who cannot retire when they had hoped to. There are two types of costs for these frustrated employees– one associated with higher healthcare premiums and another due to higher wages paid to longer-tenured employees who have not retired. We all appreciate the value that older employees bring to the workplace, but for those who want to retire and can't, financial wellness education makes a difference.

So, when you add up all these costs and compare them to the cost of financial education, the ROI is very large and the payback period is pretty immediate.

Table 2

1,000 Employees	Year 1	Year 2	Year 3	Year 4	Year 5
1. Employer FICA Savings from HSA & FSA participation	30,600	61,200	91,800	122,400	153,000
2. Employee Engagement Savings	800,000	1,600,000	2,400,000	3,200,000	4,000,000
3. Timely Retirement Savings	596,000	1,192,000	1,788,000	2,384,000	2,980,000
Total ROI	1,426,600	2,853,200	4,279,800	5,706,400	7,133,000

Summary

Personal financial wellness is a new component of employee wellness. It is related to health wellness but is important in its own right. Substantial portions of your employees experience serious personal financial distress each year. The financial wellbeing of employees has declined during the recent economic crisis. Employees are stressed. Stress is the source of significant health problems. The stress also reduces employee engagement, which in turn reduces productivity. Employees who wish to retire but who are unable to do so because of personal financial difficulties create costs to the business. These costs include lower productivity, higher healthcare costs and higher payroll costs. There are also direct costs associated with higher FICA taxes and benefits administration costs. Taken together, the benefits of assisting employees to understand and self-manage their physical and financial wellness are compellingly large. In the future, organizations will view employee wellness from a broader perspective. Employee wellness will include both physical and financial wellness. This broader perspective will benefit employees by meeting their needs more comprehensively while also substantially increasing organizational health.

References

DiBenedetto, J.E. & Jones, J.E (2012) Rebuild the engagement survey engine, Talent Management Magazine,

Dweck, C.S. & Leggett, E.L. (1988) A social-cognitive approach to motivation and personality. Psychological Review, 95, 256-273.

Garman, E. T., Leech, I. E., & Grable, J. E. (1996). The negative impact of employee financial behaviors on employees. Financial Counseling and Planning, 7, 156-168

Garner, C.A. (2006) Should the decline in personal savings be a cause for concern? Economic Review, Second Quarter, Federal Reserve Board

Harter, J.K.; Schmidt, F.L.; & Hayes, T.L. (2002). Business-unit-level relationship between employee satisfaction, employee engagement, and business outcomes: A meta-analysis. Journal of Applied Psychology, 87(2), 2002, 268-279.

Infurna, F.J, Gerstorf, D. & Zarit, S.H. (2011) Examining dynamic links between perceived control and health: Longitudinal evidence for differential effects in midlife and old age. Developmental Psychology, 47 (1), 9-18.

Mandel, L. (2008) The financial literacy of young American adults. The JumpStart Coalition for Personal Financial Literacy. Washington, DC

Nilson Report, April 2009; http://www.nilsonreport.com/recentissues.htm

Sagie, A., Birati, A., and Tziner, A. (2002) Assessing the costs of behavioral and psychological withdrawal: A new model and an empirical illustration. Applied Psychology: An International Review, 51(1), 67-89.

Squires, P., Harris, R., & Mintz, M. (2010) Evidence for the validity and reliability of the Mental Skills Assessment. Paper presented at the 2010 Annual Conference of the Association for Applied Sport Psychology (AASP), Providence, RI.

Stress in America (2011) American Psychological Association, Washington, DC

Key Ideas

- Personal financial wellness refers to employees who have the knowledge, confidence and motivation to proactively manage their personal finances to achieve their goals. This includes mastering key concepts, making wise selections about benefits, having a positive cash flow, saving for college and retirement, and achieving the peace of mind that comes with financial wellness.

- Nearly 25 percent of home owners are "under water" which means their mortgage is greater than the value of their home.

- The drop in housing values has a direct impact on employees and employers. For example, if an employer wishes to promote a top-performing employee to a new position and it requires the employee to relocate, the top performer may not be able to afford the move or the promotion because he or she is deeply under water.

- Historically in the US the average household rate of savings is about 8 percent .

- In the last dozen years (2000 – 2011) the savings rate has been unusually low. It averaged 3.6 percent. There were some years in which the savings rate was less than 2 percent (2001, 2004) and it was negative in 2005, people spent more than they earned (Garner, 2006).

- The percentage of households that held second mortgages rose from 2.5 percent in 2000 to 12.5 percent in 2006. Credit card debt rose by 59 percent from 2000 to its peak of $957.5 billion in 2008.

- According to an annual survey of adults in the US conducted by the American Psychological Association (APA, 2011), money (75 percent), work (70 percent) and the economy (67 percent) continue to be the three most frequently cited causes of stress.

- According to the APA survey the most common effects of stress are irritability or anger (42 percent); fatigue (37 percent); lack of interest, motivation or energy (35 percent); headaches (32 percent); and upset stomachs (24 percent).

- Direct costs include higher employer FICA payments because employees are not participating in 401K plans at all or at high levels. Consequently, employees are not deferring taxable income and the employer and employee must pay FICA on dollars that could have been avoided if contributions to 401K plans were higher.

- Additional direct costs due to increased administrative expenses associated with wage garnishments, requests for cash advances, loans from savings plans and requests to work overtime.

Questions

1. Filling the blank from the following list of the concepts of financial wellness: Making wise decisions about benefits, _____, saving for college and retirement, and peace of mind.

   a. Having stock options

   b. Having positive cash flow

   c. How to balance a check book

   d. Making a rainy day fund

2. How does the drop in housing value impact employers?

   a. Relocating employees becomes difficult because they cannot sell their home, or buy a new one

   b. It causes employees to become depressed and less productive.

   c. All of the persons money goes to paying for a house, so there is no room to better themselves.

   d. Instead of paying money for gas to get to work, they are spending in on their homes

3. What does OCB stand for?

   a. Organizational Client Behavior

   b. Organizational Cash Benefits

   c. Organizational Citizenship Behavior

   d. Organizational Citizenship Benefits

Identifying Key Performance Indicators in Workplace Wellness Vendors

By Andrew Stephenson

With the recent explosion of corporate health and wellness over the past decade, we have witnessed the evolution of a genuine stand-alone health industry. Amongst the myriad of emerging vendors how does one determine the value of services being offered?

This article uses best-practice and benchmarking research on the efficacy of successful corporate health and wellness initiatives to identify key factors that organizations considering an investment should seek. Finding the best possible value in a wellness service for an organization depends on pairing the unique needs of that organization with specific measurable outcomes from providers. Knowing the correct questions to ask can be the differentiator in finding synergy with the most appropriate vendor, leading to successful and profitable program outcomes.

Are all programs created equal? Can all programs actually add value to your organization?

There is no doubt that a *good* program will provide value to almost any organization. Research by government bodies, scientific experts and real world trial and error basically emits a constant ooze of compelling evidence highlighting the economic pluses of workplace health promotion programs at all levels: personal, organizational and community. But what constitutes as *good* and how do you find it in an increasingly swollen provider market?

A good program will successfully identify and address the root causes of health and productivity costs to your business. The financial return, from a business sense manifests through improved productivity and sustainability of a healthier workforce, in addition to improved job engagement, satisfaction and the reduced costs of medical care.

Poor health hurts your business, but what is the key driver of poor health? The chief adversary of optimal wellness are the poor lifestyle and health behavior choices made by our population, the CDC estimates that they are responsible for as much as 70 percent of healthcare costs. When an individual's health deteriorates, there are concomitant erosions in a range of parameters, such as physical capacity, energy levels and tolerance to stress; all of which greatly affect their ability to be productive at work. An employee not working to their potential becomes a direct expense to your organization. The extent to which health affects an employee's productivity has been well established and measured in terms of thousands of dollars annually; increasing exponentially depending on the number of health risk factors a person exhibits.

When reviewing potential workplace wellness initiatives, you are looking for elements that make a program cost effective. In the same way that mounting health risk factors can inhibit an employee's ability to perform well at work; decreasing health risk factors and improving employee's salubrious behaviors will improve their energy levels, work performance, and, according to recent information, their engagement in their job. If this last benefit is true (enhanced job engagement) then not only do you get better value in the sense of work-per-salary-dollar in the short-term, you will also improve retention, spawning a more experienced, innovative and competitive workforce in the long-term. When the savings generated from improved employee productivity, reduced absenteeism, reduced employee turnover and medical cost savings overtake the amount it costs to implement and manage your workplace health promotion program you begin to generate a return on your investment (ROI).

Thus one of the most significant factors in producing a return, and a key differentiating measure of value will be a program's ability to change the health behaviors of your workers. Does a given program you may be reviewing present an opportunity to actually facilitate *real* changes in the lifestyle behaviors and subsequent health risks of *real* people... your people?

In order to achieve the outcome of measurable change, there are two elements a prospective program or vendor must possess: an ability to get a high rate of active participation AND an ability to generate change within those participants.

- A program that involves every single one of your employees, but does not encourage any of them to change will have little impact.

- A hypothetical intervention with 100 percent behavior change outcome that none of your employees participates in will also have little or no impact.

The notion that these characteristics form a foundation for successful programs is not new, and has been well established in literature and yet in practice they are still not widely achieved. If your organization is considering a move towards investing in employee health, be scrupulous in reviewing potential partners to manage or deliver these services. Whether you are running the gauntlet at a health and safety trade show, reviewing marketing brochures, perusing the web or inviting bids for a contract - learn to blow smoke away from marketing mirrors and understand the numbers. Keep it simple.

Does your potential provider demonstrate success in generating wide-spread active participation of workforce populations? If they report participation rates of 'target groups', 'high risk employees' or the rate at which 'those who began the program finished the program' it may not justify automatic dismissal, but it should stimulate you to ask more questions. Benchmarking research suggests that the participation rates for the most successful workplace health promotion programs are at least 60 percent of the entire work population. Further, noted researchers suggest that the bar must be set much higher, and that truly high value outcomes will be found in programs that can deliver 90 percent participation or above. With average participation in many current workplace health programs snagged around 30 percent or below, it is fair to say that many organizations are not capitalizing on their investment.

Does your potential provider demonstrate evidence-based interventions, or demonstrate a clear link between their services and behavioral theory? If they offer a lot of *interesting looking* activities, you need to ask yourself about how cohesive the components are, and how effective they will be at not only facilitating genuine change within your workforce, but sustaining that change long-term.

There are other aspects of evaluating vendors you may consider, such as their methods of risk assessment, program review and outcome analysis. Ensuring that the program delivery modalities are suitable to your workplace is also essential, however many of these aspects will be organization-specific. These finer characteristics will help you pinpoint your ideal vendor from your short-list. It's the creation of your short-list from the greater pool in which the principles of potential value most come in to play. Does the vendor demonstrate an intimate understanding of workplace health promotion? Does the program have a demonstrated ability to achieve widespread and sustained change of employee health behaviors? This is the single measure by which you can determine the true value potential of profitable and sustainable programs.

As this arm of the health industry matures, there is a growing field of potential vendors, partners and resources to consider. The benefit, however is that these types of programs have now been in existence long enough to enable us to distinguish between the types of approaches that work, and those that do not, meaning you *can* find successful partners, as long as you know what you are looking for.

References for quoted figures:

1 "The Health and Cost Benefits of Work-site Health Promotion Programs"; Goetzel & Ozminkowski, Annu. Rev. Public Health (29), 2008

2 Dee Edington "Zero Trends: Health as a Serious Economic Strategy", 2009

3 Center for Disease Control website: www.cdc.gov

4 National Business Group on Health website: www.businessgrouphealth.org

Key Ideas

- A good program will successfully identify and address the root causes of health and productivity costs to your business. The financial return, from a business sense, manifests through improved productivity and sustainability of a healthier workforce, in addition to improved job engagement, satisfaction and the reduced costs of medical care.

- When an individual's health deteriorates, there are concomitant erosions in a range of parameters, such as physical capacity, energy levels and tolerance to stress; all of which greatly affect their ability to be productive at work. An employee not working to their potential becomes a direct expense to your organization. The extent to which health affects an employee's productivity has been well established and measured in terms of thousands of dollars annually; increasing exponentially depending on the number of health risk factors a person exhibits.

- A program that involves every single one of your employees, but does not encourage any of them to change will have little impact.

- A hypothetical intervention with 100 percent behavior change outcome that none of your employees participates in will also have little or no impact.

- If they report participation rates of 'target groups', 'high risk employees' or the rate at which 'those who began the program finished the program' it may not justify automatic dismissal, but it should stimulate you to ask more questions.

- Does the program have a demonstrated ability to achieve widespread and sustained change of employee health behaviors? This is the single measure by which you can determine the true value potential of profitable and sustainable programs.

Questions

1. A program that involves every single one of your employees, but does not encourage any of them to change will have little impact.

   a. True

   b. False

2. The extents of lost productivity per employee can be measured in what dollar amounts?

   a. Hundreds

   b. Thousands

   c. Tens of Thousands

   d. None of the above

3. This is the measure by which you can determine the true value potential of profitable and sustainable programs.

   a. Ability to a wide variety of employees

   b. Ability to sustain changes

   c. All of the above

   d. None of the above

How to Recruit Champions for your Wellness Team
By Colleen Reilly

All cultures have leaders—people who understand the guiding principles of that culture and can help motivate a large group to take action and be successful. A wellness culture is no different.

Your organizational wellness program will be met with different reactions: enthusiasm, skepticism, interest, passion, apathy, and doubt. No one person can build a culture of wellness that effectively responds to all of these reactions. You need a *team* of leaders—wellness champions—who can personally motivate employees to work toward their wellness goals. This team of wellness leaders will help you to lay the foundation for your culture of wellness and help it to grow and prosper every day.

Who are they?
Properly identifying wellness leaders in your organization is very important since these individuals will set the tone for your entire program and develop your culture.

A good place to start is by approaching leaders in your organization who you know may have an interest in wellness. Keep your eyes and ears open for avid exercise and health food enthusiasts and seek out people who believe in the program and may have a personal testament to how focusing on wellness has worked for them in both their personal and professional life.

It's best to recruit a diverse team of leaders—a team of champions that can build physical, professional, personal, and financial wellness among your employees will give individuals a myriad of human resources to approach when they have questions, concerns, or new ideas for programming.

Also, be sure to recruit champions from various levels of your organization. Some associates may find it intimidating to approach an executive for support, but they wouldn't have a second thought about approaching a peer.

The only prerequisite for your champion team is that the team members have an enthusiastic, positive attitude toward wellness that they are willing to share.

How do they get started?

Once you have selected your wellness champion team, the first important step is to make sure that they are educated about your program, goals, initiatives, and expectations.

Schedule an orientation session in which you can take time to talk about your population's health risks, share your plans to help minimize these risks, and get feedback on programming ideas. Discuss the tools and resources that are available to employees and set some expectations for the champion team. Let the team members know what their role will be on the individual, departmental, and organizational levels. If you expect champions to bring you on-going feedback, let them know. Maybe you'd like to set a goal for each champion team member to lead a monthly lunch-and-learn meeting or have them encourage employees to walk around the office building during breaks.

Let's talk.

A key component to having a successful team of wellness champions is communication. Whether you feel that monthly, bi-weekly, or weekly meetings are necessary, be sure to schedule specific time for the team to communicate as a whole on a regular basis. These meetings will help you solicit feedback from your champion team, inform them of progress on current and new initiatives, and help you build a team atmosphere that can carry over to all of your employees.

Another important aspect of communication on your wellness team is feedback loops. Open the lines for them to communicate with you or other team members anytime. You may find it helpful to create an e-mail distribution list for this wellness team to facilitate discussions and to give employees company-wide one e-mail address to which they can provide feedback of their own.

In addition, you may want to assign certain team members to certain types of feedback to prompt on-going dialogue. For instance, you could have one team member that helps to evaluate new programming ideas, one that keeps a pulse on the financial wellness of associates, and another to examine complaints and brainstorm what changes could be made for future programs.

Turn them loose.
Well, not exactly. Your wellness program is obviously going to be subject to corporate guidelines and objectives. However, allowing your wellness champions to take ownership by customizing programs to their specific office locations and/or work environments will lead to a greater feeling of satisfaction and enthusiasm among team members.

Listen to their ideas and involve them in brainstorming sessions about new programming—and take their concerns and suggestions seriously because they are the most involved in the implementation of your program and will have a first-person account of how programs are received across employee groups. This feeling of ownership will translate into a greater support for wellness and a contagious positivity for your organization.

Reward them.
Last but not least, be sure to recognize and reward your wellness champions. See to it that peers in the organization are aware of their contributions and big successes. Personal acknowledgement from the executive team can also be very motivating and rewarding.

In addition to recognition, incentives and rewards can help motivate your champion team and increase interest for others to join the team in the future. When it comes to wellness, there is no such thing as "too many chiefs." Consider adding a bonus based on your team's performance or host a celebratory luncheon when your team achieves a major goal for the year. These rewards go a long way to show your champions how much you appreciate them and how important they are to the success of wellness in your organization.

Get busy.
A wellness champion team can add tremendous value and efficiency to your wellness program. Your team will help to increase participation and promotion of wellness programs, distribute wellness materials, provide vital marketing and public relations support of programs within your organization, and inspire associates to get on their own personal paths to wellness.

When you choose the right people, educate them, empower them, and reward them, you will find that your wellness team is a vital partner in nurturing your wellness program for the long term.

Key Ideas

- Also, be sure to recruit champions from various levels of your organization. Some associates may find it intimidating to approach an executive for support, but they wouldn't have a second thought about approaching a peer.

- The only prerequisite for your champion team is that the team members have an enthusiastic, positive attitude toward wellness that they are willing to share.

- A key component to having a successful team of wellness champions is communication. Whether you feel that monthly, bi-weekly, or weekly meetings are necessary, be sure to schedule specific time for the team to communicate as a whole on a regular basis

- When it comes to wellness, there is no such thing as "too many chiefs."

Questions

1. All of your champions should be from upper management.

   a. True

   b. False

2. Communicating as a team should occur no more then once a month

   a. True

   b. False

Legal Aspects of Corporate Wellness Plans
By Gregory J. Viviani

This section reviews certain legal issues pertaining to the structure of employer-sponsored wellness programs. This memo addresses legal issues related to the ERISA nondiscrimination rules[226], the ADA[227], GINA[228] and Title VII[229]. This this memo does not address the tax consequences to employees that are associated with employer sponsored wellness programs.

PART A – THE ERISA LAW

I.Overview of the Relevant Portions of the ERISA Law

Section 702 of ERISA generally prohibits discrimination in group health plan coverage based on *"health status-related factors"*.

Discrimination based on health status-related factors is prohibited in terms of (i) an employee's or dependent's right to be covered under the plan, and (ii) the amount that an employee is being charged for coverage under the plan.

As a simple example, assume an employer sponsored plan charges employees $200 per month for coverage; and that the spouse of the employee has diabetes. Enrollment in the plan cannot be denied to the employee or spouse because the spouse has diabetes. Nor can the employee be charged more than $200 per month because the spouse has diabetes.

Section 702 of ERISA defines the following as health status-related factors:

- Health status.

- Medical condition. Includes both physical and mental illness, pregnancy or congenital malformation. All conditions covered, whether because of illness or injury.

- Claims experience.

- Receipt of healthcare.

- Medical history.

- Genetic information. Includes information about genes, gene products and inherited characteristics. Includes information regarding carrier status, family history, etc.

- Evidence of insurability (including conditions arising out of acts of domestic violence).

- Disability.

II.Exemptions for Wellness Programs

Section 702(b)(2)(B) of ERISA that states that a group health plan or health insurance issuer should not be prevented from establishing premium discounts or rebates, or modifying copayments or deductibles "in return for adherence to programs of *health promotion* and *disease prevention*". Simply put, this provision is intended to create an exemption for *certain* types of wellness programs.

The Department of Labor ("DOL") Regulations relating to wellness programs is found at 29 CFR Section 2590.702(f). For ease of reference, this article will refer to a wellness program that meets the DOL regulatory requirements as a "Qualified Wellness Program".

A. Wellness Programs Not Connected with a Health Status-Related Factor

As an initial point, the DOL Regulations make it clear that not all wellness programs are subject to regulation under ERISA.

If the wellness program is made available to all similarly situated individuals, the program is only subject to the ERISA nondiscrimination rules if:

1. The program has a financial reward or financial penalty that is connected to the program, and

2. The program is in fact based on a *health status-related factor*.

A financial reward or penalty associated with the program can exist in any variety of ways. Examples of rewards are reduced employee contributions and reduced deductibles or copayments. An example of a financial penalty would be higher employee contributions for failure to participate in or meet the requirements of the wellness program.

With the foregoing as background, the DOL Regulations state that the following types of programs are not subject to HIPAA because they are deemed not to be connected to a health status-related factor:

- A program that reimburses all or part of the cost for memberships in a fitness center.

- A diagnostic testing program that provides a reward for participation and does not base any part of the reward on outcomes.

- A program that encourages preventive care through the waiver of the copayment or deductible requirement under a group health plan for the costs of, for example, prenatal care or well-baby visits.

- A program that reimburses employees for the costs of smoking cessation programs without regard to whether the employee quits smoking.

- A program that provides a reward to employees for attending a monthly health education seminar.

On the other hand, for example, a program that is connected to an individual's body mass or cholesterol level will be subject to the regulation because the program *is* related to a *health status-related factor.* As is explained below, that type of program may still be permitted if it can qualify as a "Qualified Wellness Program."

B. Qualified Wellness Program

The DOL Regulations prescribe five basic requirements that must be met in order for a wellness program to be a Qualified Wellness Program. Those requirements are described below.

1. 20 percent Limit on Total Financial Reward

A reward can be in the form of a discount or rebate of an employee premium or employee contribution, a waiver of all or part of a cost-sharing mechanism (such as deductibles, copayments, or coinsurance), the absence of a surcharge, or the value of a benefit that would otherwise not be provided under the plan. Some examples include:

- Lower employee contributions, deductibles or co-payments.

- A surcharge for smokers (or a reduction in charges for non-smokers).

- An employer-funded credit, discount or rebate toward benefit costs.

- A bonus to any employee who quits smoking for 1 year.

To meet the requirements of the DOL Regulations, the general rule is that the total of all financial rewards for an employee that are connected to health status related factors must be limited to no more than 20 percent of the plan's total cost of employee-only coverage. Under the Patient Protection and Affordable Care Act (the "PPACA"), the percentage limit is scheduled to be increased to 30 percent in 2014.[230] Note that to the extent that a wellness might have rewards that are not based on health status related factors, those awards do not count toward the 20 percent (or 30 percent) limit.[231]

However, if, in addition to employees, any class of dependents (such as spouses or spouses and dependent children) may participate in the wellness program, the reward must not exceed 20 percent of the cost of the coverage in which an employee and any dependents are enrolled.

For purposes of determining whether the 20 percent limit is met, the reward for a wellness program must be coupled with any other rewards for other wellness programs under the group health plan, if those other wellness programs also require satisfaction of a standard related to a health status-related factor.

For purposes of determining whether the 20 percent limit is met, the cost of coverage is determined based on the total amount of employer and employee contributions for the benefit package under which the employee is (or the employee and any dependents are) receiving coverage. In other words, it is based on the total cost of the coverage to the plan.

2. Reasonably Designed to Promote Health or Prevent Disease

The program must be reasonably designed to *promote* health or *prevent* disease. A program satisfies this standard if it meets all of the following rather vague requirements:

- It has a reasonable chance of improving the health of or preventing disease in participating individuals.

- It is not overly burdensome.

- It is not a subterfuge for discriminating based on a health factor

- It is not highly suspect in the method chosen to promote health or prevent disease.

The foregoing requirements are basically quoted from the DOL Regulations. The rather vague standard that the DOL has put forth needs some further explanation. In that regard, the Preamble to the final Regulations sates the following:

The "reasonably designed" requirement is intended to be an easy standard to satisfy. To make this clear, the final regulations have added language providing that if a program has a reasonable chance of improving the health of participants and it is not overly burdensome, is not a subterfuge for discriminating based on a health factor, and is not highly suspect in the method chosen to promote health or prevent disease, it satisfies this standard. There does not need to be a scientific record that the method promotes wellness to satisfy this standard. The standard is intended to allow experimentation in diverse ways of promoting wellness. For example, a plan or issuer could satisfy this standard by providing rewards to individuals who participated in a course of aromatherapy. The requirement of reasonableness in this standard prohibits bizarre, extreme, or illegal requirements in a wellness program.[232]

3. Reward Opportunity at Least Once Per Year.

Each individual must be able to qualify for the reward at least once per year.

4. Availability to Similarly Situated Individuals

The program must be available to all similarly situated individuals. This requirement is the most difficult and subtle concept that is addressed by the DOL Regulations. The general notion is that to be Qualified Wellness Program, the program cannot simply provide the financial reward to individuals who meet specific medical criteria. The program has to be designed to reward participation in the program.

In order to meet this requirement of the DOL Regulations, the wellness program *must* find a way to address individuals who, during the relevant time period, cannot meet the wellness standard that the program has established for receiving the financial reward, if either of the following circumstances exist:

- It is "unreasonably difficult" for the individual to meet the wellness standard during the relevant time period "due to a medical condition".

- It is "medically inadvisable" for the individual to try to meet the wellness standard during the relevant time period.

In either of these situations, the wellness program must either (i) establish a reasonable alternative standard for the individual, or (ii) simply waive the applicable standard for the individual (and thus provide the financial reward anyway).

The wellness program may seek verification, such as a statement from an individual's physician that a health factor makes it unreasonably difficult or medically inadvisable for the individual to satisfy or attempt to satisfy the otherwise applicable standard for receiving the financial reward.

5. Disclosure of Reasonable Alternative Standard

All plan materials describing the wellness program must disclose the availability of a reasonable alternative standard. The DOL Regulations state that the following disclosure language may be used:

"If it is unreasonably difficult due to a medical condition for you to achieve the standards for the reward under this program, or if it is medically inadvisable for you to attempt to achieve the standards for the reward under this program, call us at [insert telephone number] and we will work with you to develop another way to qualify for the reward."

6. Examples of Qualified Wellness Programs

The DOL Regulations contain six examples of wellness programs that are designed to illustrate the foregoing rules.[233]

III. Penalties

Essentially, there are two potential sources of liabilities that can be imposed upon an employer if it were to adopt some type of illegal policy in regard to wellness programs: (1) employee claims under ERISA, and (2) excise taxes under the Internal Revenue Code.

A. Employee Claims Under ERISA

One source of liability for a non-compliant employer would be for employee claims brought under ERISA. The DOL also would have authority to bring an action against the employer to enforce the provision of ERISA and to seek redress for the affected employees.

Under ERISA, attorney fee awards are discretionary. Thus, an employer could be required to pay the attorney fees of plaintiffs. Punitive damages are not allowable under ERISA.

B. Excise Taxes

There is an excise tax that can be imposed upon an employer that has a healthcare plan that does not comply with the requirements of the law.[234] The basic tax amount is $100 per day for each person with respect to whom the violation occurs (e.g., the employees who are affected by the illegal wellness program).

There is an exception from the tax if (i) the failure to comply was due to reasonable cause and not due to willful neglect, and (ii) the failure to comply is corrected within 30 days of the date the employer knows, or should know, that the failure to comply exists. The law also would cap the excise tax at $500,000 per year if the failure to comply was due to reasonable cause and not due to willful neglect.

The Secretary of the Treasury may waive application of the tax if (i) the failure to comply was due to reasonable cause and not due to willful neglect, and (ii) the tax is "excessive relative to the failure involved."

PART B – ADA ISSUES

I.   Overview of the ADA

The design of wellness programs also can be affected by several provisions of the Americans with Disabilities Act (the "ADA").[235] ADA requirements are enforced by the Equal Employment Opportunity Commission ("EEOC").

Under the ADA, there are three potential concerns:
- To the extent that an individual employee is considered to be disabled, a "reasonable accommodation" may have to be made for that person.

- The ADA has certain provisions that pertain to the privacy of employee medical records.

- The ADA has a provision that generally prohibits an employer from requiring an employee to undergo any type of medical examination.

All three of these points are discussed below. The first two points do not appear to be much of a concern for a wellness plan. That is because they are somewhat duplicative of certain requirements of the HIPAA law that wellness plans will already have to meet.

As is discussed below, the last point could be a concern, depending on the design of the wellness plans. However, at this point in time, it does not appear that this particular concern should impact the design of most wellness plans.

1. Reasonable Accommodation for a Disabled Employee
Under the ADA, as a general proposition, an employer is prohibited

from discriminating against an employee who is "disabled". The ADA would prohibit discrimination with respect to all terms and conditions of employment, including fringe benefits such as a wellness plan.

If an individual is disabled, the employer may need to offer that employee a "reasonable accommodation" that takes into account the employee's disability. The ADA would require that the employer engage in an interactive process to try to develop a reasonable accommodation for the employee.

Since "disability" is also listed under the HIPAA law as a "health status-related factor", the provisions of the HIPAA law already prohibit a group healthcare plan from (i) denying enrollment to an employee or dependent on account of disability, and (ii) charging an employee a higher premium cost on the basis of a disability of the employee or a dependent.

One suggestion for an employer is that all communications related to any medical standards in the wellness plan also specifically note that reasonable accommodations can be made for disabled employees.

2. ADA Privacy Rules
Under the ADA, medical records of an employee must be kept confidential and maintained separately from the rest of the employer's personnel files. Moreover, the medical records cannot be used to discriminate against the employee.

The ADA privacy rules are separate and distinct from the HIPAA privacy rules, and apply only to the employer, not a health insurance plan provider.

Since an employer group health plan is already going to have to comply with the HIPAA privacy rules that protect "personal health information", the existence of the ADA privacy rule should not have much, if any, impact on the operations of an employer sponsored wellness program.

3. Medical Examination Issues
a. Overview
The ADA has restrictions on medical examinations of employees

that could be a potential problem for a wellness program if financial incentives are tied to an employee's willingness to undergo some type of medical procedure in relation to the wellness plan.

At this juncture, the EEOC has not issued any specific guidance addressing the interaction of the ADA and wellness plans. Thus, as is explained below, it appears that most employers who sponsor wellness plans can justifiably rely on a provision of the ADA that provides an exemption for a "bona fide benefit plan".[236]

b. General Rules

As a general rule, the ADA prohibits an employer from requiring an employee to undergo a medical exam unless it is job-related and consistent with business necessity.[237] Obviously, company-wide wellness plans will not meet that test.

The EEOC has issued "Enforcement Guidance" that takes a very expansive view of the term "medical examination".[238] Under the EEOC view, the term "medical examination" will include many procedures that are commonly associated with wellness plan. The general rule is that a "medical examination" is a procedure or test that seeks information about an individual's physical or mental impairments or health, with all facts and circumstances considered. However, the EEOC specifically states:

1. Medical examinations include the following:

- vision tests conducted and analyzed by an ophthalmologist or optometrist;

- blood, urine, and breath analyses to check for alcohol use;

- blood, urine, saliva, and hair analyses to detect disease or genetic markers (e.g., for conditions such as sickle cell trait, breast cancer, Huntington's disease);

- blood pressure screening and cholesterol testing;

- nerve conduction tests (i.e., tests that screen for possible nerve damage and susceptibility to injury, such as carpal tunnel syndrome);

- range-of-motion tests that measure muscle strength and motor function;

- pulmonary function tests (i.e., tests that measure the capacity of the lungs to hold air and to move air in and out);

- psychological tests that are designed to identify a mental disorder or impairment; and,

- diagnostic procedures such as x-rays, computerized axial tomography (CAT) scans, and magnetic resonance imaging (MRI).

2. Medical examination do NOT include the following:

- tests to determine the current illegal use of drugs;

- physical agility tests, which measure an employee's ability to perform actual or simulated job tasks, and physical fitness tests, which measure an employee's performance of physical tasks, such as running or lifting, as long as these tests do not include examinations that could be considered medical (e.g., measuring heart rate or blood pressure);

- tests that evaluate an employee's ability to read labels or distinguish objects as part of a demonstration of the ability to perform actual job functions;

- psychological tests that measure personality traits such as honesty, preferences, and habits; and,

- polygraph examinations.

The potential problem for many wellness plans are plan provisions that require a blood draw, or saliva or urine sample, as a means of identifying whether an employee has certain types of health conditions. If that is so, for purposes of the ADA, the wellness plan is will be considered to be conducting a medical examination.

c. The Voluntary Medical Exam Exemption

The ADA nevertheless has an exemption that permits an employer to ask an employee to undergo a medical examination, if it is done on a *voluntary* basis as part of an employee healthcare program. As is explained below, in the context of a wellness plan that has financial incentives, the "voluntary" requirement appears to be a problem with this exception.

Here is a quote from the EEOC "Enforcement Guidance", explaining its view of this particular provision of the law:

The ADA allows employers to conduct voluntary medical examinations and activities, including voluntary medical histories, which are part of an employee health program without having to show that they are job-related and consistent with business necessity, as long as any medical records acquired as part of the wellness program are kept confidential and separate from personnel records. These programs often include blood pressure screening, cholesterol testing, glaucoma testing, and cancer detection screening. Employees may be asked disability-related questions and may be given medical examinations pursuant to such voluntary wellness programs.

A wellness program is "voluntary" as long as an employer neither **requires** participation **nor penalizes employees who do not participate.**
At first blush, one might rightly assume that a wellness plan should be considered to be in compliance with the foregoing exemption for voluntary medical exams, as long as employees must voluntarily sign up for the wellness plan. However, although the EEOC has not established any formal written guidance on this point, the EEOC has challenged the validity of some employer wellness plans that were designed in that fashion.

The concern of the EEOC is not entirely clear. It seems to relate to the "penalty" language. One apparent position of the EEOC is that the wellness plan will not qualify for the exemption if an employee must pay a higher employee contribution for health plan coverage if the employee does not choose to participate in the wellness plan. In other words, the wellness plan does not qualify for the exemption because there is a "penalty" for not undergoing the medical exam.

As simplistic as it seems, it also appears that this potential issue can be alleviated by simply restructuring the wellness plan incentive so that it is a lower employee contribution amount for those who do elect to participate in the wellness plan. In other words, flip it around so that there is a discount provided for plan participation, instead of a penalty.

Please note that at this time, it is still not clear that using an "incentive" or "discount" approach will entirely eliminate the EEOC's concerns about the wellness plans. For example, it is possible that the EEOC still might take the position that the existence of a very large incentive or discount might effectively make the employee's participation in the wellness plan involuntary.

For example, assume a wellness plan provides a 50 percent discount on the employee's cost of coverage if the employee simply undergoes a screening that involves a blood draw. The large incentive would not be prohibited under the ERISA restrictions on wellness plan because it is not being tied to actual test results. In other words, the availability of the discount is not based on a health status related factor. In that case, the sheer size of the discount might make the EEOC more inclined to argue that participation in the wellness plan is not actually "voluntary".

d. The Bona Fide Benefit Plan Exception

Fortunately, that is not the end of the ADA analysis. The ADA also has an exemption that can apply with respect to the terms of a "bona fide benefit plan" that is not a "subterfuge" for evading the purposes of the ADA.[239] The Enforcement Guidance of the EEOC does not address this particular provision of the ADA.

At this juncture, there is one federal district court case directly on point – Bradley Seff v. Broward County.[240] In that case, the employer (Broward County, Florida) instituted a voluntary wellness plan that had a health risk assessment and biometric screening done via a blood draw. Under the plan, if an employee was diagnosed to have one of five specific diseases, the employee was offered the opportunity of participating in a disease management program. That program included coaching and certain medication at no cost to the employee.

In 2010, the county instituted a $40 per pay surcharge on employees who did not participate in the wellness plan. Mr. Seff sued, claiming that the plan violated the ADA's prohibition on employer-mandated medical exams. The court held in favor of the employer, finding on the facts that the wellness plan was part of the county's group health plan and was not a "subterfuge" for evasion of the ADA.

The outcome of the Broward County case is comforting. However, the court's decision is on appeal. In addition, the court's decision was based on the facts in that particular case, and there are a wide range of wellness plan designs, many of which are much more aggressive than the Broward County Plan design. Thus, other courts may reach differing conclusions based on other types of wellness plans, not to mention the views of the particular judge. Thus, it will likely be several years before there is a final resolution of this issue.[241]

PART C – GINA

I. Overview of the GINA Law

In general, the GINA law is a "civil rights" type of law. GINA generally establishes "nondiscrimination" rules that apply to group healthcare plans. Those healthcare plan rules were added ERISA.[242]

The GINA law is within the purview of the Equal Employment Opportunity Commission (the "EEOC").[243] The EEOC has issued final regulations pertaining to GINA.[244]

Certain excise tax provisions under the Internal Revenue Code ("IRC") also can apply to an employer if it or its group health plan does not comply with the GINA nondiscrimination rules and other restrictions on the collection and use of genetic information.[245]

II. GINA Restrictions

The advertised concept of the GINA law it is designed to prevent "discrimination" on the basis of genetic information. However, the actual law goes much farther than that, in some ways that may affect the design of wellness plans.

"Genetic information" is already listed as a "health status-related factor" under the ERISA nondiscrimination rules. Thus, as a general proposition, genetic information cannot be used to deny enrollment in a group healthcare plan or to charge employees higher amounts for their coverage. In addition, genetic information also may be part of an employee's or dependent's "personal health information" that is protected from disclosure under the HIPAA law. So in some respects, the GINA may overlap a bit with current ERISA and HIPAA protections.

With those thoughts aside, here is an explanation of the GINA:

A. Background Definitions

There are a number of highly technical definitions in the GINA law that may be of interest to an employer when it is considering the design of wellness plans. They are described below.

"Genetic Information" of an individual is defined as:

- the individual's genetic tests (see definition below),

- the genetic tests of family members, and

- the manifestation of a disease or disorder in family members of such individual

- any request for, or receipt of, genetic services (see definition below), or participation in clinical research which includes genetic services, by the individual or any family member of such individual.

Genetic information includes genetic information about a fetus of a pregnant individual or family member. It also includes genetic information about an embryo held by an individual or family member. It does not include information about the sex or age of any individual. The law has a very expansive definition of the term "family member".

"Genetic Services" is defined to include:

- a genetic test

- genetic counseling (including obtaining, interpreting, or assessing genetic information); or

- genetic education

"Genetic Test" generally means "an analysis of human DNA, RNA, chromosomes, proteins, or metabolites, that detects genotypes, mutations, or chromosomal changes". The EEOC Regulations define Genetic Test as follows:

(f) Genetic test --(1) In general. "Genetic test" means an analysis of human DNA, RNA, chromosomes, proteins, or metabolites that detects genotypes, mutations, or chromosomal changes.

(2) **Genetic tests include**, but are not limited to:

- A test to determine whether someone has the BRCA1 or BRCA2 variant evidencing a predisposition to breast cancer, a test to determine whether someone has a genetic variant associated with hereditary nonpolyposis colon cancer, and a test for a genetic variant for Huntington's Disease;

- Carrier screening for adults using genetic analysis to determine the risk of conditions such as cystic fibrosis, sickle cell anemia, spinal muscular atrophy, or fragile X syndrome in future offspring;

- Amniocentesis and other evaluations used to determine the presence of genetic abnormalities in a fetus during pregnancy;

- Newborn screening analysis that uses DNA, RNA, protein, or metabolite analysis to detect or indicate genotypes, mutations, or chromosomal changes, such as a test for PKU performed so that treatment can begin before a disease manifests;

- Preimplantation genetic diagnosis performed on embryos created using invitro fertilization;

- Pharmacogenetic tests that detect genotypes, mutations, or chromosomal changes that indicate how an individual will react to a drug or a particular dosage of a drug;

- DNA testing to detect genetic markers that are associated with information about ancestry; and

- DNA testing that reveals family relationships, such as paternity.

(3) The following are **examples of tests or procedures that are not genetic tests:**

- An analysis of proteins or metabolites that does not detect genotypes, mutations, or chromosomal changes;

- A medical examination that tests for the presence of a virus that is not composed of human DNA, RNA, chromosomes, proteins, or metabolites;

- A test for infectious and communicable diseases that may be transmitted through food handling;

- Complete blood counts, cholesterol tests, and liver-function tests.

(4) Alcohol and Drug Testing

- A test for the presence of alcohol or illegal drugs is not a genetic test.

- A test to determine whether an individual has a genetic predisposition for alcoholism or drug use is a genetic test.

****

B. Group Health Plan Restrictions

As general proposition, a group health plan and a plan's insurer are prohibited from doing any of the following:

- Requesting or requiring an employee or family member to undergo a Genetic Test.

- Requesting, requiring or purchasing Genetic Information for "underwriting purposes" (see below).

- Requesting, requiring or purchasing Genetic Information of an individual prior that individual enrolling in the plan.

- Under ERISA, using genetic information to adjust premiums or contribution requirements for employees and their dependents.

For this purpose, underwriting purposes include:

- rules for, or determination of, eligibility (including enrollment and continued eligibility) for benefits under the plan or coverage

- rules for, or determination of, eligibility (including enrollment and continued eligibility) for benefits under the plan or coverage

- the application of any pre-existing condition exclusion under the plan or coverage

- other activities related to the creation, renewal, or replacement of a contract of health

C. Application to Wellness Plans

Wellness plans can qualify for a limited exemption from the foregoing general rules that prohibit requesting or requiring genetic information.

Under the EEOC Regulations, to qualify for the exception, a Wellness Plan must meet the General Rules outlined below and not violate the "Restrictions on Financial Inducements" outlined below.

1. General Rules

1. The provision of genetic information by the individual is voluntary. In the eyes of the EEOC, this means that the Wellness Plan or employer cannot either (i) require the individual to provide genetic information, or (ii) penalize those who choose not to provide it.

2. The individual provides prior knowing, voluntary, and written authorization, which may include authorization in electronic format. This requirement is only met if the wellness plan uses an authorization form that:

    a. Is written so that the employee is reasonably likely to understand it;

    b. Describes the type of genetic information that will be obtained and the general purposes for which it will be used; and

    c. Describes the restrictions on disclosure of genetic information.

3. Individually identifiable genetic information is provided only to the employee (or family member if the family member is receiving genetic services) and the licensed healthcare professionals or board certified genetic counselors involved in providing such services. The information cannot be accessible to managers, supervisors, or others who make employment decisions, or to anyone else in the workplace.

4. Any individually identifiable genetic information provided under this exception is not disclosed to the employer, except in aggregate terms that do not disclose the identity of specific individuals.

2. Restrictions on Financial Inducements

As a general rule, a Wellness Plan or employer may not offer a financial inducement for individuals to provide genetic information.

a. Health Risk Assessments

Financial inducements for completion of health risk assessments that include questions about family medical history or other genetic information are permitted only if the wellness plan or employer makes it perfectly clear that the financial inducement will be made available even if the participant does not answer questions regarding genetic information.

Here is an example:

> A wellness plan offers $ 150 to employees who complete a health risk assessment with 100 questions, the last 20 of them concerning family medical history and other genetic information. The instructions for completing the health risk assessment make clear that the inducement will be provided to all employees who respond to the first 80 questions, whether or not the remaining 20 questions concerning family medical history and other genetic information are answered. This health risk assessment does not violate GINA.

b. After Genetic Information is Obtained

Once an employee has voluntarily provided genetic information (e.g., family medical history) that indicates that person is at increased risk of acquiring a health condition in the future, a Wellness Plan may offer financial inducements to encourage that person (i) to participate in disease management programs or other programs that promote healthy lifestyles, and/or (ii) to meet particular health goals as part of a health or genetic service.

However, to comply with GINA, these programs must also be offered to individuals with current health conditions and/or to individuals whose lifestyle choices put them at increased risk of developing a condition.

Here is an example:

> Employees who voluntarily disclose a family medical history of diabetes, heart disease, or high blood pressure on a health risk assessment and employees who have a current diagnosis of

one or more of these conditions are offered $ 150 to participate in a wellness program designed to encourage weight loss and a healthy lifestyle. This does not violate Title II of GINA.

The program in the previous example offers an additional inducement to individuals who achieve certain health outcomes. Participants may earn points toward "prizes" totaling $ 150 in a single year for lowering their blood pressure, glucose, and cholesterol levels, or for losing weight. This inducement would not violate Title II of GINA.

III. Penalties for Failure to Comply with GINA

Similar to the wellness plan discussion above, essentially, there are two potential sources of liabilities that can be imposed upon an employer if it were to violate the GINA: (1) employee claims under ERISA, and (2) certain civil penalties and excise taxes.

PART D - TITLE VII

Title VII of the Civil Rights Act of 1964 prohibits discrimination against any individual with respect to his or her compensation, terms, conditions, or privileges of employment, because of, among other things, the individual's race, national origin or sex.

Some legal commentators have raised the question of whether some types of wellness plan designs might run afoul of Title VII. A possible example that has been given is a situation where the wellness plan has financial rewards or incentives, or financial penalties, which may be tied to a wellness standard that persons of a particular race or national origin may find it difficult to meet.

It would seem logical that potential concern about Title VII issues should be alleviated if the plan satisfies the HIPAA rules that require the establishment of reasonable alternative standards for individuals for whom it is "unreasonably difficult" or "medically inadvisable" to meet the wellness plan's regular standard.

To date, there do not appear to be any court cases that have directly addressed this type of potential Title VII concern. Nor has the EEOC come out with any statement of position or other guidance on this issue.

Key Ideas

- Section 702 of ERISA generally prohibits discrimination in group health plan coverage based on "health status-related factors".

- Discrimination based on health status-related factors is prohibited in terms of (i) an employee's or dependent's right to be covered under the plan, and (ii) the amount that an employee is being charged for coverage under the plan.

- This article will refer to a wellness program that meets the DOL regulatory requirements as a "Qualified Wellness Program".

- The general notion is that to be Qualified Wellness Program, the program cannot simply provide the financial reward to individuals who meet specific medical criteria. The program has to be designed to reward participation in the program.

- The general rule is that a "medical examination" is a procedure or test that seeks information about an individual's physical or mental impairments or health, with all facts and circumstances considered.

- The ADA nevertheless has an exemption that permits an employer to ask an employee to undergo a medical examination, if it is done on a voluntary basis as part of an employee healthcare program.

- GINA generally establishes "nondiscrimination" rules that apply to group healthcare plans. Those healthcare plan rules were added ERISA.

- The advertised concept of the GINA law it is designed to prevent "discrimination" on the basis of genetic information

- As general proposition, a group health plan and a plan's insurer are prohibited from doing any of the following:

- Requesting or requiring an employee or family member to undergo a Genetic Test.

- Requesting, requiring or purchasing Genetic Information for "underwriting purposes" (see below).

- Requesting, requiring or purchasing Genetic Information of an individual prior that individual enrolling in the plan.

- Under ERISA, using genetic information to adjust premiums or contribution requirements for employees and their dependents

- Title VII of the Civil Rights Act of 1964 prohibits discrimination against any individual with respect to his or her compensation, terms, conditions, or privileges of employment, because of, among other things, the individual's race, national origin or sex.

Questions

1. What is meant by a qualified wellness program?
   a. A program which meets DOL requirements
   b. A program which has a good ROI
   c. A program which has existed for 3 or more years
   d. A program which is administered by a third party

2. A medical examination is allowed to be given to an employee by the ADA under what circumstance?
   a. If the exam is given anonymously
   b. If there is no penalty for taking the exam
   c. If the employer does not act on any information gained from the exam
   d. If the employee undertakes the exam voluntarily

3. What is the purpose of the GINA law?
   a. To prevent health discrimination against women
   b. To prevent genetic discrimination
   c. To ensure wellness plans fall under government guidelines
   d. None of the above

4. Which of the following is not a health status-related factor?
   a. Medical History
   b. Claims Experience
   c. Disability
   d. Alcohol Use

Value-Based Purchasing at 25: Looking Back & Looking Ahead

By James B. Couch, M.D., J.D., FACPE

1.The Rise and Prolonged Fall of Employer-Provided Health Insurance: The Triumph of Volume over Value

A. *Private Employer-Provided Health Insurance as a Substitute for Wage Increases during World War II*

Private health insurance connected to employment traces its primary origins to World War II. During that conflict, to support the war effort, wages were frozen. To keep the factories humming, some employers began to offer health insurance instead of wage increases. However, these companies were still the exception to the vast majority who did not during World War II. Nevertheless, the seed was planted.

B. *The Post-War Boom in Employer-Provided Health Insurance: The Power of Unions and the Rise of Managed Care*

Following World War II and the rise of the Baby Boom and America's rise to superpower status, many more companies began to offer health insurance tied to employment to get the Great American Jobs Machine rolling during the 1950s and 1960s Post-War Boom. Major unions, especially the United Auto Workers (UAW), began to make first dollar health insurance coverage a condition for their workers during labor negotiations. This practice continued and accelerated for the next several decades. That, and the union's strong-armed negotiations for their members wages, other benefits, right to work and retirement programs had much to do with the across the board, improvements in the condition of middle-class Americans until at least the early 1980s.

1. *The Rise of Managed Care*

Although some variants of managed care date back almost a hundred years, the forms and organizations that have survived to the present day began their rise since World War II (e.g. Kaiser, Group Health Cooperative of Puget Sound, Harvard Community Health Plans, et. al.). These not-for-profit community-based groups supported the importance of primary care and care coordination. They adhered to the principles and practices of preventive medicine, wellness and the types of health assessment and improvement programs which are now part and parcel of modern patient-centered medical homes and accountable care organizations.

Employees and their dependents working and living in those parts of the country where these early managed care pioneers are still prevalent have been generally satisfied with them. They traditionally have had the highest ratings by consumers and the best quality scores (when their providers have been evaluated based on their adherence to best evidence-based practices). Many patients and providers who continue to belong to them today are third- and fourth-generation members. They have come to expect (and even be comforted by) the group mentality and accountability measures (incumbent upon both providers and members) which are inherent to these types of not-for-profit managed care plans. In general, these are not the people who gave managed care a bad name (deserved or not) during the 1980s and 1990s.

2. *Wall Street Enters the Managed Care Health Insurance Market*
In the early 1980s major insurance companies like Aetna, Cigna (formed through the merger of Connecticut Life Insurance and INA in 1981), Prudential, MetLife and Travelers (among others) entered the managed care markets. Some of these at the time (e.g. Aetna, Cigna, Travelers, Humana, et. al.) were investor-owned companies, whose shares traded on Wall Street. Consequently, how well these investor-owned companies were able to manage their members' costs (relative to premiums—the medical loss ratio) had a growing impact on both their profitability and share price (and money available for huge executive salaries, bonuses, retirement and severance packages).

Over the next 10 to 20 years, these companies faced a growing backlash from consumer groups and patients concerning the many perceived and actual roadblocks that health plans (with the support or complicity of their employer customers) put up to restrict access to a wide range of providers, facilities and interventions (both diagnostic and therapeutic). Primary care physicians who contracted with these insurers, unlike their highly esteemed counterparts in the not-for-profit health plans, came to be reviled as dreaded "gatekeepers."

Back in the mid-1990s, for a very brief period of time, managed care was actually able to stem the near double-digit annual increases in health care costs that had become expected. However, as a result of the continuing consumer backlash against the access restrictions in most managed care plans, these investor-owned health plans began to offer less restrictive managed care variants.

One of these less restrictive variants was a preferred provider organization (PPO). As members of PPOs, patients could see physicians who had been "preferred" because they had agreed to specific levels of discounts in their fees. To try to capture the best of both worlds, insurers also marketed point of service (POS) plans permitting patients to opt in or out of various restrictions to diagnostic and therapeutic alternatives for their conditions at the point of care when being seen by POS-contracted providers.

With the growing popularity of these less restrictive variants of managed care (i.e. the non-HMO capitated plans), the relentless rise in healthcare costs resumed during the first decade of the new century. This incessant rise in costs and private insurance premiums to cover them has continued to the present day (with only the recent Great Recession temporarily halting the rate of this rise).

C. The Root Cause of Runaway Healthcare Cost Inflation: The Third-Party Payment Fee for Service Financing System

The economy is now beginning to improve. Many of the provisions of health care reform continue to be implemented (before the effects of reform can begin to work to lower costs while improving quality). Consequently, there is expected to be a significant spike in costs and premiums between now and at least the middle of this decade. Increasingly, researchers and policy analysts on all points of the political spectrum have agreed on what needs to be changed to be able to preserve the healthcare system for future generations: America needs to move from a volume-driven to a value-driven system.

The current, predominant fee for service reimbursement system continues to severely fragment the delivery and financing of care, driving up its costs (since one person's waste is another's profit); divorcing responsibility for the financial consequences of bad health and clinical decisions by patients and providers, alike; and creating the false impression that "more care is somehow better care."

II. Value-Based Purchasing as the Only Viable Alternative Reimbursement Methodology to Preserve the Private Market for Employer-Provided Health Insurance

A. *History of Value-Based Purchasing—Definitions Here and Abroad*

  1. *Definitions and Dimensions—Pioneers in the 1980s*
  The first time that a term quite similar to "value-based purchasing" appeared in print was in May 1987 (Couch, JB, Medical Care Value Purchasing: Why Now and How to Prepare for It; DRG Monitor; 1987; 4(9):1-8). This article on "medical care value purchasing" discussed how the Pennsylvania Healthcare Cost Containment Council (known then and now as the PHC4) was attempting to establish a value-driven market. In this market, large employers would begin to purchase healthcare services (through health plans, and, perhaps, even directly from hospitals and physician groups) based on their demonstrable value (i.e. their quality and cost effectiveness). Quality and cost effectiveness were measured by the clinical outcomes and financial costs of treating patients with specific conditions and undergoing particular procedures. These outcomes and costs were compared to what were expected for these parameters based on patients' pretreatment severity of illness as measured by a proprietary system, the MedisGroups system, by MedeQual Systems, in Westborough, MA. The employer-dominated PHC4 mandated that all 307 hospitals in Pennsylvania purchase, implement and use this software system for these purposes.

  In November 1987, a follow-up article on medical care value purchasing fully developed its core principles and practices concerning how it should work. For medical care value purchasing to work effectively, the following needed to be in place:

  a. Definitions of provider quality and cost-effectiveness mutually agreed upon by providers and purchasers;

b. Systems for measuring provider quality and cost-effectiveness mutually agreed upon by providers and purchasers;

c. Standards mutually agreed upon by providers and purchasers against which severity-adjusted provider quality and cost-effectiveness could be compared;

d. Criteria mutually agreed upon by providers and purchasers for selecting providers on the basis of their measured clinical performance as compared to these standards;

e. The redesign of healthcare benefit programs to create incentives to channel subscribers toward high-value providers and away from low-value providers; and

f. Methods to establish and continually adjust provider reimbursement levels on the basis of the demonstrated value of their healthcare services to subscribers. (Couch, J.B., Medical Care Value Purchasing: Update and Emerging Applications; DRG Monitor; 1987; 5(3):1-8)

"Medical care value purchasing" has now been renamed the "value-based purchasing of healthcare services" (after a brief detour when it was referred to as "pay for performance" in the late 1990s and early 2000s). However, the principles and practices for value-based purchasing in 2012 are not significantly different from what they were laid out to be for medical care value purchasing a quarter century ago in 1987.

What has changed, however, is the much greater urgency to embrace and implement these same principles and practices. There is a compelling need to switch over as quickly as possible from volume-driven to value-driven healthcare reimbursement systems, to prevent healthcare costs from severely hampering American companies' competitiveness in an increasingly price-sensitive global marketplace. Without this switch, we are also on track for the level of taxpayer-financed healthcare costs to subsume the entire federal budget by the middle of this century.

2. *Overcoming a Near-Death Experience in the American Medical Association: Early Group Promoters of Value-Based Purchasing*

(by the Michigan Blues, Automakers and Business Coalitions) Throughout the 1990s

Value-based purchasing almost suffocated in its crib in the late 1980s/ early 1990s. Couch and Nash, in an editorial in the "Annals of Internal Medicine" in November 1988, did manage to rename it in its current form as "value-based purchasing" (albeit briefly). (Couch, JB, Nash, DB, Severity of Illness Measures: Opportunities for Clinicians; Ann.Intern.Med. 1988; 109:771-3). However, that editorial (the first mention of "value- based purchasing" in a leading peer-reviewed medical journal) caught the attention of the leadership of the American Medical Association at the time.

Despite this author's ongoing efforts as a member of the AMA House of Delegates over a four-year period to promote value-based purchasing as the wave of the future, that admonition fell on deaf ears at the House of Medicine's highest policymaking body. Following this author's valedictory speech about value-based purchasing on the floor of the AMA House of Delegates at its annual meeting in Chicago in June 1991, the House promptly rejected it and reported its dismay with it in an article in "American Medical News" in August 1991, titled: "AMA Not Ready for New Quality Philosophy".

Nevertheless, during the 1990s, progressive employers and business coalitions took on the cause of value-based purchasing and ran with it. These leaders included the Greater Detroit Area Health Council (GDAHC), led by Jim Kinney, Ph.D., and Patricia Salber, M.D., while she was "on loan" to the Michigan Blues. Others included progressive members of the National Business Coalition on Health (such as Jim Mortimer at the Midwest Business Group on Health, Patricia Powers at the Pacific Business Group on Health, Dr. Frank Brocato at the Employers Purchasing Alliance and Leon Warshaw, M.D., at the New York Business Group on Health). Large employer members (such as General Electric, AT&T and the Marriott Corporation, et al.) of the National Business Group on Health (then known as the Washington Business Group on Health) also became advocates.

Despite the proliferation of value-based purchasing efforts by these and other groups during the 1990s, these leaders of the movement could only engage in pilot programs. These initiatives were still considered to be quite a bit outside the mainstream of how both providers and payers operated and made their "real money." Nevertheless, these groups helped greatly to resurrect value-based purchasing from its "near-death experience" at the hands of the AMA in the early 1990s.

3. *The Business Roundtable-Founded Leapfrog Group and Private Foundation (Robert Wood Johnson) Programs and Initiatives in the 2000s*

With the new century and millennium, value-based purchasing began to become a bit more in the mainstream, at least from the perspective of large employers. The Business Roundtable, comprised of the CEOs of Fortune 500 companies, decided that they were not going to live with double-digit increases in their employee benefit programs' health costs any longer. They came together, first in 1998, and founded the Leapfrog Group (http://www.leapfroggroup.org) in 2000. The 60 or so Fortune 500 companies signing on as charter members pledged to redesign their employee benefit programs to entice their employees, their dependants and retirees to seek out those hospitals and physicians who had committed to the following core principles and practices:

a. Staffing their intensive care units with physicians trained and certified specifically in critical care medicine;

b. Using computerized physician order entry (CPOE) systems;

c. Engaging in evidence-based hospital referral (so that patients with certain conditions would receive care utilizing particular types of procedures at those institutions with the most experience and best clinical outcomes in treating such patients with those procedures).

Over the past decade, the Leapfrog Group expanded these core founding principles and practices into a comprehensive survey of questions for hospitals to answer. These series of questions substantiating that hospitals followed these three fundamental "safety leaps" were augmented further by a series of questions testing hospitals' adherence to 17 of the

31 National Quality Forum-approved safety measures. Over 1200 hospitals respond to this annual survey currently. Being designated a Top Leapfrog Group facility is a title highly sought by leading hospitals and health systems.

The Robert Wood Johnson Foundation also spurred on value-based purchasing through two nationwide initiatives titled "Rewarding Results" and "Pursuing Perfection", both launched in 2001. Through its grantees and other partners (such as the Institute for Healthcare Improvement, or IHI), these programs lasted throughout the decade. The most active leader emerging from the "Rewarding Results" initiative was the Integrated Healthcare Association (or IHA). The IHA is a major California leadership group governed by a balanced mix of leading insurers and health plans, hospitals, health systems and physician groups. It currently oversees over 180 value-based purchasing initiatives and is the major sponsor of a national annual conference on value-based purchasing and pay for performance.

4. *National Healthcare Reform Provisions Supporting Value-Based Purchasing—2010s*

Many of the value-based purchasing initiatives from the 2000s, some from the 1990s, and even the pioneer effort by the PHC4 (despite numerous "near death" experiences of its own) in the 1980s have continued into the current decade (the 2010s). They formed the foundational support for the major initiatives in value-based purchasing included in the Patient Protection and Affordable Care Act (PPACA) signed into law by President Obama on March 23, 2010. These include not only the inpatient value-based purchasing initiative (already underway with the first value-based payments to be made starting in about a year). They also include modifications to physician payments based on demonstrable quality and cost-effectiveness starting over the next few years, and financial penalties for being a readmissions or hospital acquired conditions outlier. Also, the accountable care organization, patient-centered medical homes and bundled payment initiatives (most forms of which enjoy bipartisan support) all will ultimately require a significant expansion of value-based purchasing, as defined above, to be successful.

No matter who is President and which political party controls either or both Houses of Congress starting in January, 2013, economic necessity will continue to drive the transformation of the U.S. healthcare system in the years and decades ahead. The Inpatient Value-Based Purchasing program (and the various other initiatives converting this country from a volume- to a value-driven healthcare system) will survive. The need to convert from a volume- to a value-driven healthcare system enjoys strong bipartisan support. That the PPACA does not move us quickly enough toward that commonly supported goal is a common criticism by the Republican establishment against the PPACA.

B. What Must be Accomplished, and by Whom, for Value-Based Purchasing (VBP) to Achieve its Goals and Objectives?

1. *What are VBP's Major Goals and Objectives?*

The ultimate goal of VBP is to improve continuously the quality, safety and efficiency of healthcare services delivered to specific populations. The means by which to accomplish this goal involve developing, implementing, evaluating and continuously improving the ways by which purchasers and payers of health care assess the comparative quality, safety and efficiency (value) of care delivered by individuals and groups of providers to individuals and defined populations of patients. They then reward or penalize them (financially or professionally) based on their demonstrable results. The more detailed steps to accomplish these objectives appear in section II(A)(1), under "Definitions and Dimensions."

2. *How Does VBP Differ from Value-Based Insurance Design (VBID)?*

Technically, value-based insurance design (VBID) is a part of VBP—see step 5 under the "Definitions and Dimensions" section II(A)(1) just cited. However, it differs from VBP's major goal and the objectives by which to accomplish this goal discussed immediately above. VBP's focus is on how purchasers and payers may evaluate and incent providers to improve the quality, safety and efficiency (i.e. value) of care which they deliver to individuals and populations of patients, from the patients', payers' and purchasers' perspectives.

VBID, on the other hand, focuses on how to get patients (whether employees, dependants or retirees) to make better health care decisions. These better decisions may improve their own health through lifestyle and other behavior modifications, by purchasing and using more cost-effective medicines and other treatments as directed, by seeking care from superior value providers and by obtaining that care in the least expensive, yet safe and effective care setting. VBID involves providing the financial and non-financial incentives to patients and their families to nudge them toward these healthier choices and cost-effective alternatives to managing their conditions. VBP focuses on providing both financial and non-financial incentives to stimulate providers to continuously evaluate and improve the quality, safety and efficiency of care they deliver to individuals and populations of patients, whose medical and health care costs payers and purchasers help to finance.

However, both VBP and VBID must be in place and functioning effectively in achieving their goals and objectives as described above for either of them to be optimized. Any employer or health plan undertaking either would be well advised to undertake both, lest neither will be as effective in achieving its goals and objectives.

3. *Who are the Major Stakeholders and Beneficiaries of VBP and VBID?*

The major stakeholders involved with VBP are the 5 "Ps": purchasers, payers, providers, patients and the public. While all are stakeholders, the last two of these "Ps" (patients and the public) are the two most direct beneficiaries of both VBP and VBID. Payers (health plans and insurers) and purchasers (employers) are also clear beneficiaries of both VBP and VBID.

Through effective VBP, patients will obtain continuously improving high-quality, safe and efficient care by providers incented by payers and purchaser to accomplish this in demonstrable ways. Patients will benefit from VBID by being provided with financial and non-financial incentives to make more health-conscious decisions. They will also be incented financially and non-financially to seek care from superior value providers in less expensive, more convenient (yet safe and effective) care settings with more cost-effective means for diagnosing and treating their conditions. The public, at large, will benefit from both effective VBP and VBID because each separately, and even more together, will result in a lower health burden that has to be financed either through insurance premiums and/or taxes.

Employers and payers (health plans) too will certainly benefit from both VBP and VBID. Both these practices will produce a healthier and more productive workforce. These practices will also decrease overall employee health benefit costs. These cost reductions should exceed the offsetting costs of the programs themselves, including the reduction or elimination of copay, coinsurance and deductible amounts, to encourage more cost-effective health-conscious and clinical decision making by employees, dependants, retirees and members, respectively.

Even providers will benefit, albeit to varying degrees. In general, to the extent that VBID produces a healthier and more compliant population, those providers who are rewarded for keeping patients well (as opposed to treating them after they are sick) will do well. Also, those providers who can demonstrate the superior value of their care delivery will do well through effective VBP practices by purchasers and payers. Once the new models for financing VBP and VBID are in place and understood, they should create sustainable cycles of continuous improvement among providers seeking these rewards, thereby also continuously enhancing the benefits to payers, purchasers, patients and the public.

III. Conclusions

A. *Summary*

Value-based purchasing represents the primary vehicle on which the American healthcare system needs to hitch a ride to transform it from being volume- to value-based. The single most important root cause of the runaway costs and very uneven quality and results of our current healthcare system is the third-party-financed fee for service reimbursement system. While building toward a crisis for decades, it is now at the point where nobody, regardless of political affiliation, can deny that we have to move away from this self-destructive way of paying for healthcare services.

This still-predominant financing methodology has produced an extremely fragmented way of delivering health care with relatively little demonstrable accountability for its quality and cost-effectiveness. This is unsustainable for the future. The transformation to a value-based system must occur, regardless of what happens to the PPACA, whether at the hands of an ideologically divided U.S. Supreme Court this spring, or even a Republican president, U.S. House and Senate next year.

Value-based purchasing (VBP) is a means by which progressive employers can create an environment to stimulate the continuous improvement of the quality, safety and efficiency (i.e. value) of care. They can do this by joining with like-minded payers and providers to follow the six principles and practices of value-based purchasing first published 25 years ago. In cooperation with payers and their employees, employers need to augment these VBP practices with value-based insurance design. By rewarding the health-conscious and more cost-effective clinical decision making of their employees, dependants and retirees (whose health care costs they subsidize), employers may use VBID to enhance their VBP programs and their results, and vice versa.

B. *Recommendations*

1. *Future World 2037: Value-Based Purchasing at 50*

Despite turning 25 this year, value-based purchasing is still considered by most to be in an embryonic form as far as its demonstrable effectiveness is concerned. The vast majority of the evaluations of the beneficial effects of VBP and VBID thus far have derived from pilot studies launched in a vast sea of fee-for-service healthcare. Consequently, there still hasn't been enough of a value proposition for participants (in their "day jobs") to invest sufficiently in the tools and technologies necessary to make these pilots enough of a success to justify expanding them broadly so that they could show the magnitude of those benefits. This has created a "Catch-22" situation.

However, there is (finally) a rapidly growing bipartisan recognition that the entire country is heading toward a much worse economic future unless healthcare costs are dramatically curtailed (without hurting quality). We have reached the proverbial "tipping point" for value-based purchasing to hit the mainstream; if not this decade, then certainly by the 2020s or 2030s. How will VBP look in 2037 when it turns a mature 50 years old?

When VBP turns 50 in 2037, it should finally be firing on all six of its principles and practices cylinders. By then, the necessary electronic health information technologies will be available, tested safe and effective and fully operational. These will include completely mobile, real-time clinical diagnostic and therapeutic decision support, predictive modeling, portable (if not implanted) personal health sensors and monitors and other means to continuously evaluate and improve health and functional status. Patients will have "Pocket-Sized IBM Watson supercomputers" to suggest their most likely diagnoses based on their symptoms. These "Pocket Watsons" will also recommend if it's necessary to seek medical attention (and, if so, from whom, based on their latest "value profiles" for treating such conditions). If their "Pocket Watsons" determine that it's safe for patients to treat themselves, then patients will receive highly understandable directions on how to do that most cost effectively, whether via over-the-counter medicine, lifestyle and other behavioral modifications and/or various types of non-medical treatments.

2. *How Do We Get There from Here?*

Employers have been, are and always will be the most logical groups to champion VBP and VBID as defined and discussed in this article. It is clearly in their enlightened self-interest to continue to be the leaders of these movements. They can do this by:

a. Committing to work closely with their health plan partners and the key provider groups managing the health of their workforce to invest in the six principles and practice of VBP;

b. Working with their employees to develop and implement a wide range of VBID principles and practices to promote health- conscious behaviors, lifestyle and other behavioral modifications and the means by which they can begin to seek out like-minded value-seeking providers for their and their dependants' care; and

c. Developing a wide range of quality and outcome indicators they can use to evaluate the beneficial effects both to employees and to their bottom lines as a result of their VBP and VBID programs. These indicators could include, among other things: decreases in absenteeism and presenteeism rates, improvements in the health and functional status of their employees with chronic conditions and the overall positive effects on their bottom lines, as measured not only by decreases in health costs per employee, but also improvements to their top lines deriving from increases in productivity, satisfaction, recruitment and retention of their workforce.

Contributor Biographies

Tom Abshire

Tom Abshire is the Senior Vice President for Products, Marketing and Member Engagement at Virgin HealthMiles. The company provides programs and technologies that engage your workforce in good health.

Mark Anderson MD, DABFP

J. Mark Anderson, MD is a partner at Executive Medicine of Texas (www.emtexas.com) and co-host of the nationally syndicated Staying Young Radio Show.

Justin Bellante

Justin Bellante is CEO of BioIQ, a wellness technology company that helps individuals to improve their health and organizations to reduce healthcare costs through individual empowerment, verifiable measurement and proven technology.

Mark Bloomberg MD, MBA, FACPE

Senior physician executive, HealthNEXT,
Faculty at Harvard School of Public Health
Distinguished Fellow of the American College of Physician Executives
Mark Bloomberg, MD, MBA, FACPE, senior physician executive, HealthNEXT, and he is also a faculty member at Harvard School of Public Health and is a distinguished fellow of the American College of Physician Executives. He can be reached at bloomberghealthcare@comcast.net .

Frank Bottone, Jr. Ph.D

Dr. Bottone is a Senior Publications Medical Writer at Ingenix. Dr. Bottone received his Ph.D. degree from the interdepartmental program in Nutrition, at North Carolina State University in Raleigh, NC, where his research focused on the chemo-preventive effects of dietary and other compounds. In addition to publishing numerous scientific articles in peer-reviewed journals, Dr. Bottone, Jr. is the author of two books and over a dozen magazine and newspaper articles.

Amanda Carlson-Phillips

Amanda Carlson-Phillips is the Vice President of Nutrition and Research at Core Performance. Core Performance combines innovation, coaching, and technology to deliver unmatched, sustainable results for employees and companies alike. Amanda has designed leading-edge nutrition protocols for wellness programming at Intel and C&S.

Shawn Connors

Shawn M. Connors is president of Hope Health. He believes behavior change requires a mix of both art and science. He founded the International Health Awareness Center, Inc. (IHAC) in 1981, which focuses on the importance of communication in positively affecting workplace cultures. Recently, he worked with a talented team to develop a workable, realistic health communication system, empowering thousands of workplaces and community-based clients to communicate more effectively with new media.

Dean Cooley Ph.D
University of Tasmania

James B. Couch M.D. J.D., FACPE
Managing Partner & Chief Medical Officer
Patient Safety Solutions, LLC
Hospital Market Sector Team Leader
Informed Opinion Leadership Action Group, LLC

David M. Demers MPH

David M. Demers, is director of strategic planning at Marathon Health, a provider of onsite healthcare and population health management services.

Dee Edington, Ph.D
Founder and Chairman of Edington Associates, LLC. Founder and Professor of the University of Michigan Health Management Research Center and former Director of the Center until June 2011

Dr. Raymond J. Fabius
Dr. Fabius is a faculty member of the American College of Occupational and Environmental Medicine, the new School of Population Health at Thomas Jefferson University and the American College

of Physician Executives, where he is recognized as a Distinguished Fellow. He is the author of two books on population health issues with a third to be published in September 2010.

Kathy Gruver Ph.D
She is author of The Alternative Medicine Cabinet is a speaker, author, educator and practitioner. She currently hosts her own natural health TV show.
She can be reached at:
healingcirclemassage@hotmail.com
805-680-1984
www.thealternativemedicinecabinet.com

Amit K. Gupta M.D.
Dr. Gupta is a healthcare entrepreneur and has been at the forefront of healthcare innovation and product strategy for over 20 years. He started COHIS at Boston Medical Center, which was the first online healthcare information system in 1994, receiving an award for innovation by the Dept. of Health & Human Services in 1997. He cofounded and was Healthcare Director for Neuvis (sold to IBM), where he led HIPAA compliance solutions and pharmaceutical exchanges. He was Founder & President of CareGain, a leading consumer- directed healthcare platform provider sold to Fiserv Health in 2006.

Edward J. Haaz, M.Ed.LPC, ABMPP,
Chief Behaviorist, HealthNEXT
Senior Fellow, Jefferson School of Population Health
Edward J. Haaz, M.ED., LPC, ABMPP, Chief Behaviorist, HealthNEXT, is also the President and COO of Corporate Health Solutions, Inc. He can be reached at 215-918-1232.

Steffany Haaz Ph.D.
Health Behaviorist, HealthNEXT,
Steffany Haaz, Ph.D., Health Behaviorist, HealthNEXT, is also a Certified Movement Analyst and Registered Yoga Therapist.
She can be reached at 215-918-1232.

Don Hall DrPH,
CHES Founder/Chairman of Wellsource, Inc.
Donald R. Hall, DrPH, CHES, wellness industry expert and founder

of Wellsource, Inc., knows that being healthy is good for individuals and good for businesses.

Denise J. Holland

MHA PAHM CWP is an insurance and wellness expert and certified training professional with over 15 years of experience in the health and wellness industry. She spent ten years with Blue Cross and Blue Shield of North Carolina, creating and evaluating health improvement programs. Most recently she has been the director of Employee Healthcare for a multi-national manufacturing company in Eastern North Carolina.

Lisa M. Holland

Lisa M. Holland, RN, MBA is an accomplished wellness subject matter expert with over 18 years of healthcare care industry experience. Lisa is the President of the StayFit Plan wellness program, a division of Simplicity Health Plans.
She can be reached at 216.367.3092 or
stayfitinfo@simplicityhealthplans.com

Kaye Kennedy

Kaye Kennedy is the Director of Corporate Health and Wellness for MBS Wellness.
She can be reached at: Kaye@MBSWellness-SF.com

David Kirshenbaum

Chief Operating Officer
Chief Information Officer, HealthNEXT
Senior Fellow, Jefferson School of Population Health
David Kirshenbaum, Chief Operating Officer, HealthNEXT. is also a Senior Fellow, Jefferson School of Population Health.
He can be reached at 860-206-3253.

Dr. David Koivuranta

Time Health Management is a corporate health and wellness company operated by Dr. David Koivuranta. It is founded on over a decade's worth of experience and knowledge derived from treating employees suffering from ergonomic stress, strain and disease. It's time to manage your corporate health, visit www.timehealthmanagement.com and receive a free business evaluation. Learn why our workplace wellness solutions make sense. For more information email drdave@timehealthmanagement.com or call 416-697-7918. Ask us about our 5 minute onsite ergonomic and stress reducing system that should be found in every successful business.

Rajiv Kumar
Rajiv Kumar is the Founder and Chief Clinical Officer of Shape Up The Nation, the first wellness company to use social networking to change behavior and reduce healthcare costs.

Richard Lofredo
President and Founder
The Financial Literacy Group, LLC
Richard graduated from Ramapo College of New Jersey with a Bachelor of Arts degree. He is credentialed from the American College as a Chartered Financial Consultant. Richard is also an active member of the New Jersey Chamber of Commerce and the Society of Human Resource Managers.

Fabien Loszach
Partner at Loszach Report

Casey Mainsbridge
University of Tasmania

Tiziano Marovino PT, DPT, MPH, MSc, DAAPM
VP Health Strategy and Innovation Biogenesis Group LLC
Tiziano Marovino is a clinical research physical therapist whose investigational interests have focused on medical product research testing including evaluation for device reliability, validity, and clinical effectiveness. His epidemiology/biostatistics studies were completed at Johns-Hopkins University and his doctoral degree in rehabilitation from Creighton University.

Todd McGuire
Chief Technology Officer, incentaHEALTH
Todd McGuire is the co-founder and CTO of incentaHEALTH. He can be reached at: tmcguire@incentaHEALTH.com

William McPeck MSW, CWWPC, WLCP
William McPeck, thought leader and strategist in worksite wellness and wellbeing, holds national professional certifications in worksite wellness, work-life balance and stress management.

He can be reached at:
William Mcpeck, MSW director, williammcpeck@gmail.com

Les C. Meyer
Les C. Meyer, MBA, is a seasoned healthcare strategist and vice president of HealthNEXT, senior fellow, Jefferson School of Population Health, Thomas Jefferson University, chairman, Informed Opinion Leadership Action Group (IOLAG).
He can be reached a (303) 916-0017 or
Les.Meyer@HealthAndPerformance.info

Shirley Musich Ph.D
Dr. Musich is a Senior Researcher in the Healthcare Innovation and Information Group at Ingenix, where she is responsible for providing decision support to lead employers and other Ingenix clients through health evaluation, strategy design, intervention, measurement and evaluation processes.

Michael Nadeau
Mr. Nadeau brings more than 15 years of outsourcing and human resources experience to the company. Prior to Viverae, Mr. Nadeau worked for a Dallas-based HR outsourcing company. There, he recognized the need for accountability in the workplace to keep employees healthier and reduce corporate spending on healthcare. Previously, he was an equity partner for Acuity Technology, an IT consulting company in Dallas.

Ronald J. Ozminkowski Ph.D.
Ron Ozminkowski is an economist by training and serves as chief scientific officer at OptumHealth®. He is an internationally recognized expert in the evaluation of health and productivity management programs and has published extensively on this topic.

Scott Pedersen Ph.D
University of Tasmania

Richard Pinckney MD, MPH
Richard Pinckney, MD, is a primary care physician and an Associate Professor of medicine at the University of Vermont, College of Medicine.

Nico Pronk M.D.
Nico Pronk, Ph.D., FACSM, FAWHP
Vice President and Health Science Officer, HealthPartners
Sr. Research Investigator, HealthPartners Research Foundation
Adj. Professor of Society, Human Development, and Health,
Harvard School of Public Health
Visiting Research Professor, Environmental Health Sciences,
University of Minnesota
He can be reached at:
952-967-6729 (office)
Nico.p.pronk@healthpartners.com

Colleen Reilly
Colleen Reilly MBA/MSM is the President of Total Wellbeing. She
has 15 years of experience working on every side of the employee
wellness equation and has become a sought after expert in Performance Based Corporate Wellness.
She can be reached at:
303.696.5420
colleen.reilly@employeetotalwellbeing.com

James Reynolds M.D.,
Chief Medical Officer, HealthNEXT
James Reynolds, M.D., Chief Medical Officer, HealthNEXT
He can be reached at (303) 579-0209.

Glenn Risely
Glenn Riseley is Founder and President of Global Corporate Challenge®,
the world's largest and most exciting corporate health initiative.

Mark Roberts
Mark Roberts' professional sales background includes 30 years of
sales and marketing in the tax, insurance and investment markets.
Mark is a licensed life, health and accident insurance agent in all 50
states and DC, for insurance products and discount health plans.
He can be reached at: markr@careington.com.

Julie Sabo LAT, MT
VP Employee Health Management Biogenesis Group LLC
Julie Sabo is a licensed athletic trainer and certified massage therapist

in Michigan and actively involved in population health management with Biogenesis Group.
She can be reached at: Tiz@biogenesisgroup.com

Seth Serxner Ph.D, MPH
Seth Serxner is a social scientist by training and serves as chief health officer for OptumHealth. He is a board member for the C. Everett Koop Health Project and Care Continuum Alliance. He also serves as editorial board member of the American Journal of Health.

Barton H. Sheeler
Vice President, Business Development Nurtur Online Health Solutions
Bart Sheeler currently heads up Online Health Solutions at Nurtur. He is the visionary force behind Nurtur's partnership with the Duke University Center for Living and The PHD Network (Personal Health Development Network), an online health and wellness platform.

Jonathan Spero M.D.
CEO InHouse Physicians
Jonathan Spero, MD, is CEO of InHouse Physicians and board certified in Internal Medicine. Dr. Spero is an expert in the field of targeted employee wellness programs with measureable ROIs.
Dr. Spero can be reached at jspero@ihphysicians.com.

David M. Spratt DO, FACOEM,
Senior Clinician, Employee Assessments, HealthNEXT
David M. Spratt, DO, FACOEM, Senior Clinician - Employee Assessments, HealthNEXT, was the Corporate Medical Director at Crown Cork and Seal. He can be reached at 215-918-1232 or 215-602-2627.

Paul Squires
Paul is president of Applied Skills & Knowledge, Inc. He is an industrial psychologist with twenty-five years of experience with organizational assessment and design, process improvement, training development, performance management, assessment development and validation, computer-based training and project management. Dr. Squires has authored over a dozen journal articles and books on human capital, training and measurement topics.

100 East Hanover Avenue, Suite 402, Cedar Knolls, NJ 07927
E-Mail: paul_squires@appliedskills.com

www.AppliedSkills.com
973-631-1607 x102

Andrew Stephenson

Andrew Stephenson is the U.S. Business Development Manager for Health by Design International, an award winning workplace health and injury prevention program provider. Working in the health industry in 3 countries over the past 7 years has provided abundant educational and professional development experiences

Roy Sugarman PhD

Director, Applied Neuroscience for Athletes' Performance
Dr. Roy Sugarman is a clinical neuropsychologist and the Director of Applied Neuroscience at Athletes' Performance.

Pamela Swingley

CEO & Founder of RememberItNow!
She designed RememberItNow! to help her father, and millions of others who have chronic diseases, take control of their health.

R. Dixon Thayer

Chairman and CEO, HealthNEXT, Senior Fellow, Jefferson School of Population HealthR. Dixon Thayer, Chairman and CEO, Health-NEXT, is also a Senior Fellow, Jefferson School of Population Health, He can be reached at (610) 347-6142.

Joe Torella

HUB International – President, Northeast Region and National Practice Leader, Employee Benefits

Ryan L. Turnbull MBA

VP, Employee Benefits Wellness Practice
Poms & Associates Insurance Brokers, Inc.
Mr. Turnbull the VP, Employee Benefits Wellness Practice for Poms & Associates Insurance Brokers, Inc. is a seasoned management consultant and has successfully designed strategies and programs for many of the Fortune 100 companies that seek to lower healthcare premiums, improve employee health, and increase their bottom lines and productivity.
He may be contacted at: rturnbull@pomsassoc.com

LaurieVan Wyckhouse MS, RD, LD/N
Laurie managed and taught hospital-based Diabetes Self-Management Training classes and provided diabetes education for over 30 years.
Contact Information:
Laurie Van Wyckhouse, MS, RD, LD/N
Laurie@NutriTutor.com
888-899-1924

Gregory J. Viviani
Attorney at Squire Sanders

Lynne M. White
Lynne M. White is a Business Wellbeing Guide, Consultant, Speaker and Author with 23-years of improving business and individual performance by 20 percent to over 400 percent.
She can be reached at:
503-716-6485
lynne@lynnemwhite.com
www.lynnemwhite.com

Maureen Young
Maureen Young is a Consumer Education Advocate for ANY LAB TEST NOW, a direct access lab testing company. She is a writer, healthcare advocate, and fitness enthusiast driven to explore advances in the healthcare and medical industries

About The Corporate Health & Wellness Association

http://www.wellnessassociation.com

The Corporate Health & Wellness Association (CHWA), is the national non-profit, 501(c)(6) trade association focused on health, wellness, prevention, and disease management for employers, employees and their families. Our goal is to promote health and wellness in the workplace and to foster an atmosphere of education and engagement with health and wellness programs in the workplace. Our mission is:

- To raise awareness of the benefits to employers of implementing health and wellness programs and the importance of healthy living

- To provide source information, statistics and research data on health and wellness through research and surveys

- To serve as a central point for communication in the corporate wellness industry

- To allow the corporate wellness industry to come together to find more efficient and effective ways to implement corporate wellness programs

- To identify the most effective corporate wellness programs and best practices

- To identify innovative plans and products, to produce a monthly trade publication in educate our members through Corporate Wellness Magazine

- To host an annual meeting where all industry participants can come together and network.

About the Certified Corporate Wellness Specialist®

http://wellnessassociation.com/certified-corporate-wellness-specialist

The Certified Corporate Wellness Specialist® course and designation was created for professionals focused on practical training and knowledge to effectively manage a wellness program. The certification has been developed over the past several years through collaboration and sharing of best practices by employers across the country. It is the result of demand from employers and human resource professionals who wish to have a specialized certification program showing their expertise, knowledge; and to set themselves apart. The certification is designed for anyone looking to successfully implement a wellness program or obtain a complete, comprehensive understanding of corporate wellness. The certification program consists of eight hours of training from national leaders from across the nation in addition to a 100+ question exam. The course can be taken online or during the Annual Corporate Health and Wellness Association's annual Corporate Wellness Conference.

About *Corporate Wellness Magazine*

http://www.corporatewellnessmagazine.com

Corporate Wellness Magazine (CWM) is the only online publication dedicated to health and wellness in the workplace. Its purpose is to educate employers, employees, insurance agents, brokers, and other members about best practices and developments in corporate wellness. It is the official publication of the Corporate Health and Wellness Association.

About Corporate Wellness Conference

http://www.CorporateWellnessConference.com

The Corporate Health & Wellness Association's (CHWA) annual event, the Corporate Wellness Conference is part of one the largest conferences, the Employer Healthcare & Benefits Congress. The Corporate Wellness Conference brings together top senior level domestic and international benefits, human resource and wellness managers, insurers, TPA's, agents and brokers who are involved in implementing and maintaining corporate wellness programs. This event also focuses on Global & Multinational Corporate Wellness Programs. The annual CHWA event focuses on case studies and best practices presented by the leading employers.

Index of References

1   (Sun Life Financial , 2011)

2   (Mulvey, 2011)

3   (Benefits Canada, 2011)

4   Ryan, M. Chapman, LS. Rink, MJ. 2008. Planning worksite health promotion programs: models, methods, and design implications. American Journal of Health Promotion. July – August, Vol. 22 (6), pp. suppl 1-12, iii following p. 452.

5   Robinson, Christine. 2010. "The Keys to Turbo-Charging Intrinsic Motivation." The Journal for Quality and Participation. October, 2010, pp. 4 – 8.

6   Reiss, Steven. Who Am I? The 16 Basic Desires that Motivate Our Actions and Define Our Personalities. 2002. Berkley Trade.

7   2011 Healthcare Survey (2011), Aon Hewitt

8   Working Well: A Global Survey off Health Promotion and Workplace Wellness Strategies (2009), B. Hall

9   ibid

10 How Employers Use Incentives to Keep Employees Healthy: Perks, Programs and Peers (2009), Health2Resources

11 Working Well: A Global Survey off Health Promotion and Workplace Wellness Strategies (2009), B. Hall

12 ibid

13 When and Why Incentives (Don't) Work to Modify Behavior (2011), Gneezy et al.

14 Financial Incentives for Weight Loss: Results From a Workplace Wellness Program (2012), J. Cawley and J. Price

15 The Oxford Handbook of the Social Science of Obesity (2011), Jones-Corneille et al

16 J. Cawley and J. Price, op. cit.

17 Financial Incentive–Based Approaches for Weight Loss - A Randomized Trial (2008), Volpp et al

18 Multi-business Study into the Effect of Low Impact Physical Activity on Employee Health and Wellbeing (2011), D. Batman and S. Cartwright

19 Deloitte, U.S. Survey of Healthcare Consumers, 2011

20 Chicago Tribune, October 3, 2011

21

22 Hendricks, R., A Model for National Healthcare: The History of Kaiser Permanente (New Brunswick, NJ: Rutgers University Press, 1993), 13-17

23 Abrams, H.K. Some hidden history of occupational medicine. Environmental. Research, 59: 23–25, 2002.

24 Realizing the Potential of Onsite Health Centers, Watson Wyatt, 2008

25 Rousmaniere, P., "An emerging vision for employee health: the business of offering onsite corporate medical clinics as the new hub for healthcare cost containment", Risk & Insurance, April 15, 2009.

26 Pelletier, KR. "A review and analysis of the clinical and cost-effectiveness studies of comprehensive health promotion and disease management programs at the worksite: update VI 2000-2004". Journal of Occupational and Environmental Medicine. 2005; 47:1051-1058.

27 Chapman, L., Meta-evaluation of worksite health promotion economic return studies: 2005 update. American Journal of Health Promotion, 2005; 19:1-11.

28 Euclid, The Elements, Translated with an introduction and commentary by Sir Thomas L. Heath, Dover, (3 vols.), 2nd edition, 1956

29 Actuarial Issues Related to Pricing Healthcare Under Healthcare Reform, American Academy of Actuaries, Monograph Number 10, July 1994, p. 21.

30 Key Milestones in the CMS Program, Centers for Medicare and Medicaid Services

31 Peter R. Kongstvedt, The Managed Healthcare Handbook, Fourth Edition, Aspen Publishers, Inc., 2001

32 Pena-Dolhun, E., et.al. Unlocking specialist's attitudes toward primary care gatekeepers-original research, Journal of Family Practice, December, 2001.

33 President Clinton signed the Mental Health Parity Act of 1996 (P.L. 104-204) into law on September 26, 1997

34 US Healthcare Costs, Kaiser Family Foundation, http://www.kaiseredu.org/topics_im.asp?imID=1&parentID=61&id=358

35 Mehrota, A., et.al., Comparing Costs and Quality of Care at Retail Clinics With That of Other Medical Settings for 3 Common Illnesses, Annals of Internal Medicine, 2009; 151:321-328.

36 The Power of Utilizing Incentive Campaigns: Integrating Health & Wellness Into Your Core Business Strategy, Wellness Council of America, 2008.

37 Department of Labor, Field Assistance Bulletin, No. 2007-04.

38 Taitel, M, et al, "Incentives and Other Factors Associated With Employee Participation in Health Risk Assessments",

Journal of Occupational and Environmental Medicine, Volume 50, No. 8, August, 2008, pp. 863-872.

39   See http://www.healthcarebluebook.com/ and http://www.healthgrades.com/

40   See http://www.marathon-health.com

41   Lombardo, M, Eichinger, R., For Your Improvement: A Guide for Development and Coaching, 4th Edition, Lominger International, Korrn/Ferry Publishing, 2006.

42   Prochaska, J, Velicier, W., The Transtheoretical model of behavior change, American Journal of Health Promotion, Sept.-Oct., Vol. 12, pp. 38-48, 1997.

43   Miller, W, Rollnick, S., Motivational Interviewing: Preparing People for Change, The Guilford Press, 2002.

44   See http://www.lominger.com

45   Miller, W. and Rollnick, S., Motivational Interviewing: Preparing People for Change, Guilford Press, 2002.

46   Tang, P., Lansky, D., The missing link: bridging the patient-provider health information gap, Health Affairs, 24, No. 5, 2005.

47   Whittemore, R., et. al., A nurse-coaching intervention for women with type 2 diabetes, Diabetes Education, Vol. 5, Sept-Oct., 2204, pp. 795-804.

48   Rollnick, S., Miller, W., Motivational Interviewing in Healthcare: Helping Patients Change Behavior, Kindle Publishers, 2007.

49   HEDIS 2010: Technical Specifications for Physician Measurement, October, 2009, NCQA at www.ncqa.org.

50   The Seventh Report of the Joint National Committee on Prevention, Detection, Evaluation and Treatment of High Blood Pressure, National Heart Lung Blood Institute, 2004

51   Third Report of the Expert Panel on Detection, Evaluation, and Treatment of High Cholesterol in Adults, National Heart Lung Blood Institute, 2004

52   The Effect of Intensive Treatment of Diabetes on the Development and Progression of Long-Term Complications in Insulin Dependent Diabetes Mellitus, New England Journal of Medicine, Volume 329: 977-986, September, 1993.

53   The Relationship between Modifiable Health Risks and Healthcare Expenditures: An Analysis of the Multi-Employer HERO Health Risks and Cost Database. Goetzel, R., et al, American Journal of Health Promotion, Vol. 15, Number 1, Sept./Oct. 2000, pp. 45 - 52

54   National Ambulatory Medical Care Survey, Advance Data from Vital and Health Statistics, Number 374, June, 2006.

55   Healthcare Management Guidelines, Volume 1: Inpatient and Surgical Care, Milliman and Robertson, Inc., November, 1996.

56   AHA Hospital Statistics, 2008 Edition.

57   Healthcare Price, Cost and Utilization Benchmarks, Volume V, HCPro, Inc., 2008.

58   McCaig, L., et.al., National Hospital Ambulatory Medical Care Survey, Advance Data from Vital and Health Statistics, Number 372, June 23, 2006.

59   Kaiser Family Foundation, Hospital Emergency Room visits per 1,000 Population, See http://www.statehealthfacts. org .

60   The Value of Biometric Screening in an Employer Population, Healthways Center for Health Research, 2008.

61   Frazee, S., et.al., "Leveraging the Trusted Clinician: Documenting Disease Management Program Enrollment", Disease Management, Volume 10, No. 1, November, 2007, pp. 16-29

62   Ibid

63   Ibid

64   Whitaker, J., Reversing Hypertension, Warner Books, 2001.

65   Chapman, L., Proof Positive: An Analysis of the Cost-Effectiveness of Worksite Wellness, Sixth Edition, 2007.

66   Naydeck, B., et.al., The Impact of the Highmark Employee Wellness Programs on 4-Year Healthcare Costs, JOEM, Volume 50, No. 2, February, 2008, pp. 146-155.

67   Pelletier, K., A Review and Analysis of the Clinical and Cost-Effectiveness Studies of Comprehensive Health Promotion and Disease Prevention Programs at the Worksite, American Journal of Health Promotion, 2001; Volume 16, pp. 107-116.

68   http://www.dol.gov/compliance/laws/comp-erisa.htm

69   Ibid.

70   Chapman, Larry. Proof Positive: An Analysis of the Cost Effectiveness of Worksite Wellness. Chapman Institute, 2009

71   GfK Custom Research NA, New York, NY. Third Annual Wellness in the Workplace Study, Sept, 2011.

72   Goetzel RZ, Long SR, Ozminkowski RJ, Hawkins K, Wang S, Lynch W. Health, Absence, Disability, and Presenteeism Cost Estimates of Certain Physical and Mental Health Conditions Affecting US Employers. Journal of Occupational and Environmental Medicine, 2004;46,4:398-412

73 Agency for Healthcare Research and Quality: The Guide to Clinical Preventive Services. Recommendations of the US Preventive Services Task Force, 2006. © 2012 OptumHealth

74 Linnan L, Bowling M, Childress J, et al. Results of the 2004 National Worksite Health Promotion Survey. American Journal of Public Health. 2008;98(8):1503-1509.

75 Chapman L. Meta-evaluation of worksite health promotion economic return studies: 2005 update. American Journal of Health Promotion. 2005;19(6):1-11.

76 Goetzel RZ, Ozminkowski RJ, Villagra V, Duffy J. Return on investment in disease management: A review. Healthcare Financing Review. 2005;26(4):1-19.

77 Baicker K, Cutler D, Song Z. Workplace wellness programs can generate savings. Health Affairs. 2010;29(2):1-8.

78 Musich S, McDonald TM, Hirschland D, Edington DW. Excess healthcare costs associated with excess health risks in diseased and non-diseased health risk appraisal participants. Disease Management and Health Outcomes. 2002;10:251-258.

79 Edington DW. Emergin research: a view from one research center. American Journal of Health Promotion. 2001;15:341-349.

80 Musich SA, Adams L, Edington DW. Effectiveness of health promotion programs in moderating medical costs in the USA. Health Promotion Internatinal. 2000;15:5-15.

81 McGlynn E, The Quality of Care Delivered to Adults in the United States, NewEngJMed 348:26, June 26, 2003; pp.2635-45;

82 Berry L, Mirabito A, Baun W, What's the Hard Return on Employee Wellness Programs? Harvard Business Review, Dec. 2010;

83 Baicker K, Cutler D, Song Z, Workplace wellness programs can generate savings; Health Affairs 2010;29:304-311

84 Aldana SG. Financial impact of health promotion programs: a comprehensive review of the literature. Am J Health Promotion 2001; 15:296-320

85 Presenteeism: At Work --- But Out of It, Harvard Business Review, October 2004

86 Lee T, Care Redesign – A Path Forward for Providers, NewEngJMed 367:5, August 2, 2012, pp. 466-72

87 Loeppke, R., et al., Health and Productivity as a Business Strategy: A Multi-Employer Study, JOEM.2009; 51(4):411-428

88 http://www.civhc.org/CIVHC-Initiatives/Data-and-Transparency/Metrics-and-Dashboards.aspx/ (accessed August 23, 2012)

89 Parry T, Sherman B, A Pragmatic Approach for Employers to Improve Measurement in Workforce Health and Productivity, Population Health Management, Volume 15, Number 2, 2012;

90 . "GLOBEX UPDATE HEALTH & BENEFITS." Globex. Globex International, January 2011. Web. 4 Sep 2012. <http://www.globexintl.com/public/wp-content/uploads/news_123.pdf>.

91 ""The MetLife Study of Global Health & Wellness: A Look at How Multinational Companies Are Responding to the Need for a Healthier Workforce." Metlife.com. MetLife Multinational Solutions in Conjunction with the MetLife Mature Market Institute, 2010. Web. 10 Sept. 2012. <https://www.metlife.com/assets/institutional/products/benefits-products/MetLifeGlobalHealthWellness.pdf>.

92 ibid

93 "Multinational Workforce Health: Building a Sustainable Global Strategy." Towerswatson.com. Towers Watson, 2011. Web. 10 Sept. 2012. <http://www.towerswatson.com/assets/pdf/4572/Towers-Watson-Multinational-Workforce-Health.pdf>.

94 ibid

95 ibid

96 Ibid

97 Purcell, Kristen; Entner, Roger; and Henderson, Nichole. The Rise of Apps Culture. The Pew Internet and American Life Project. September 14, 2010.

http://pewinternet.org/Reports/2010/The-Rise-of-Apps-Culture/Overview.aspx

98 Raine, Lee. The Rise of the e-Patient. The Pew Internet and American Life Project. October 7, 2009.

http://www.pewinternet.org/Presentations/2009/40-The-rise-of-the-e-patient.aspx

99 ibid

100 ibid

101 ibid

102 Fox, Susannah; and Purcell, Kristen. Chronic Disease and the Internet. The Pew Internet and American Life Project. September March 24, 2010. http://pewinternet.org/Reports/2010/Chronic-Disease.aspx

103 Purcell, Kristen. The Power of Mobile. The Pew Internet and American Life Project. September September 13, 2010.

104 Smith, Aaron. Mobile Access 2010. The Pew Internet and American Life Project. September July 7, 2010. http://www.pewinternet.org/Reports/2010/Mobile-Access-2010.aspx

105 Purcell, Kristen; Entner, Roger; and Henderson, Nichole. The Rise of Apps Culture. The Pew Internet and American Life Project. September 14, 2010. http://pewinternet.org/Reports/2010/The-Rise-of-Apps-Culture/Overview.aspx

106 ibid

107 Ibid

108 Fox, Susannah; and Purcell, Kristen. Chronic Disease and the Internet.

109 ibid

110 U.S. Dept. of Commerce, Census Bureau and Intl. Trade Admin.; Advocacy-funded research by Kathryn Kobe, 2007

111 CHI Research, 2003 (www.sba.gov/advo/research/rs225.pdf); U.S. Dept. of Labor, Bureau of Labor Statistics.

112 . "Striving for a Healthier America Through Availability and Uptake of Workplace Wellness Programs in the Small Business Community." . The Trust for America's Health & The Small Business Majority, 03/13/2012. Web. 31 Aug 2012. <http://www.smallbusinessmajority.org/_docs/resources/031312_SBM_TFAH_Workplace_Wellness.pdf>.

113 ibid

114 "Striving for a Healthier America Through Availability and Uptake of Workplace Wellness Programs in the Small Business Community."

115 Kaiser Family Foundation, Survey of Employer Health Benefits.

116 Reuteman, Rob. "Making Wellness Work for Small Business." CNBC.com. N.p., 14 Nov. 2011. Web. 31 Aug. 2012. <http://www.cnbc.com/id/45261950/Making_Wellness_Work_for_Small_Business>

117 "Striving for a Healthier America Through Availability and Uptake of Workplace Wellness Programs in the Small Business Community."

118 . "The National Healthy Worksite Program." Centers for Disease Control. National Center for Chronic Disease Prevention and Health Promotion: Division for Population Health , 04/26/2012. Web. 31 Aug 2012. <http://www.cdc.gov/nationalhealthyworksite/docs/NHWP_Overview_508_5.3.12.pdf>.

119 Rains, Julie . "Designing a Small-Business Wellness Program." Open Forum. N.p., 01/18/2012. Web. 31 Aug 2012. <http://www.openforum.com/articles/designing-a-small-business-wellness-program>.

120 http://www.ahrq.gov/research/ria19/expendria.pdf

121 McKay, Betsy. (2009) Cost of Treating Obesity Soars. The Wall Street Journal .Retrieved from http://online.wsj.com/article/SB10001424052970204563304574314794089897258.html

122 G. L. (2009). The ROI on Weight Loss at Work. Harvard Business Review. Retrieved from http://hbr.org/2009/12/the-roi-on-weight-loss-at-work/ar/1

123 Rasmussen Center for Cardiovascular Disease Prevention. (2009). Cost of Cardiovascular Disease. Retrieved from http://www.cardiovasculardiseaseprevention.org/cost.asp

124 Heart Disease and Stroke Prevention: Addressing the Nation's Leading Killers: At A Glance 2011. (2010). Retrieved March 12, 2012, from http://www.cdc.gov/chronicdisease/resources/publications/AAG/dhdsp.htm

125 Zook, Tony. (2006, April 24) The ROI of Wellness. Forbes. Retrieved from http://www.forbes.com/2006/04/21/wellness-programs-gold-standards-cx_tz_0424wellness.html

126 Hewitt, J.A., Whyte, G.P., Moreton, M., van Someren, K.A., Levine, T.S., 2008. The effects of a graduated aerobic exercise programme on cardiovascular disease risk factors in the NHS workplace: a randomised controlled trial. J Occup Med Toxicol. 28, 3:7.

127 McMurray, R.G., Ainsworth, B.E., Harrell, J.S., Griggs, T.R., Williams, O.D. 1998. Is physical activity or aerobic power more influential on reducing cardiovascular disease risk factors? Med Sci Sports Exerc. 30, 1521-1529.

128 Adult Obesity. (2012). Retrieved March 12, 2012, from http://www.cdc.gov/obesity/data/adult.html

129 Chronic Diseases and Health Promotion. (2010). Retrieved March 12, 2012. http://www.cdc.gov/chronicdisease/overview/index.htm

130 Heidenerich, P.A., Trogdon, J.G., Khavjou, O.A., Butler, J., Dracup, K., Ezekowitz, M.D., ... Woo, Y. J. (2011). Statement From the American Heart Association: Forecasting the Future of Cardiovascular Disease in the United States. Journal Of The American Heart Association, 935. Retrieved from http://circ.ahajournals.org/content/123/8/933.full.pdf

131 L.W.Green, M.W.Kreuter. Health program planning: an educational and ecological approach (4th ed.).: McGraw-Hill, New York; 2005.

132 Hancock T. The Ottawa Charter at 25. Canadian journal of public health. Revue canadienne de sante publique. Nov-Dec 2011;102(6):404-406.

133 WHO. Health Equity Through Intersectoral Action: An Analysis of 18 Country Case Studies. World Health Organization, Geneva: Her Majesty the Queen in Right of Canada, represented by the Minister of Health; 2008.

134 Christensen CM, Baumann H, Ruggles R, Sadtler TM. Disruptive innovation for social change. Harv Bus Rev. Dec 2006;84(12):94-101, 163.

135 Jayasinghe S. Conceptualising population health: from mechanistic thinking to complexity science. Emerging themes in epidemiology. 2011;8(1):2.

136 Van Beurden EK, Kia AM, Zask A, Dietrich U, Rose L. Making sense in a complex landscape: how the Cynefin

Framework from Complex Adaptive Systems Theory can inform health promotion practice. Health Promot Int. Nov 29 2011.

137 Ellis B, Herbert SI. Complex adaptive systems (CAS): an overview of key elements, characteristics and application to management theory. Informatics in primary care. 2011;19(1):33-37.

138 Paina L, Peters DH. Understanding pathways for scaling up health services through the lens of complex adaptive systems. Health policy and planning. Aug 5 2011.

139 Ellis B. Complexity in practice: understanding primary care as a complex adaptive system. Informatics in primary care. 2010;18(2):135-140.

140 Sturmberg JP, O'Halloran DM, Martin CM. People at the centre of complex adaptive health systems reform. Med J Aust. Oct 18 2010;193(8):474-478.

141 Sturmberg JP, Martin CM. The dynamics of healthcare reform--learning from a complex adaptive systems theoretical perspective. Nonlinear dynamics, psychology, and life sciences. Oct 2010;14(4):525-540.

142 Jordon M, Lanham HJ, Anderson RA, McDaniel RR, Jr. Implications of complex adaptive systems theory for interpreting research about healthcare organizations. J Eval Clin Pract. Feb 2010;16(1):228-231.

143 Green LA. Prescription for health: round 1 initial results. Ann Fam Med. Jul-Aug 2005;3 Suppl 2:S2-3.

144 Flocke SA, Kelly R, Highland J. Initiation of health behavior discussions during primary care outpatient visits. Patient Educ Couns. May 2009;75(2):214-219.

145 Simons VA, Flynn SP, Flocke SA. Practical behavior change counseling in primary care. Prim Care. Sep 2007;34(3):611-622, vii.

146 Flocke SA, Crabtree BF, Stange KC. Clinician reflections on promotion of healthy behaviors in primary care practice. Health Policy. Dec 2007;84(2-3):277-283.

147 Green LA, Cifuentes M, Glasgow RE, Stange KC. Redesigning primary care practice to incorporate health behavior change: prescription for health round-2 results. Am J Prev Med. 11/2008 2008;35(5 Suppl):S347-S349.

148 Dodoo MS, Krist AH, Cifuentes M, Green LA. Start-up and incremental practice expenses for behavior change interventions in primary care. Am.J.Prev Med. 11/2008 2008;35(5 Suppl):S423-S430.

149 Sturmberg JP. EBM: a narrow and obsessive methodology that fails to meet the knowledge needs of a complex adaptive clinical world: a commentary on Djulbegovic, B., Guyatt, G. H. & Ashcroft, R. E. (2009) Cancer Control, 16, 158-168. J Eval Clin Pract. Dec 2009;15(6):917-923.

150 Sturmberg JP, Martin CM. Knowing--in medicine. J Eval Clin Pract. Oct 2008;14(5):767-770.

151 Botelho RJ. Family & Peer Health Coaching: Changing Ourselves, Our Families, Organizations, Communities & Cultures. A leadership and social network guide to create professional & social movements. Rochester, NY: MHH Publications; 2012.

152 WHO. Preamble to the Constitution of the World Health Organization as adopted by the International Health Conference, New York, 19 June - 22 July 1946; signed on 22 July 1946 by the representatives of 61 States (Official Records of the World Health Organization, no. 2, p. 100) 1948, 7 April

153 World Health Organization, Commision on the Social Determinants of Health.. Closing the gap in a generation: Health equity through action on the social determinants of health. 2009 2009.

154 Huber M, Knottnerus JA, Green L, et al. How should we define health? BMJ. 2011;343:d4163.

155 Saracci R. The World Health Organisation needs to reconsider its definition of health. BMJ. May 10 1997;314(7091):1409-1410.

156 Nations U. United National Universal Declaration of Human Rights: New York,NY; 1948.

157 Peterson CS, M. Character Strengths and Virtues: A Handbook and Classification: Oxford University Press; 2004.

158 Deci EL, Eghrari H, Patrick BC, Leone DR. Facilitating internalization: the self-determination theory perspective. J.Pers. 3/1994 1994;62(1):119-142.

159 The Road to Resilience. http://www.apa.org/helpcenter/road-resilience.aspx.

160 Antonovsky A. Unraveling the Mystery of Health: How People Manage Stress and Stay Well. San Francisco: Jossey-Bass Publishers; 1987.

161 Antonovsky A. Health, Stress, and Coping: New Perspectives on Mental and Physical Well-Being. San Fancisco, CA: Jossey-Bass Publishers; 1979.

162 Niemiec CP, Ryan RM, Patrick H, Deci EL, Williams GC. The energization of health-behavior change: Examining the associations among autonomous self-regulation, subjective vitality, depressive symptoms, and tobacco abstinence. The Journal of Positive Psychology. 2010/03/01 2010;5(2):122-138.

163 Ryan RM, Frederick C. On Energy, Personality, and Health: Subjective Vitality as a Dynamic Reflection of Well-Being. Journal of Personality. 1997;65(3):529-565.

164 Ryan RM, Deci EL. A Self-Determination Theory Approach to Psychotherapy: The Motivational Basis for Effective Change. Canadian Psychology. 2008 2008;49(3):186-193.

165 Greene J, Hibbard JH. Why Does Patient Activation Matter? An Examination of the Relationships Between Patient Activation and Health-Related Outcomes. J Gen Intern Med. Nov 30 2011.

166 Hibbard JH, Mahoney E. Toward a theory of patient and consumer activation. Patient Educ Couns. Mar 2010;78(3):377-381.

584

167 Bandura A. Health promotion by social cognitive means. Health Educ Behav. Apr 2004;31(2):143-164.

168 Bandura A. Self-Efficacy - Toward A Unifying Theory of Behavioral Change. Psychological Review. 1977 1977;84(2):191-215.

169 Salovey P, Rothman, A.J., Detweiler, J.B., Steward W.T. Emotional States and Physical Health. American Psychologist. January 2000;55(1):110-121.

170 Cameron LD, Leventhal, H. The self-regulation of health and illness behaviour. New York, NY: Routledge; 2003.

171 Vohs KD, Baumeiste, R.F. . Handbook of Self-Regulation, Second Edition: Research, Theory, and Applications. England: Guilford; 2010.

172 de Ridder D TD, Bertha, J., de Wit, F. Self-regulation in Health Behavior. Chichester, England: John Wiley & Sons, LTD; 2006.

173 Hofmann W, Baumeister RF, Forster G, Vohs KD. Everyday temptations: An experience sampling study of desire, conflict, and self-control. J Pers Soc Psychol. Dec 12 2011.

174 Hofmann W, Friese M, Strack F. Impulse and Self-Control From a Dual-Systems Perspective. Perspectives on Psychological Science. March 1, 2009 2009;4(2):162-176.

175 de Ridder DTD, Lensvelt-Mulders G, Finkenauer C, Stok FM, Baumeister RF. Taking Stock of Self-Control: A Meta-Analysis of How Trait Self-Control Relates to a Wide Range of Behaviors. Personality and Social Psychology Review. August 30, 2011 2011.

176 Johnson BA. Managing Polarities: Identifying and Managing Unsolvable Problems. Amherst. Massachusetts: HRD Press. Inc; 1992.

177 Mogford E, Gould L, Devoght A. Teaching critical health literacy in the US as a means to action on the social determinants of health. Health Promot Int. Mar 2011;26(1):4-13.

178 Lindstrom B, Eriksson M. From health education to healthy learning: implementing salutogenesis in educational science. Scandinavian journal of public health. Mar 2011;39(6 Suppl):85-92.

179 Lorig KR, Ritter PL, Dost A, Plant K, Laurent DD, McNeil I. The Expert Patients Programme online, a 1-year study of an Internet-based self-management programme for people with long-term conditions. Chronic.Illn. 12/2008 2008;4(4):247-256.

180 Holman H, Lorig K. Patient self-management: a key to effectiveness and efficiency in care of chronic disease. Public Health Rep. 5/2004 2004;119(3):239-243.

181 Reed RL, Battersby M, Osborne RH, Bond MJ, Howard SL, Roeger L. Protocol for a randomised controlled trial of chronic disease self-management support for older Australians with multiple chronic diseases. Contemporary clinical trials. Nov 2011;32(6):946-952.

182 Fixsen D, Naoom S, Blase K, Friedman R, Wallace F. Implementation Research: A Synthesis of the Literature. 2005 2005.

183 Bogart LM, Uyeda K. Community-based participatory research: Partnering with communities for effective and sustainable behavioral health interventions. Health Psychol. 7/2009 2009;28(4):391-393.

184 Langley GJ, Nolan KM, Nolan TW, Norman CL, Provost LP. The improvement guide: A practical approach to enhancing organizational performance. San Francisco, CA: Jossey-Bass; 1996.

185 Macaulay AC, Jagosh J, Seller R, et al. Assessing the benefits of participatory research: a rationale for a realist review. Global health promotion. Jun 2011;18(2):45-48.

186 Jagosh J, Pluye P, Macaulay AC, et al. Assessing the outcomes of participatory research: protocol for identifying, selecting, appraising and synthesizing the literature for realist review. Implementation science: IS. 2011;6:24.

187 Wong G, Greenhalgh T, Westhorp G, Pawson R. Realist methods in medical education research: what are they and what can they contribute? Med Educ. Jan 2012;46(1):89-96.

188 Greenhalgh T, Wong G, Westhorp G, Pawson R. Protocol--realist and meta-narrative evidence synthesis: evolving standards (RAMESES). BMC medical research methodology. 2011;11:115.

189 Pawson R, Greenhalgh T, Harvey G, Walshe K. Realist review--a new method of systematic review designed for complex policy interventions. Journal of health services research & policy. Jul 2005;10 Suppl 1:21-34.

190 Liberato SC, Brimblecombe J, Ritchie J, Ferguson M, Coveney J. Measuring capacity building in communities: a review of the literature. BMC public health. 2011;11:850.

191 Downey LH, Anyaegbunam C, Scutchfield FD. Dialogue to deliberation: expanding the empowerment education model. Am.J.Health Behav. 1/2009 2009;33(1):26-36.

192 Horowitz CR, Robinson M, Seifer S. Community-based participatory research from the margin to the mainstream: are researchers prepared? Circulation. 5/19/2009 2009;119(19):2633-2642.

193 Wells K, Jones L. "Research" in community-partnered, participatory research. JAMA. 7/15/2009 2009;302(3):320-321.

194 Goh YY, Bogart LM, Sipple-Asher BK, et al. Using community-based participatory research to identify potential interventions to overcome barriers to adolescents' healthy eating and physical activity. J.Behav.Med. 6/21/2009 2009.

195 Kennedy C, Vogel A, Goldberg-Freeman C, Kass N, Farfel M. Faculty perspectives on community-based research: "I see this still as a journey". J.Empir.Res.Hum.Res.Ethics. 6/2009 2009;4(2):3-16.

196 Jernigan VB. Community-Based Participatory Research With Native American Communities: The Chronic

Disease Self-Management Program. Health Promot.Pract. 4/17/2009 2009.

197 Nastasi BK, Hitchcock J. Challenges of evaluating multilevel interventions. Am.J.Community Psychol. 6/2009 2009;43(3-4):360-376.

198 Hebert JR, Brandt HM, Armstead CA, Adams SA, Steck SE. Interdisciplinary, translational, and community-based participatory research: finding a common language to improve cancer research. Cancer Epidemiol.Biomarkers Prev. 4/2009 2009;18(4):1213-1217.

199 Bass BM, Riggio RE. Transformational Leadership: Psych Press; 2005.

200 Devore S, Champion RW. Driving population health through accountable care organizations. Health Aff (Millwood). Jan 2011;30(1):41-50.

201 Goldsmith J. Accountable care organizations: the case for flexible partnerships between health plans and providers. Health Aff (Millwood). Jan 2011;30(1):32-40.

202 Lieberman SM, Bertko JM. Building regulatory and operational flexibility into accountable care organizations and 'shared savings'. Health Aff (Millwood). Jan 2011;30(1):23-31.

203 Shortell SM, Casalino LP, Fisher ES. How the center for medicare and medicaid innovation should test accountable care organizations. Health Aff (Millwood). Jul 2010;29(7):1293-1298.

204 Center RG. The patient centered medical home: history, seven core features, evidence and transformational change. 2007; http://www.graham-center.org/online/etc/medialib/graham/documents/publications/monographs-books/2007/rgcmo-medical-home.Par.0001.File.tmp/rgcmo-medical-home.pdf.

205 Berwick DM, Nolan TW, Whittington J. The triple aim: care, health, and cost. Health Aff (Millwood). May-Jun 2008;27(3):759-769.

206 Marcus Thygeson N, Solberg LI, Asche SE, Fontaine P, Gregory Pawlson L, Scholle SH. Using Fuzzy Set Qualitative Comparative Analysis (fs/QCA) to Explore the Relationship between Medical "Homeness" and Quality. Health Serv Res. Feb 2012;47(1 Pt 1):22-45.

207 Scholle SH, Saunders RC, Tirodkar MA, Torda P, Pawlson LG. Patient-centered medical homes in the United States. The Journal of ambulatory care management. Jan-Mar 2011;34(1):20-32.

208 Downs TJ, Larson HJ. Achieving Millennium Development Goals for health: building understanding, trust and capacity to respond. Health Policy. 10/2007 2007;83(2-3):144-161.

209 Gabbay RA, Bailit MH, Mauger DT, Wagner EH, Siminerio L. Multipayer patient-centered medical home implementation guided by the chronic care model. Joint Commission journal on quality and patient safety / Joint Commission Resources. Jun 2011;37(6):265-273.

210 Goroff M, Reich MR. Partnerships to provide care and medicine for chronic diseases: a model for emerging markets. Health Aff (Millwood). Dec 2010;29(12):2206-2213.

211 Oprea L, Braunack-Mayer A, Rogers WA, Stocks N. An ethical justification for the Chronic Care Model (CCM). Health expectations: an international journal of public participation in healthcare and health policy. Mar 2010;13(1):55-64.

212 Gofin J, Foz G. Training and application of community-oriented primary care (COPC) through family medicine in Catalonia, Spain. Fam Med. Mar 2008;40(3):196-202.

213 Art B, De Roo L, De Maeseneer J. Towards unity for health utilising community-oriented primary care in education and practice. Educ Health (Abingdon). Aug 2007;20(2):74.

214 Iliffe S, Lenihan P. Integrating primary care and public health: learning from the community-oriented primary care model. International journal of health services: planning, administration, evaluation. 2003;33(1):85-98.

215 Christensen CM, Grossman JH, Hwang J. The Innovator's Prescription: A Disruptive Solution for Healthcare: McGrall-Hill, New York; 2009.

216 Note: HealthNEXT RFP has a parenthetical reference to "see appendix for studies"

217 Journal of Occupational Environmental Medicine (50:633–641), "Association between nine quality components and superior worksite health management program results," Terry PE, Seaverson EL, Grossmeier J, Anderson DR., 2008

218 ibid

219 Health Affairs (29:304–311), "Workplace wellness programs can generate savings," Baicker K, Cutler D, Song Z, 2010

220 American College of Occupational and Environmental Medicine (Vol. 54, No. 4), "A Review of the Knowledge Base on Healthy Worksite Culture," Aldana, Ph.D., Steven G., et al, April 2012

221 ibid

222 ibid

223 ACSM's Health & Fitness Journal (Vol. 16, No. 3), "An Optimal Lifestyle Metric: Four Simple Behaviors That Affect Health, Cost, and Productivity," Pronk, Nico, Ph.D.

224 Globally, Americans save less than citizens of many countries such as Japan (14 percent), Singapore (10 percent), Sweden, and Denmark but more than citizens of Greece, Italy, Spain and other European countries (source: BEA).

225 Prochaska's Transtheoretical model of behavior change is compatible with self-management skills. His theory argues that there are five phases of behavior change. They are (1) Pre-contemplation phase in which there is no intention to change behavior, (2) Contemplation phase in which there is an awareness of a problem and serious

time spent thinking about addressing it, (3) Preparation phase in which the individual decides to take action within a short period of time, (4) Action phase in which the individual takes action to change behavior, and (5) Maintenance phase in which the individual directs his or her efforts to preventing relapse and make permanent behavior change.

226 Originally passed as part of the Health Insurance Portability and Accountability Act of 1996 ("HIPAA"), P.L. 104-191, August 21, 1996, adding them into the Employee Retirement Income Security Act of 1974 ("ERISA").

227 The Americans with Disabilities Act, 29 U.S.C. §12101 et seq.

228 Genetic Information Nondiscrimination Act of 2008 (P.L. 110-233)

229 Title VII of the Civil Rights Act of 1964 (P. L. 88-352).

230 See Section 2705 of the Public Health Service Act, as amended by the PPACA (P.L. 111-148).

231 See Department of Labor FAQs, Part V, regarding the PPACA - http://www.dol.gov/ebsa/pdf/faq-aca5.pdf A.

232 See 71 FR 75014, at 75018 (December 13, 2006).

233 See 29 CFR §2590.702(f)(3).

234 Internal Revenue Code §4980D, 26 U.S.C. §4980D.

235 29 U.S.C. §12101 et seq.

236 42 U.S.C. .§12201(c)

237 42 U.S.C. §12112(d)(4)(A).

238 See http://www.eeoc.gov/policy/docs/guidance-inquiries.html, issued in July of 2000

239 42 U.S.C. §12201(c).

240 See 778 F.Supp. 2d 1370 (S.D. Fla. April 11, 2011). This case is currently on appeal.

241 Other case law supports the notion that most wellness plans will not have a difficult time meeting the other requirements of the statute. See, e.g., Krauel v. Methodist Medical Center, 95 F.3d 674, at 678 (8th Cir., 1996); EEOC v. Aramark Corp., 208 F.3d 266 (D.C. Cir. 2000); and Tenbrink v. Federal Home Loan Bank, 920 F. Supp. 1156 (D. Kan. 1996).

242 See §702(c) and (d) of ERISA (29 U.S.C. §1182(c) and (d)).

243 See 42 U.S.C. Chapter 21F, §§2000ff-1 et seq.

244 See 29 C.F.R. Part 1635 (75 FR 68932).

245 See Internal Revenue Code Sections 9802(c)(and (d) and 4980D (26 U.S.C. §§9802(c) and (d) and 4980D).

Notes

Notes